S0-BRO-214

World

Regional

Geography

Oliver H. Heintzelman

Richard M. Highsmith, Jr.

DEPARTMENT OF GEOGRAPHY
OREGON STATE COLLEGE

WORLD REGIONAL GEOGRAPHY

New York

Prentice-Hall, Inc.

1955

To

J. Granville Jensen

friend and colleague,

this book is sincerely dedicated.

Preface

World regional geography presents a concise view of the world as the home of man. A practical, logical, and systematic approach to the field of geography is provided, along with a survey of the world in terms of this outlook. The nature and elements of geography are first presented in skeleton form, and then are emphasized throughout the chapters as their functions become apparent. The world is divided into fourteen regional types. For each of these, the physical environment is first described and analyzed in view of its potentialities and limitations. Man is then brought onto the scene, and his manner of living in the region and utilizing its endowments are examined. Each regional study is concluded with an *Outlook* section, which notes trends and possibilities for the future.

These basic understandings are essential in our world today, where overlapping interests in resources, trade, technology, culture, and international policies are constantly evolving new meanings and importances.

Many persons have made significant contributions to the consummation of this book. Five critics saved us from many blunders. Fifteen geographers, each with intimate knowledge of a particular region and experience in teaching introductory or world-survey courses, were called upon to read the chapters. Their suggestions have been of inestimable value, and we wish to acknowledge their assistance, and at the same time to exonerate them from any misstatements or inconsistencies on our part.

Stanley A. Arbingast, University of Texas
Douglas B. Carter, Johns Hopkins Laboratory of Climatology

Dale E. Courtney, Bowling Green State University
Howard J. Critchfield, Western Washington College of Education
Clark I. Cross, University of Florida
Theodore Herman, Utah State Agricultural College
M. John Loeffler, University of Colorado
Michael P. McIntyre, Wayne University
Elbert E. Miller, University of Utah
Wilfred G. Myatt, Oregon State College
Albert W. Smith, University of Colorado
Keith W. Thompson, University of Adelaide
J. Allen Tower, Birmingham-Southern College
Curtis M. Wilson, Oregon College of Education
Robert N. Young, Stanford University

We are especially grateful to J. Granville Jensen, who read the entire manuscript and gave many helpful suggestions, and to Marijane H. Highsmith, who gave many hours of "spare" time to decipher our longhand, correct grammar and spelling, and type the manuscript form.

We wish also to thank Ray M. Northam for his excellent work in preparing all the maps and diagrams.

O. H. H.
R. M. H.

Contents

CHAPTER 1

Geography, The Correlative Science

THE TWENTIETH CENTURY HAS WITnessed the physical reality of one world! Technology and invention have changed concepts of time and space. Modern communication has brought the lands and peoples of the world closer together. The application of technology is constantly lowering and breaking the barriers of isolationism. The growing demand for commodities is creating new ties and interdependences. The "far-off places with the strange-sounding names" are no longer beyond our range of interest. Fifty years ago Baghdad was a romantic name in far-off Asia; today it is only hours away from New York by air. Events in China, Argentina, or Yugoslavia may influence our way of life. Our horizons today encompass a world that is round and one.

DROUGHT STRIKES COFFEE PLANTATIONS IN BRAZIL! RICH IRON DEPOSITS DISCOVERED IN CANADA!

Such headlines are significant to all the world today. Nations and peoples can no longer be self-sufficient. The implication of shortages and surpluses in commodities is everywhere. We live in an era of interdependence!

No region, nation, nor people has been favored with all the necessities of the modern industrial society. Each modern nation constantly draws materials from all corners of the earth to supply the needs of living. Why do many nations of the world import coffee from the Tropical Highlands? Why does the Ganges-Brahmaputra valley produce the majority of the world's jute? Why does the Orient have a monopoly on silk? Why is the Ruhr Valley of western Europe a great industrial area? Why is the Central Valley of California a checkerboard of commercial agriculture? Why are the lowlands of South China so intensely utilized by millions, while the great Amazon Basin of Brazil remains sparsely populated and essentially undeveloped? Many of the reasons for these puzzling contrasts can be discovered by geographic analysis. Geography interprets such contrasts, studies such interdependences, and analyzes such problems of agriculture, natural resource development, and industry.

Geography is a correlative science, drawing together the many facets of earth and man into complete mosaics to be viewed in their totality. It helps provide understanding of a nation's position in the world. It gives insight into the lives of people outside our own area by appraising the resources available to them and analyzing their manner of living, thereby giving us an understanding and appreciation of their problems and potentialities. Geography is concerned with the *interrelationships* of man and earth and the significant ways in which they differ from place to place.

The surface of the earth consists of a variety of ever-changing patterns. Rivers slowly widen their valleys and build deltas; wind and rain erode the hills and mountains; waves constantly alter the shore lines. Nature often manifests her latent power by making rapid and disastrous alterations. Storms sweep across the land destroying life and property. Earthquakes open great cracks, new mountains are born in the sea, and lava flows blot out existing landscapes. The gradual variations of seasonality, in turn, effect their changes. The dark earth turned by the plow in spring takes on a mantle of green to be replaced later by the yellow and brown of autumn. Nature's vegetation, too, changes with the seasons as its foliage grows and is shed with periods of heat and cold, rain and drought.

Man modifies natural earth patterns by developing and arranging his works on the surface. He builds dams to provide water for irrigation systems, and to generate power for delivery over a wire network. He drains marshes and clears forests. He builds transportation systems to connect towns and cities. As he develops new techniques there are greater and more varied modifications. The features of the natural and cultural landscapes never remain static.

The patterns of the earth environment have a dual personality. The contributions of the natural or physical environment are everywhere interwoven with the results of man's utilization and development. The physical environment provides the base, the interdependent elements supplied by nature: climate and weather, landforms, water, vegetation, animal life, soils, and minerals. The potentialities of the foundation vary with the different combinations of natural features. Some combinations produce deserts and others, luxuriant vegetation. Some areas are richly endowed with minerals. Some attractive areas produce high capabilities for supporting people; others repel man until new techniques enable him to cope with the adverse conditions. The variety of factors and the areal distribution of the possible combinations create the diversity of regions on the earth's surface that must be understood if we are to fully comprehend the problems or the possibilities confronting the world's people.

Man is the central theme in geography. The patterns of man's occupancy vary with his numbers and his stage of development, as well as with the potentialities of his physical environment. Through living on the natural foundation of earth and using its resources, man creates a superstructure—settlements, land utilization patterns, industries, and communication lines . . . the human elements of geography.

A geographic study of any area is concerned with these questions: (*1*) What possibilities and problems are presented by the physical environment for supporting people? (*2*) What progress has been made by man in adapting the land and its resources to suit his needs? (*3*) How has man made these adaptations? (*4*) What are the possibilities for continued or more intensive use?

Like other sciences, geography has a method of study which varies with the nature of the problem. The procedure of regional investigation is shown in the following outline.

THE METHOD OF REGIONAL GEOGRAPHY

I. Analysis and appraisal of the elements of the physical environment
   - A. Factors favorable to the support of man
   - B. Factors unfavorable to the support of man
   - C. Problems that may be mastered or remedied by technology

II. Examination of the inhabitants
   - A. Numbers and distribution
   - B. Stage of technological development
   - C. Peculiar culture traits that may influence the manner of living and use of the environment

III. Examination, description, and explanation of man's activities and occupancy patterns by correlation and synthesis of human and physical elements

IV. Evaluation of the region's potentialities from the view of supporting more population or supporting present population on a higher level

Clearly geography is a cross-field study concerned with analysis and correlation of two classes of interrelated elements, those that are supplied by nature, and those that are products of human occupancy. Some background in the geographic elements is desirable before proceeding with a regional study of the world.

PHYSICAL ELEMENTS

Space relationships

Space relationships—location, size, and shape—are fundamental geographic factors. Each may have distinguishable effects upon the development of a place, region or nation. Relative location may influence economic, cultural, or political relationships. Land utility for agriculture is affected by location with respect to markets, transportation, and nearness to labor supply. Industry is affected by these same factors, plus the accessibility of raw materials and energy sources. New York City is favored by a superior harbor, central location on the Atlantic Coast, and easy access to the interior—the richest hinterland in the world. Cultures are influenced by neighbors—the international boundary between the United States and Canada has never been an effective cultural barrier. Newspapers, magazines, motion pictures, and radio and television programs cross the border freely. Political, economic, and commercial relations between the two nations have always been very friendly.

There is a close correlation between the size of a country and the relative possibilities for variety in climate, landforms, vegetation, soils, minerals, and other resources. The large size of the United States offers variety in each. This has made possible a diversified economy firmly based upon commercial agriculture and industrial utilization of rich and varied resources. The small country of Denmark, in contrast, has approximate uniformity of climate and surface throughout and its resource endowments are limited. Denmark is a specialized agricultural nation which produces surpluses of dairy, poultry, and swine products, but must import many other commodities. Great size can have military advantages; production centers can be widespread, and an attacking power's supply lines must necessarily be long. During the early stages of World War II, the U.S.S.R. was able to trade some of its western space for time while organizing defenses and production farther east. Size is not always an advantage, however; there may be problems of access and transportation. Nations with large areas of deserts, mountains, or tropical rainforest may have difficulty in organizing and developing their space.

The shapes of the political and physical units of the world are varied. They may be compact in one contiguous body, with all borders approximately equidistant from a central point, attenuated with length much greater than width, broken with one or more parts separated from the main body, fragmented with numerous disconnected parts, or complex with various combinations of these several forms. It can be readily understood that a compact shape, such as that of France, Switzerland, or the United States, has both economic and political advantages. Transport nets can radiate from central points, the problems of unification are simplified, and defense is easier. An attenuated form like that of Norway, Czechoslovakia, or Chile gives long frontiers that may favor cultural contact and trade, but that present problems of defense and the necessity for long transportation lines. Broken and fragmented forms, represented respectively by Pakistan and Indonesia, present similar difficulties. The broken area of the former is particularly undesirable because the wide territory of India separates the western and eastern parts of Pakistan.

It should be noted that the effectively occupied and developed section of a country may present a quite different shape from that of the total political unit. This is illustrated by Canada, which has a relatively complex shape, but has an attenuated pattern in its area of economic development. Harsh environmental conditions have limited the major settlement to areas near the southern border.

Weather and climate

Climate is the most basic element of the natural environment. Landforms, soils, hydrology, and vegetation all feel the impact of its authority. Its influences on man are far-reaching. The crops he grows, the clothes he wears, and the buildings in which he lives and works are intimately related to climate.

Weather is the day-to-day condition of the atmosphere. Climate, not merely an average, is the composite of weather, including extremes, frequencies, and the annual march of events in the atmosphere. Weather is like the pages of a book, each one a new, varied experience; climate is the sum total, the volume. An understanding of weather and climates found throughout the world demands a knowledge of their ingredients or basic elements: (*1*) air temperature, (*2*) atmospheric moisture including clouds, fog, humidity, and precipitation, and (*3*) pressure and winds. The varying occurrence and proportion of these elements provides a variety of climates, ranging from the monotony of the tropics to the extreme diversity of the middle latitudes.

Air temperature. From the sun comes an endless stream of short-wave radiation which is the basis of earth's light and heat. Only one two-billionth of the sun's energy is intercepted by the earth. An average of 42 per cent of the intercepted energy is lost directly to space, through reflection from the upper atmosphere, 15 per cent is absorbed by the atmosphere, and the remaining 43 per cent is received directly by the earth's surface. Upon absorption of the incoming solar radiation, the earth in turn becomes a radiating body, broadcasting energy of longer wave length. Thus the earth's blanket of atmosphere is largely heated indirectly by energy radiated from the earth itself.

Atmospheric moisture. Heat transforms vast quantities of the earth's water into vapor, which is present in varying amounts in all parts of the lower atmosphere. Living things, especially plants, also contribute to atmospheric moisture by transpiration. This water vapor later condenses and returns to the earth as rain, snow, hail, sleet, or dew. There is a constant exchange between the atmosphere and the earth's water supply. The land receives water by condensation and precipitation from the atmosphere, the sea by precipitation and run-off, and the atmosphere receives water vapor by evaporation from the sea and the land and through transpiration by plants. Heat is required to evaporate water. The heat is not lost but is locked within the water vapor as latent heat of condensation.

The air's capacity for water vapor depends largely upon its temperature; as temperature decreases capacity also decreases, and vice versa. When air can hold no more water vapor at existing temperature and pressure, it is said to be saturated. The amount of water vapor actually present in the air compared to the amount it could hold if saturated at that same temperature is referred to as *relative humidity.* As air is cooled it eventually reaches the saturation temperature, or "dew point." When air is cooled below the dew point, it releases excess water vapor by condensation. On the earth's surface, condensation takes place on vegetation, sidewalks, and other such objects in the form of dew. If the temperature is below 32° Fahrenheit, condensation appears in the form of frost. In the atmosphere condensation takes place around hygroscopic nuclei—salt from ocean spray, bits of dust, and particles of smoke. This condensation is visible as fog and clouds. During the process of condensation, the latent heat stored in the water vapor is released.

The presence of a cloud cover does not necessarily mean precipitation; clouds indicate potential, more than actual, precipitation. The actual precipitation from clouds takes place when many minute particles of water or ice crystals coalesce to form a mass too heavy to remain suspended. Rain, snow, sleet, or hail then falls to replenish the earth's supply of moisture lost through evaporation, and the cycle is completed.

Pressure and winds. Wind is air in horizontal motion—movement paralleling the earth's surface. Pressure difference is the immediate cause of wind; unequal heating of the earth's surface is the basic cause of pressure differentials. When air becomes heated (as over a land mass in summer), its air pressure decreases, forming a low pressure area; conversely, air pressure increases with decreased temperature (as over a land mass in winter). The atmosphere, being free to move, tends to equalize pressure differentials. Wind is thus created as air flows from high pressure areas to areas of lower pressure. Winds blow from "highs" to "lows."

Distributed over the earth is a pattern of pressure cells and resulting winds, consisting fundamentally of a series of alternate high and low pressures and alternate east and west wind systems. Near the equator, where the earth receives a maximum of incoming solar radiation, there is a broad, discontinuous zone of low pressure known as the *equatorial low.* "The doldrums," as this belt is often called, are generally characterized by rising air, calms, variable winds (except along coasts, where sea breezes are important), and local thunderstorms which may be extremely violent.

Two belts of high pressure cells, known as the subtropical highs, circle the earth at approximately 20° to 35° north and south latitude. These belts, sometimes called "the horse latitudes," are characterized by descending and warming air. Winds in these belts are variable, and clear, dry weather prevails. The trades, blowing equatorward from the subtropical highs, are known as the steadiest winds on earth, especially when they blow over water surfaces. Low pressure cells in the vicinity of 60° to 65° north and south latitude are known as the subpolar lows. These are areas of storminess, particularly in the winter season.

The cyclonic westerly winds, originating on the poleward margins of the subtropical highs, flow toward these low pressure zones. The cyclonic westerly winds in the Southern Hemisphere are known by seamen as the "roaring forties," since no great land masses disrupt their movement and they are strong and persistent. Land masses in the Northern Hemisphere cause the cyclonic westerlies to be more variable, both in strength and direction, than their Southern Hemisphere counterparts. The polar highs coincide with the north and south polar ice caps, and are the source areas for the polar easterly winds that blow equatorward toward the subpolar lows.

A convergence of winds occurs in the low pressure belts, the trades in the equatorial low, and the cyclonic westerlies and polar easterlies in the subpolar lows. These meeting places of the winds are characterized by storms and capricious weather. Where the winds are flowing out of high pressure belts, particularly in the subtropical highs, air descends from aloft, giving a warming and drying effect, and usually producing fair weather.

Winds do not flow directly north or south toward the low pressure zones, but follow oblique courses, due to the earth's rotation. Winds in the Northern Hemisphere are deflected to the right and those of the Southern Hemisphere are deflected to the left (see Figure 1-1).

The entire pressure and wind system is extremely complex. The belted pressure pattern of the Northern Hemisphere is broken into a series of separate high and low pressure centers, due to the powerful influences of the great land masses of North America and Asia and their associated ocean bodies. All the wind and pressure belts, furthermore, shift seasonally.

The climate of a particular place is the result of complex factors that influence the atmosphere. These factors, known as climate controls, help answer questions such as: Why is there snow on the equator? Why does the northwest coast of North America receive such heavy precipitation? Why is the St. Lawrence River closed to navigation each winter when the ports of northern Norway, many degrees farther north in latitude, remain ice-free? Why are there great deserts in Africa and Asia?

Of all the climatic controls, latitude or sun control is most significant. Sun control is re-

FIGURE 1-1. *The world's wind and pressure systems.*

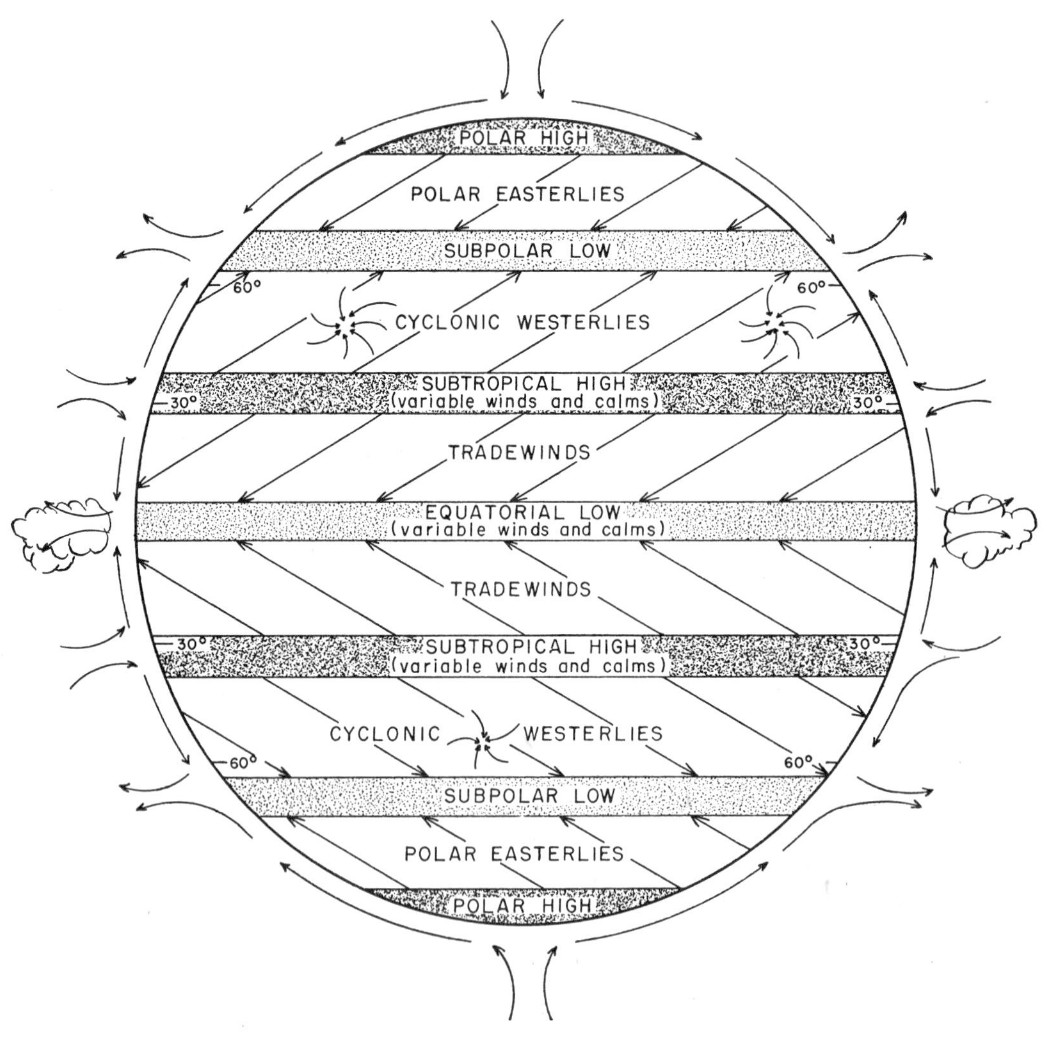

lated to seasonality, changing lengths of day, and the intensity and duration of solar radiation. All these in turn have far-reaching effects on the physical and cultural phenomena of the earth. Basic to an understanding of sun control is a study of earth motions and positions in relation to the sun.

The earth's eastward rotation on an intangible axis accounts for day and night in each 24-hour period. A second movement is the revolution of the earth around the sun in a slightly elliptical orbit each 365¼ days. The earth's axis has an inclination of 23½ degrees from vertical to the plane of the elliptic, an imaginary plane passed through the sun and extended through all points of the earth's orbit (see Figure 1-2). The position of the axis remains constant (this is called *parallelism* of the earth's axis). The combination of rotation, revolution, inclination, and parallelism accounts for differences in the distribution of solar energy over the earth, lengths of day and night, and the seasons.

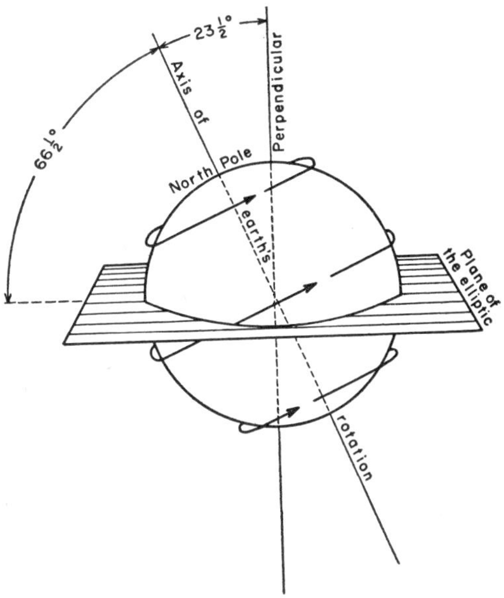

FIGURE 1-2. *The inclination of the earth's axis to the plane of the elliptic.*

The sequence of the seasons follows the revolution of the earth around the sun. In the following discussion, the earth's orbital journey and its position in respect to the sun is described with reference to the Northern Hemisphere. A study of Figure 1-3 will be helpful in interpreting the description. March 20 or 21,[1] the vernal or spring equinox, is used as the starting point. At this date the noonday sun is directly overhead at the equator and the length of day and night is equal for all parts of the earth. This gives rise to the term *equinox*—equal day and night. The earth has completed one-fourth of its revolution by June 21 or 22, the summer solstice and longest day of the year. The sun is now directly overhead at the Tropic of Cancer (23½° N). The entire area within the Arctic Circle experiences 24 hours of daylight. The next quarter-turn finds the earth in a position (on September 21 or 22) in which the sun is again directly over the equator—the autumn equinox. Day and night are again equal all over the earth. During the six-month period (March to September) the North Pole receives continuous sunlight. When three-fourths of the journey is completed (on December 22 or 23, the winter solstice and shortest day of the year), the sun is directly overhead at the Tropic of Capricorn (23½° S). At this time the entire area south of the Antarctic Circle (66½° S) is bathed in light and experiences 24 hours of continuous daylight, while the sun is no longer visible north of the Arctic Circle (66½° N). During this six-month period (September to March) the South Pole experiences continuous sunlight while at the North Pole, the sun is completely out of sight. The annual revolution is completed on March 21 or 22. The sun, during the circuit, appears to be migrating north and south between the Tropic of Cancer and the Tropic of Capricorn, the two extreme positions of the sun's vertical rays. Days begin to lengthen from the time of the winter solstice to the summer solstice date; conversely, days shorten from June 21 or 22 to December 21 or 22. Only in areas between the two tropic lines are days and nights of almost equal duration throughout the year. The Northern Hemisphere's spring and summer

[1] Difference in dates is because a calendar year has 365 days whereas 365¼ days complete a revolution. (The quarter-days are accumulated and added as an extra day every fourth year.)

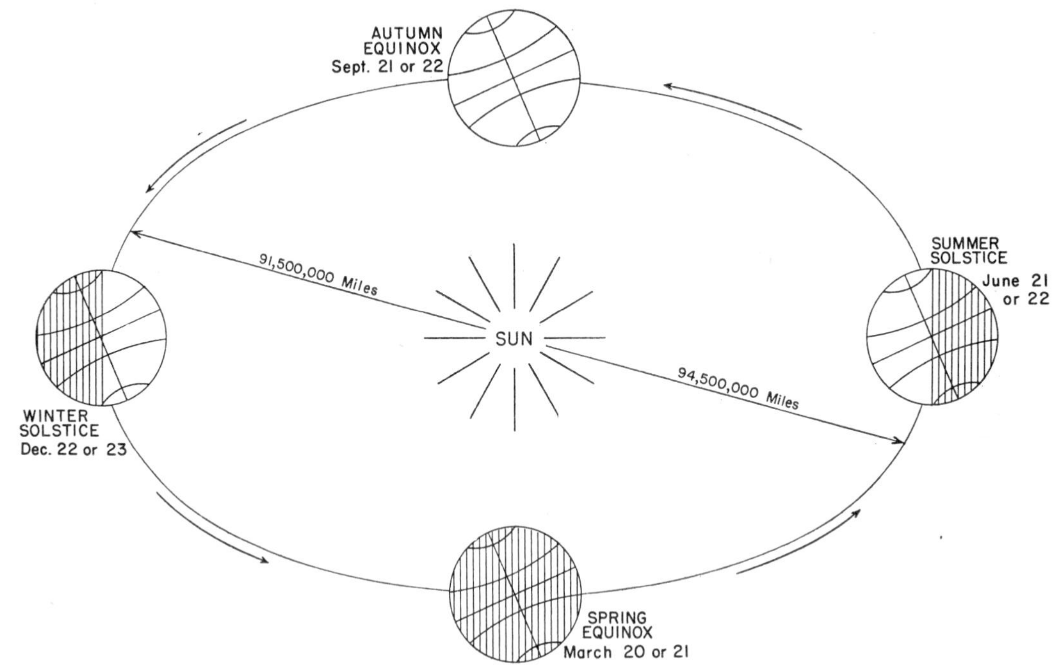

FIGURE 1-3. *The march of the seasons.*

occur in the middle and higher latitudes when the sun's vertical rays are north of the equator. Fall and winter occur while the sun is south of the equator. Areas between the tropic lines, constantly under the influence of the overhead sun, do not develop these temperature fluctuations (winter and summer). The sequence of seasons is reversed in the Southern Hemisphere.

FIGURE 1-4. *Vertical and oblique rays of the sun.*

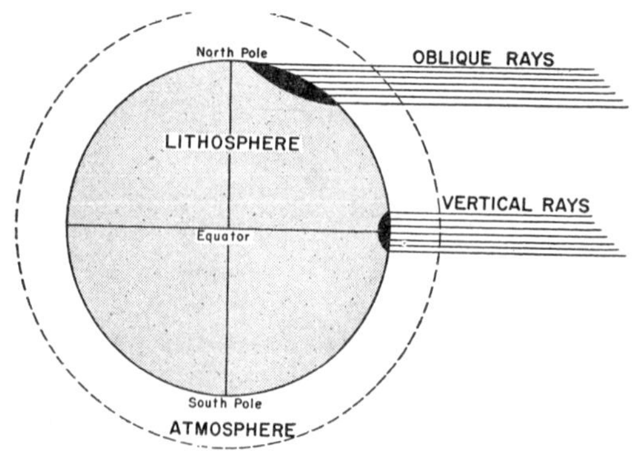

The amount of solar energy or *insolation* received by any portion of the earth's surface is chiefly dependent upon the hours of sunlight and the angle of the sun's rays to the surface. Between the Tropics of Cancer and Capricorn the sun's near-vertical rays provide intense heating. Poleward of the tropic lines the angle of the rays with the earth's surface becomes increasingly oblique. Oblique rays are less effective than direct rays, since heat energy is spread over a larger surface and the rays must also pass through a thicker layer of absorbing atmosphere (see Figure 1-4). Hence, the earth-heating effect of a middle-latitude winter sun is less than that of a summer sun. The heating effect of the sun over the tropic zone is greater than it is over middle latitudes and poleward areas.

Light and heat are two determining factors in plant growth. The number of frost-free days is an important consideration in agricultural production. Although many plants are able to withstand short cold snaps and some are able to winter through prolonged sub-freezing weather, damage to plants from cold is still the chief hazard throughout many agricultural areas. The tropical regions, except for high elevations, enjoy a continuous frost-free season with no interruptions in the periods of growth. Frost generally becomes more prevalent toward the poles, culminating in the perpetual frost of the polar regions. Areas in high latitudes having short frost-free periods or growing seasons are somewhat compensated in summer by 17 to 18 or more hours of sunlight each day.

The differential heating of land and water is another important climatic control. Land and water surfaces may intercept an equal amount of insolation, yet have unequal rates of heating and cooling. Since water is translucent, solar heat penetrates to considerable depths. The circulation of water, vertical and horizontal, is extremely important in governing the distribution of energy throughout a large land mass. Water requires about five times more heat to raise its temperature one degree Fahrenheit than does relatively dry land. Water not only requires more time to heat than land but, due to the greater volume of stored heat, takes longer to cool. Land is opaque and is not subject to tides, currents, and similar movements, consequently its heating is concentrated in a small surface volume. Land, therefore, heats and cools more rapidly than water. The consequence of this differential heating and cooling is exemplified in the fact that when it is continental or land-controlled, climate is characterized by large seasonal, as well as daily, extremes of temperature, whereas marine or ocean-controlled climate is more moderate.

Winds are a third major climatic control because of their direct and indirect effect on temperature and precipitation. Their two most important functions are (*1*) the movement of heated air from low latitudes to higher latitudes—without this circulation there would be a constant increase of temperature in the low latitudes and a decrease in the middle and high latitudes, and (*2*) the transport of water vapor over land, where it may condense and replenish the earth's water needs. Both local and regional changes in temperature are associated with winds. In the Northern Hemisphere a south wind usually means a rise in temperature, whereas north winds bring lower temperatures. Winds sweep dust and salt into the air which serve as a nuclei for the condensation of water vapor. The direction and movement of ocean currents and drifts are also affected by winds.

Ice-free ports in the high latitudes of Norway, deserts along the fringe of northern Chile, fog-shrouded coasts in northern Japan—all these are due mainly to the control of climate by ocean currents. The world system of ocean currents transfers warm water from low to higher latitudes; conversely they import cold water from the polar areas (see Figure 1-5). The warm waters of the North Atlantic Drift make winter temperatures in countries of northwest Europe remarkably mild for the latitude. Cold water paralleling tropical coasts not only cools these areas but causes aridity. Thick fogs are associated with converging cold and warm currents such as are found along the northeast coasts of North America and Asia.

In addition to the major controls that have been discussed, mountain barriers, altitude, storms, air masses, exposure, and a number of minor controls are also important. These will be discussed in later chapters dealing with world regions where their influences are especially significant.

Landforms

For the earth in general, landforms stand second only to climate in the magnitude of their effects on the distribution, activities, and adaptations of man. Because of the many interrelations and interactions of the elements of environment, however, broad rules cannot always be applied to specific localities. Landforms, influenced by climate, are themselves a climatic control, producing local contrasts as well as broader regional implications.

The earth has a surface area of nearly 200 million square miles, of which land totals approximately 29 per cent. More than three-fourths of the land area is contained in the large masses comprising Eurasia, Africa, and the Americas. Oceania and Antarctica con-

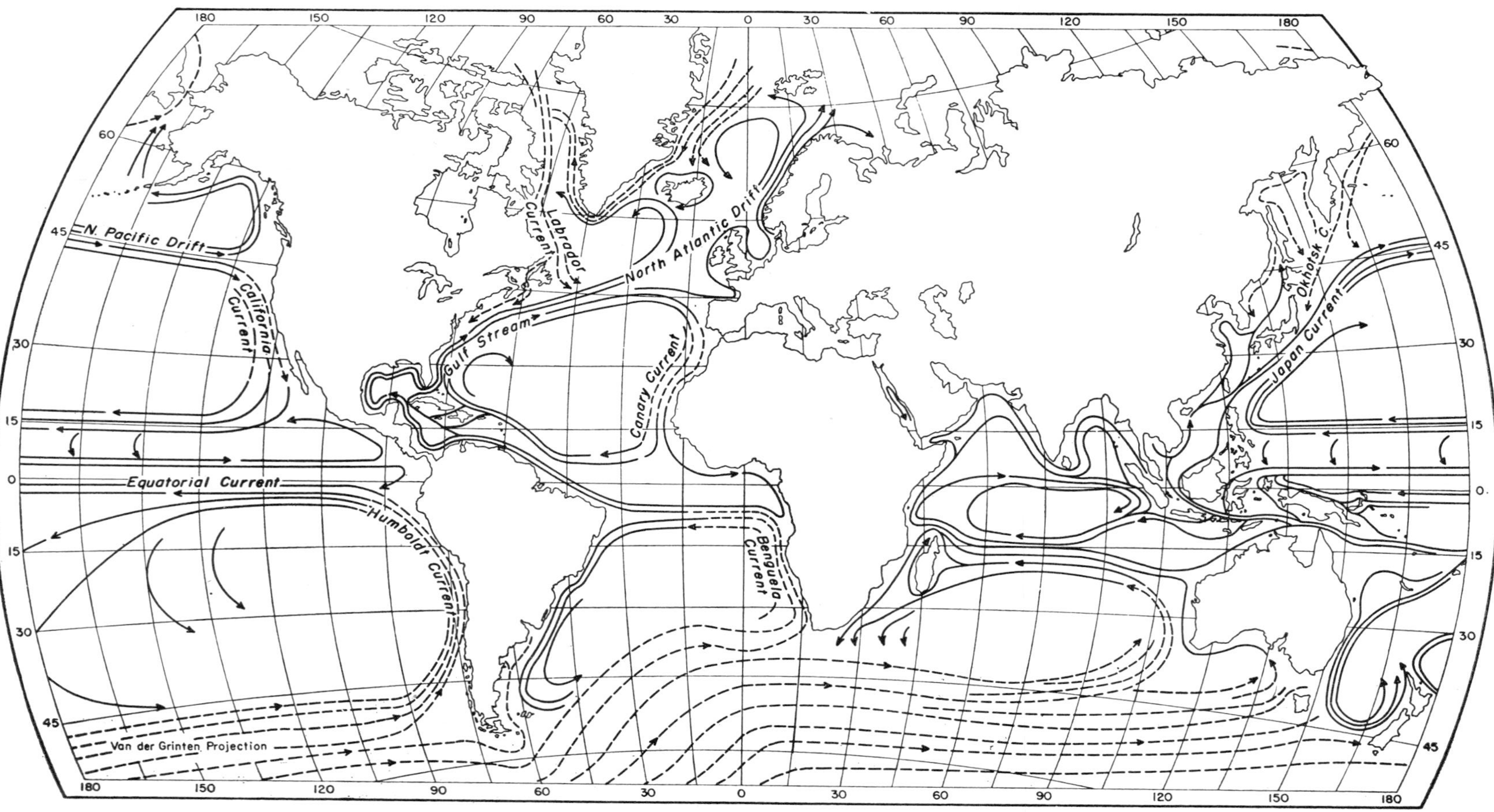

FIGURE 1-5. *The pattern of world ocean currents.*

stitute the bulk of the remainder. The preponderances of the earth's land surfaces are in the Northern Hemisphere. The form of the land appears varied when viewed in detail; its features are irregularly distributed.

The major landforms are classed in four groups: plains, plateaus, hills, and mountains. The bases for this classification are the proportion of slope land to level land, and local relief, which is the difference in elevation between high and low altitudes within an area. *Plains* are generally, but not always, areas of relatively low elevation; local relief of less than 500 feet is the principal criterion. For example, the Great Plains of North America are at elevations of more than 1500 feet, while the Atlantic Coastal Plain is for the most part under 500 feet. There are wide expanses of the Great Plains, however, with local surface relief of less than 500 feet. Thus both plains have in common a relatively smooth surface despite a thousand-foot difference in elevation. *Plateaus* are similar to plains, but usually stand well above the surrounding country on at least one side and have local relief exceeding 500 feet. *Hill lands* are surfaces with local relief between 500 and 2000 feet, and so dissected that much of their area is in slopes and only a small portion in summits. *Mountains,* like hills, have a small portion of their area in summits and a large portion in slopes; however, mountains are more than just large hills. The local relief of mountains exceeds 2000 feet and they are generally more massive.

APPROXIMATE PER CENT OF CONTINENTS IN MOUNTAINS, HILLS, PLATEAUS, AND PLAINS [2]

	Mountains	*Hills*	*Plateaus*	*Plains*
Asia	20	24	24	32
Europe	4	21	8	67
Africa	3	1	71	25
North America	13	11	24	52
South America	11	9	24	56
Oceania	9	19	24	48
Totals *	12	14	33	41

* Excluding Antarctica.

[2] From Frank A. Pearson and Floyd A. Harper, *The World's Hunger*. Ithaca, N. Y.: Cornell University Press, 1945, Table 16.

Each of these four major classes exhibits an endless variety of minor features. For example, within the range of 500 feet relief the details of a plain may include flat land, depressions, valleys, and low ridges. In mountainous areas the diversity may be even greater, ranging from young, rugged mountains with sharp, spire-like peaks towering above the perpetual snow and steep valleys, to old highlands with rounded crests and open valleys.

Two opposing groups of forces, *tectonic forces,* which originate within the earth, and *gradational forces,* which originate outside the earth, are constantly at work changing the earth's surface, producing landforms and altering their shapes. The first group, deriving energy from within the earth's interior, tends to build up the relief of the land. Variations in elevation are continuously being produced by forces that bend, warp, and break the earth's surface, depressing some portions and elevating others. These same results have been accomplished in some areas by the extrusion of molten material or lava onto the surface. The second group, in direct opposition to the first, is working to bring the earth down to a uniform level by the processes of gradation, which are tearing down the elevations and filling the depressions, this is accomplished through the work of gravity, water, wind, and ice.

Hydrology

Water is a physiological requirement for life of all kinds, but in the modern world man's needs have expanded far beyond the relatively low quantities required for sustaining life. Tremendous demands are made upon water supplies to meet the needs of irrigation, industry, power, city sanitation, and recreation. Today the possibilities for an area's development are directly related to the quantity and quality of water resources available.

Essentially all water that is used by man is in constant motion—a part of the vast circulatory system known as the hydrologic cycle (see Figure 1-7). In this cycle, water evap-

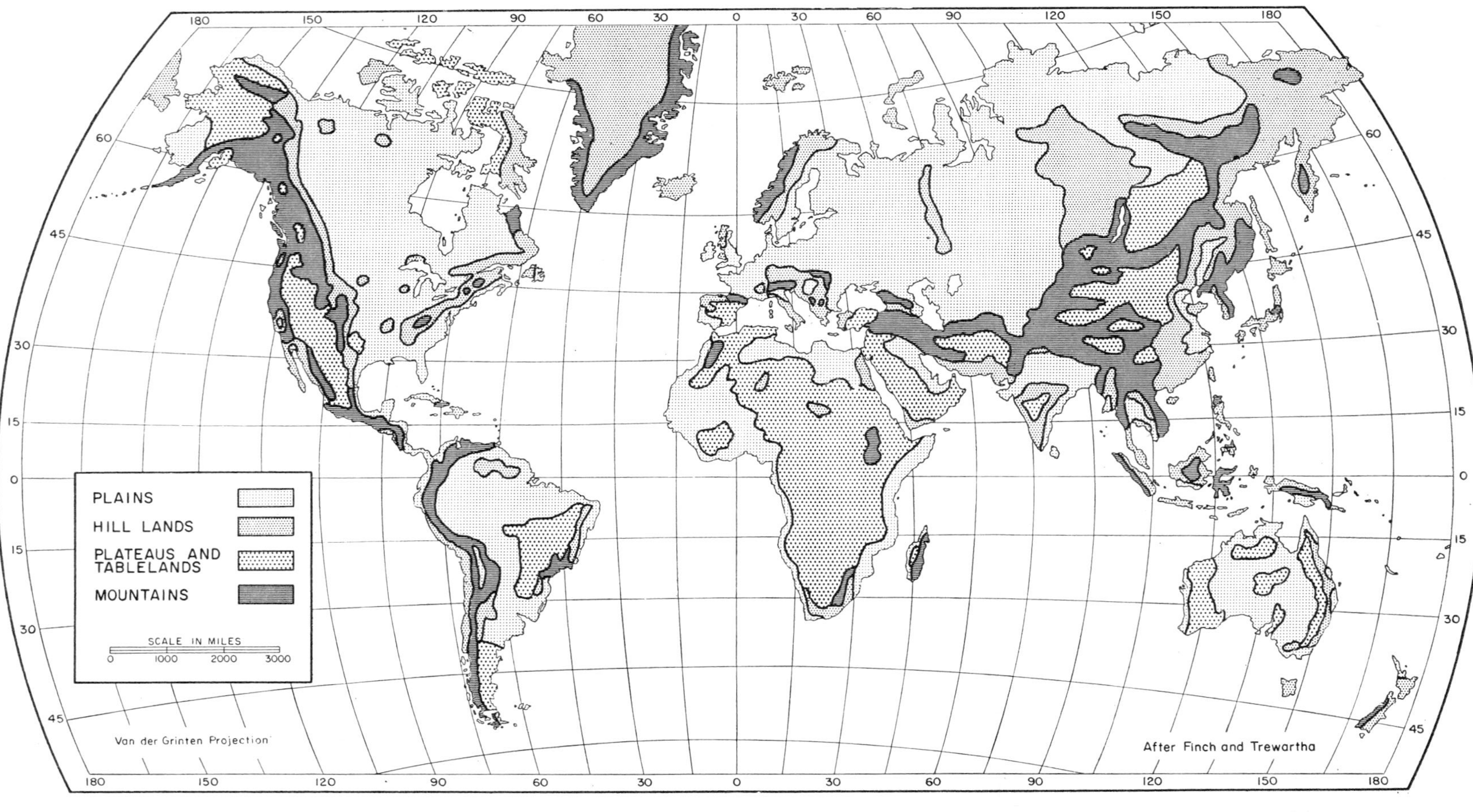

FIGURE 1-6. *The world distribution of major landform masses.*

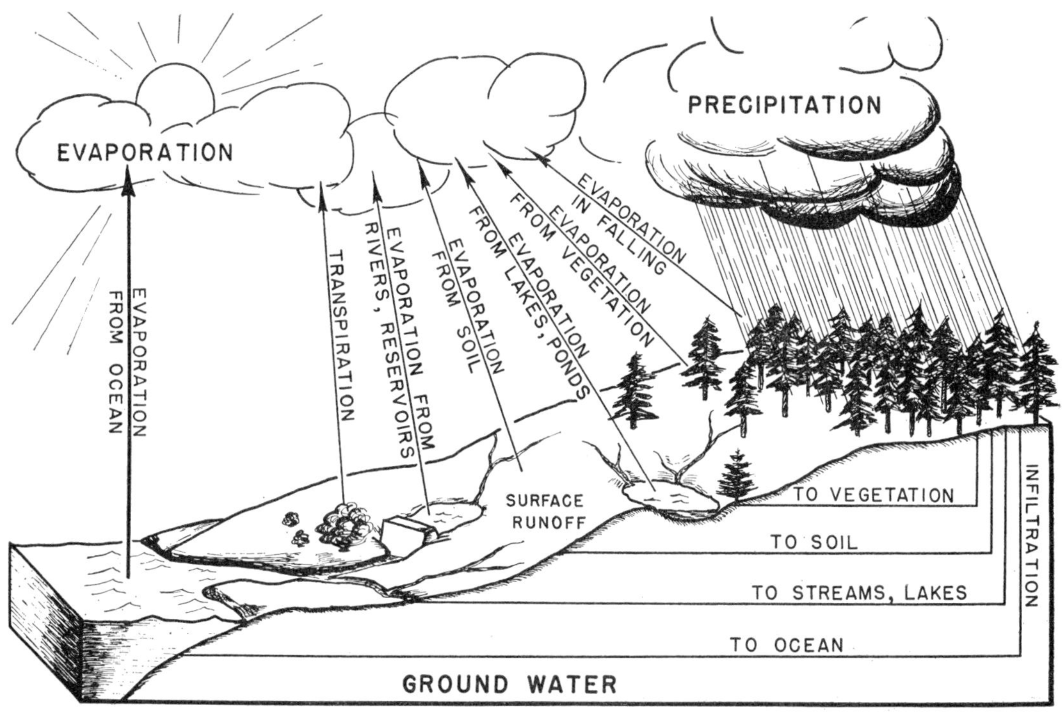

FIGURE 1-7. *The hydrologic cycle.*

orates wherever it is exposed to air, rises into the atmosphere as water vapor, condenses and returns to the earth's surface as rain or snow. Some of the water is quickly shed from the surface into stream channels; some may penetrate the soil to be held for a time, later to be evaporated or transpired by vegetation; some of the water may pass below the reach of plant roots through the subsoil to the underground reservoir where it fills the openings in the rocks above the solid, impervious zone. Under the force of gravity the ground water flows slowly through the rocks toward lower areas of natural or artificial discharge, such as springs, rivers, lakes, swamps or wells. The water that reaches the earth's surface may travel a straight and simple path or a tortuous and complicated one, but it all is destined to go back to the oceans.

Water supplies are related largely to precipitation and evaporation rates, but are also influenced by such features as soil structure, vegetation cover, and the nature of the bedrock. Regions with adequate precipitation at all seasons usually have few water supply problems, while those with low or seasonal precipitation often have shortages. Two primary reservoir elements in the hydrologic cycle can be tapped by man for water supplies: surface sources, particularly streams and lakes, and ground water reservoirs reached by wells. At present, only minor amounts of sea water are used, some in raw form and some converted to fresh water. Research is being conducted in an attempt to make the conversion of sea water to fresh water economically feasible. Such an accomplishment would have great bearing upon development in coastal areas with deficient water supplies.

Native vegetation

One of the outstanding elements giving character to a region is its cover of natural vegetation. Mantling the earth with a pattern of varying color, it constitutes one of the world's valuable resources, ranging from stands of merchantable timber to vast

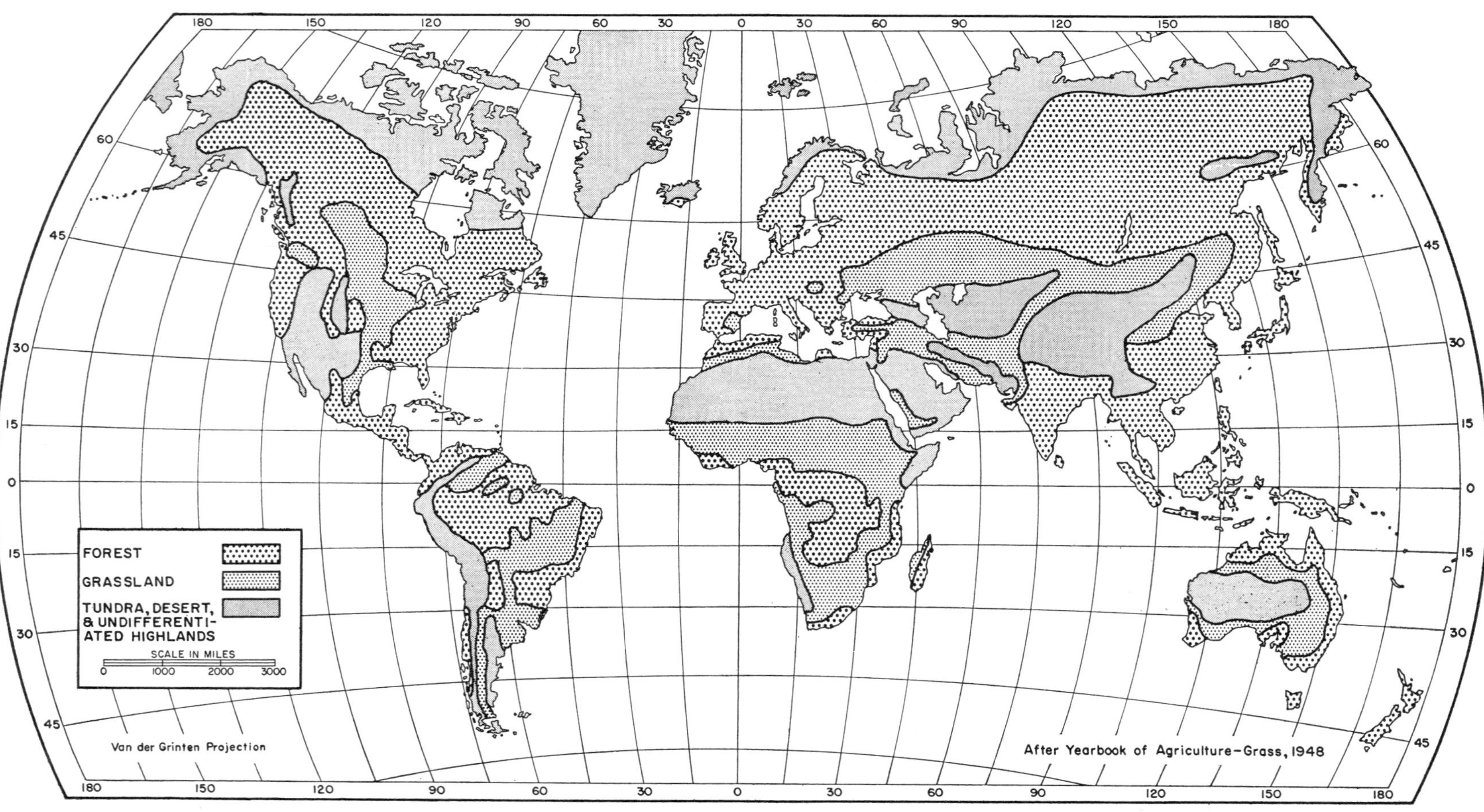

FIGURE 1-8. *The world distribution of major vegetation classes.*

seas of grass. Climate, soil, and surface features all play roles in influencing the type, abundance, and variety of vegetation. There is an especially close correlation between zones of climate and zones of vegetation.

Plant life is divided into three broad vegetative groups. *Forests* dominate the humid areas, ranging from the broadleaf evergreens of the Rainy Tropics to the deciduous and coniferous forests of the middle and higher latitudes, with transitions of scrub, park-like, and mixed forest. *Grasslands* of the savanna, prairie, and steppe occupy the zones of lesser and seasonal precipitation. Completing the pattern is the sparse *scrub* and low vegetation of the dry and cold deserts. Although vegetative groups are similar in like environments, species may differ in the groups from continent to continent.

Native animal life

Animal life is as varied and as wide-spread as natural vegetation. Its geography, however, is more complex, and its distribution does not fall so distinctly into broad patterns in response to climate. Animals are mobile, whereas plants are fixed to their environments and must make structural adjustments. Animals are able to adjust themselves to the varying demands of their environments. Some go into dormant stages during periods of cold or aridity; some migrate in search of food, others migrate for mating. Similar environments do not always have similar fauna, in contrast to vegetation. The grasslands of Africa and South America have widely differing types and numbers of animal species. Australia, with a physical environment similar to portions of other continents, has a unique fauna. Ancient land barriers and bridges are partly responsible for these differences in distribution.

Insects are the most abundant category of the earth's animal life. Although some are useful, man is constantly at work to control others, due to their spreading of disease and their attacks on crops. Mammals, fish, birds, reptiles, and amphibians are higher orders of animal life. Of these, the various species of fish are the most valuable, although some benefit is gained from all. Some primitive peoples still depend on native animals for subsistence. In man's commercial economy, fish and fur bearing animals are the most important. In regions of relatively dense population, man is hardly cognizant of the fauna in his physical environment, but in world areas less exploited by man, native animal life still forms a living, colorful part of the natural landscape.

Soil

Soil is an essential resource of the earth. It is the medium of plant growth, and all men are directly or indirectly dependent upon plants for food, clothing, and many other necessities of living. Soil, the upper weathered and biologically-molded portion of the earth's crust—a complex of minerals and organic substances, varies greatly in quality as well as in quantity from place to place. Depth, texture, structure, fertility elements, drainage, and topography are the principal variable soil characteristics which influence the kind and quantity of natural vegetation and the agricultural plants that can be grown. For example, the outstanding requirement of a soil for rice production is the ability to hold water over the surface for a long period; rich alluvial soils with impervious subsoils are ideal for this crop. Tree crops, in contrast, produce best on deep, fertile, well-drained soils in which a large root system can develop. Soils have considerable bearing upon the productive capacity of any given area, although man, through good management practices (including fertilization), can overcome some of the natural limitations.

The character of any soil is dependent upon a number of soil-forming factors, of which the most important are: (*1*) the richness of the parent rock material, which gives the soil its bulk as well as the major part of its inorganic elements, (*2*) the climate, especially rainfall and temperature, which determine the kind and intensity of weathering, (*3*) the biota, plant and animal life which are active agents in soil development while living, and, when dead, decay and are incorporated as essential organic substances, (*4*) the slope of the land, which affects run-off, drainage and

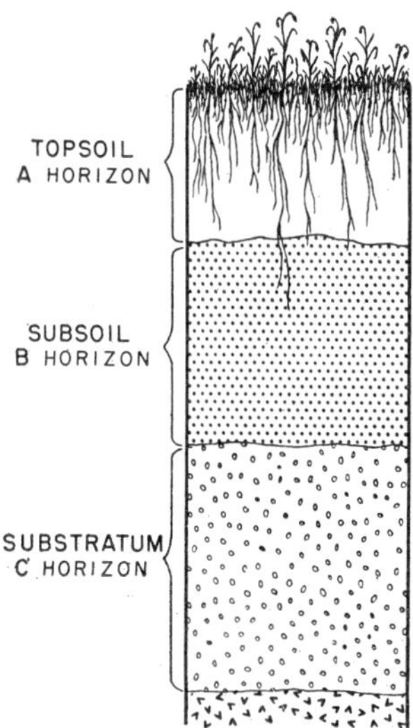

FIGURE 1-9. *Soil profile. A mature soil with a smooth topography is a natural active body, having characteristics different from the parent material. A vertical cut through a mature soil displays a profile with distinct layers called* horizons. *The* A *horizon contains weathered soil, mineral material, and a certain amount of organic matter in various stages of decomposition. Some materials have been carried by leaching into the* B *horizon, which is also weathered but contains little or no organic matter and is therefore usually lighter in color. There are accumulations of iron, aluminum, and fine clays leached from the surface layers. In arid regions there are also accumulations of salts in this layer. In the* C *horizon the modified soil material of the* B *horizon merges with the unconsolidated parent soil material, which in turn covers the solid rock.*

soil creep, and influences soil accumulation, (5) age or length of time in development, and (6) man's use, and very often misuse, of the soil.

The modern concept of development and classification of soils includes three major ideas: *first,* that soil development is a constructive process in which both physical and chemical forces are operative; *second,* that, because of differences in climate, vegetation, and the original parent materials, there are differences from place to place in the intensity and sequence of soil-forming forces, particularly in the later stages of genesis; *third,* that when soils are youthful the original geological nature of the parent material and the conditions of slope apparently determine in a large measure their character, but that as time passes, climate and associated vegetation become the dominant factor (therefore, as soils mature, especially if erosion is slight and drainage good, the inherited characteristics tend to disappear and characteristics induced by climate and vegetation appear). Over wide areas of the earth which have varying bedrock, soils, after a considerable lapse of time, tend to become similar in general characteristics if climate and vegetation are similar; such soil groups are known as zonal and together they constitute the Great Soil Groups of the world. Within the major zones, however, intrazonal and azonal soils may occur. Intrazonal soils have more or less well developed soil characteristics which result from influences such as relief or parent material rather than the normal effects of the climate and vegetation. For example, in humid regions, bog soils form in areas of very poor drainage where thick deposits of plant-remains accumulate and in arid regions saline and alkali soils form in poorly drained places where salts accumulate. In other cases, black soils have developed from soft limestone or rocks high in calcium carbonate; even in humid regions they are not acid and grass forms their dominant vegetation. Azonal soils have no well-developed soil characteristics, largely because of the youth of the parent material. Such soils include the areas of nearly pure sands, the scanty coverings of rock fragments on mountain slopes, and those developing from very recent stream-deposited materials.

The two broadest sub-divisions of the world's soils are the *pedocal,* or *zonal arid,* soils and *pedalfer,* or *zonal humid,* soils.[3] The pedocals, or calcium carbonate accumulating soils, are associated with low annual precipi-

[3] *Pedology* is the formal name of soil science. *Pedalfer* was derived from adding the *al* of aluminum and the *fe* of ferrum (iron) to the root of pedology. *Pedocal* was derived from adding the *cal* of calcium to the root of pedology.

tation (usually under 25 inches), and grass and desert shrub vegetation. The pedalfers evolved under high annual precipitation (generally in excess of 25 inches), and vegetation that was dominantly forest (exceptions are found in the higher latitudes where cool conditions foster the growth of conifers and the development of pedalfers under precipitation totals as low as 10 or 15 inches). The large amounts of water caused chemical weathering of the mineral constituents, the growth and decomposition of organic matter, and the removal of soluble salts to be intensified. Pedalfers tend to be acid since most of the carbonates were carried out of reach of plants or away through the underground drainage. Percolating water also caused a transfer of considerable amounts of the iron and aluminum from the surface layer to the subsoil.

The major zonal classes are subdivided into the Great Soil Groups on the basis of the characteristics of the mature soil profile (see Figure 1-9) produced by the influences of the details of climate and related vegetation. The names and distributions are shown in Figure 1-10 and the character of each will be discussed in its particular region.

Mineral resources

Hidden on and beneath the surface are the mineral resources, a highly significant part of the natural environment. Industrial as well as military strength is measured in terms of the quantities and combinations of these available.

Every continent has a share of the world's mineral wealth, but the nations are not equally endowed with quantities and combinations suitable for industrial development. Coal, petroleum, iron, and alloy metals are fundamental for modern industry, and scores of other minerals play essential roles. Maps showing the distribution of known minerals reveal that nature has been most generous in her gifts to the Northern Hemisphere, especially western Europe, the U.S.S.R., and the United States. Minerals contribute significantly to the economies of many other countries. There are parts of the world with mineral resources still to be exploited, and others where explorations have yet to uncover the wealth.

Minerals differ greatly in character, occurrence, distribution, and usefulness. They may be grouped into three main categories: (*1*) the *mineral fuels* including coal, petroleum, and natural gas, (*2*) the *metals,* the more important of which are iron, aluminum, copper, lead, zinc, tin, nickel, manganese, and uranium, and (*3*) the *non-metallic minerals* including fertilizers such as nitrates, potash, and phosphates; chemicals such as sulphur and salt; building materials including sand, gravel, and clay; and the precious stones.

HUMAN ELEMENTS

Population

Man is the most significant and vital element in the study of world geography. The geographer, in his concern for the interrelationships between man and earth, must necessarily consider certain aspects of man himself. Most notable among these are numbers of people, their distribution patterns, and their stages of development. The world population map (Figure 1-11) indicates clearly that the earth's 2.5 billion people are not evenly spread over its surface—this is one of the most challenging facts of world geography. The regions of the earth capable of supporting large populations by virtue of favorable climate, landforms, soils, and richness of resources are distinctly limited; large areas are at present closed to extensive human settlement by extremes in environmental conditions. Man, in his settlement, has generally avoided the areas of extremes— the lands that are too hot, too cold, too dry, too wet, too high, too rugged, too isolated. He has shunned places such as the Sahara, the Amazon Basin, the Arctic Tundra, and the lofty Himalayas. Where man has occupied unfavorable environments his numbers are usually small and his culture primitive. Population density is a geographic fact of broad significance—a relationship usually exists between numbers of people and type and intensity of land utilization. Moreover, there is a relationship between

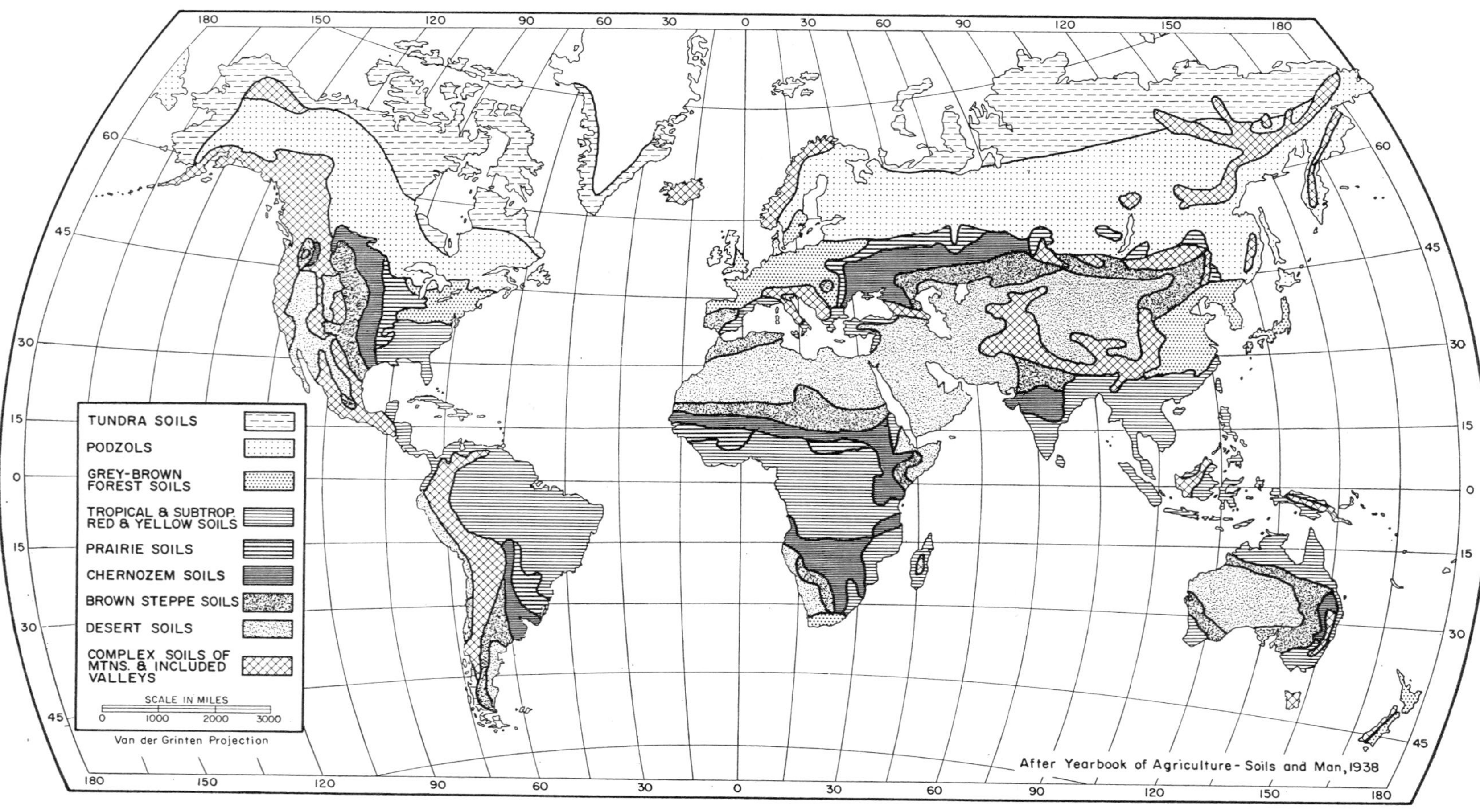

FIGURE 1-10. *The Great Soil Groups of the world.*

available resources, including arable land, and standard of living.

Any study of population should also consider the stages of development of people, especially their ever-changing technologies, which have great bearing on a group's manner of living and economic activities. By clearing forests, plowing grasslands, diverting rivers, building canals, irrigating deserts, harnessing rivers, terracing slopes, mining, and drilling for oil, man is greatly altering his interrelationships with nature. Man and his growing store of techniques make geography a dynamic science. The natural and cultural scenes change through the years. A century ago the bunch grass and sagebrush of the arid Yakima Valley of Washington supported only few people and a meager cattle-grazing activity. Through the engineering skill of man, water has been diverted to a half-million acres of the fertile land, making possible the establishment of a rich irrigated agriculture economy which today supports nearly 250,000 people. Thus the stage of man's development greatly influences his relationships with the environment; the higher his technology and the greater his "know-how," the less limiting are the influences of nature.

Economic activities

Three basic ways by which an area may support population are: agriculture, resource extraction, and manufacturing. One, none, or all may be possible in a given area, depending in a large part upon the potentialities and limitations of the physical environment. Modern man has progressed far in molding, adapting, and using his environment to supply and suit his needs; however, he falls far short in his ability to fully overcome nature.

An agricultural adaptation is largely dependent upon climate, soils, and landforms which unite in varying combinations to direct the type, extent, and intensity of crop production. Developments in fertilizers, seeds, and irrigation have extended the agricultural frontier, but still the limits are set by physical factors. Often the specific character of a given area's agriculture is markedly influenced by transportation, access to markets, labor supply, and operator preference where possibilities are numerous.

A population supported by resource extraction depends primarily upon nature's endowments. Minerals are fixed by geologic processes, forests are largely a function of climate, commercial fish depend upon a favorable water environment, and water-power development requires precipitation and mountain watersheds.

The factors determining the potentialities and limitations for manufacturing are more complex. Many are involved, but the major bases are: (*1*) raw materials to be processed, such as minerals, timber, fiber and other agricultural products; (*2*) energy resources such as coal, natural gas, oil, or water to turn the wheels of the factories and to supply heat; (*3*) labor to operate the machines and handle the material; (*4*) markets to absorb the manufactured products; (*5*) transportation to assemble the raw materials and distribute the finished products; and (*6*) capital for the purchase of raw materials, erection of factories, and payment of wages. All of these factors will seldom exist in the same place. Industry constantly seeks locations where the best combinations occur; these vary with different types of manufacture as well as with time.

Commerce, transportation, and service activities may arise as important means of supporting people wherever one or more of the basic ways of livelihood exist. The areas of the world differ greatly in their physical assets; some have surpluses in some commodities and deficiencies in others. No modern nation nor area is totally self-sufficient. Differences in raw materials and productions from place to place are the basis for trade. When commerce arises so does the need for transportation; transportation nets and handling facilities become important items of regional equipment. The activities of assembly, distribution of commodities, and maintenance of facilities provide employment. Wherever people cluster there is need for services such as the operation of food and dry goods stores, amusement houses, garages, and newspapers, as well as

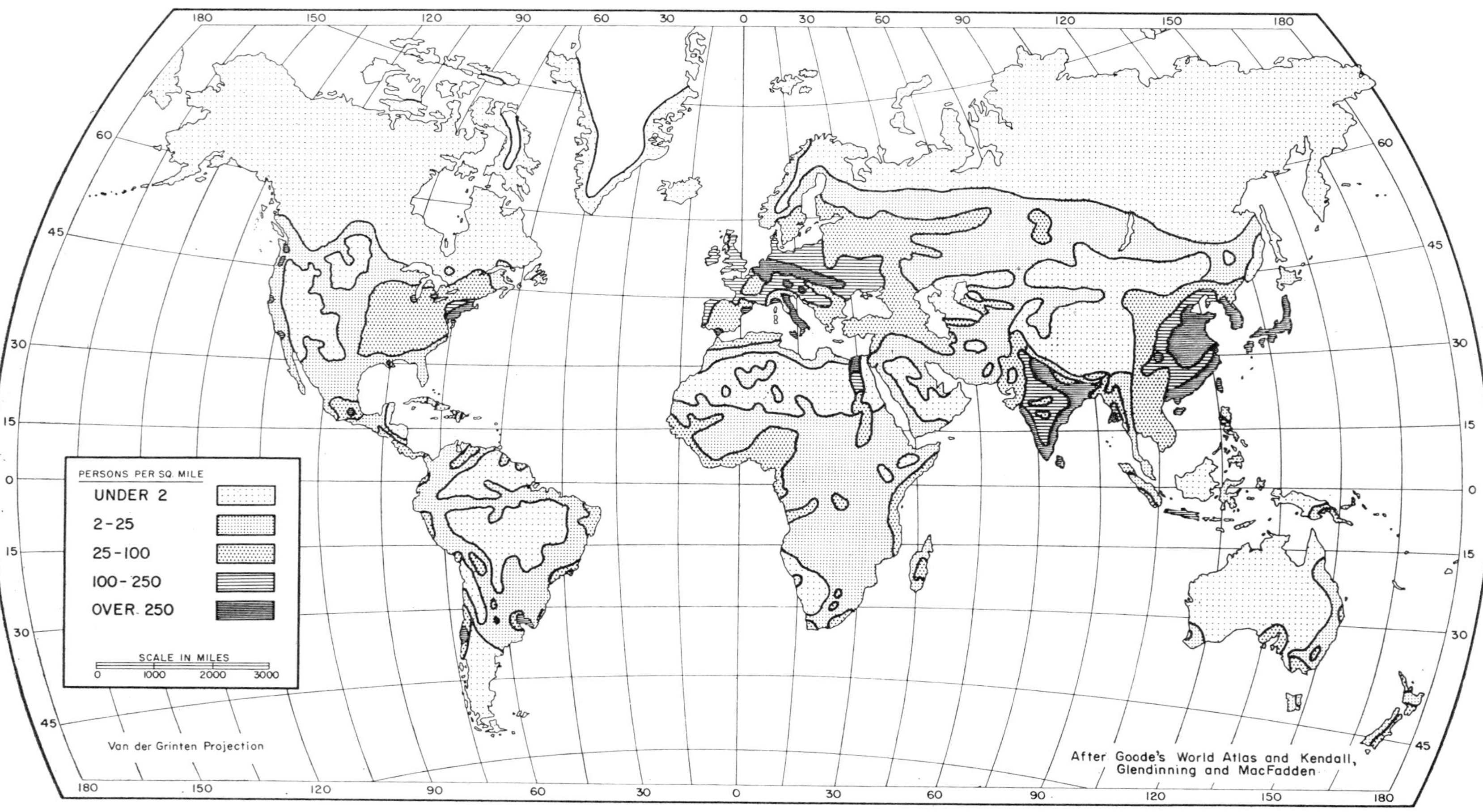

FIGURE 1-11. *The distribution of world population.*

the professional services in medicine, law, and education.

Cultural features

Man's economic activities produce visible cultural patterns. The evidences of his living on the earth and using its resources are always conspicuous in inhabited areas; normally, clues to the basic means of support are also present. In agricultural districts, field patterns, crops, livestock, and farmsteads dominate the areal scene. Where mining is significant, mine pits or buildings covering the shafts, piles of slag, and workers' villages are visible. Where fishing is a major occupation, boats, equipment, docks, and handling facilities are evident. Concentrations of factories, stockpiles of raw material and fuels, and transportation facilities attest to the importance of manufacturing in an area. In most cases, examination of the readily apparent features will reveal not only the importance of the activities but also the stage of development of the inhabitants and something of their level of living.

Shelters and settlements are other cultural features that result from man's living on the earth. One of man's primary needs is for protection from the elements; his house and other buildings form one of the most visible evidences of his habitation of the earth. The features of house-types which concern the geographer are building material and style, which may give distinctiveness to an area. Building materials used in construction are generally the types that are most readily available. The predominance of frame buildings in the Pacific Northwest area of the United States is indicative of the availability of lumber, whereas the mud and clay houses of the lower Nile Valley result from the paucity of other materials in that area. Using building materials at hand is not a fast rule; other factors may be involved. Development of transportation may make new materials available from distant sources. For example, there has been a shift from the early sod huts of the prairie lands of the central United States to the frame houses that prevail today.

The style of houses may also reflect many other factors, such as climate, standard of living, and historical background. In areas of heavy snowfall, the pitch of the roof is steep; in arid regions, the roof is commonly flat. In Southern California the stucco walls, tile roofs, and general house styles are related to the factor of early Spanish settlement, as well as to the construction materials available.

The grouping of houses into settlement types is of greater significance than the nature of individual houses, since the type of settlements found in a region generally gives a key to its economic life. Based upon grouping and function, two main settlement types may be recognized: dispersed or scattered, and clustered or agglomerated. Scattered settlements with individual house and related buildings, separated by some distance from neighboring houses, are typical of American agricultural regions. The cluster type of settlement may range in size from the small hamlets of a few houses in which the agricultural population of the Orient live, to the large urban centers of industrial regions.

Cities are functional developments. Their location, size, shape, and function are chiefly products of geographic relationships, and these attributes of a city in turn reflect much of the character of an area. Cities generally grow in conformity with the needs of an area. Many urban centers indicate rich resources and an advanced stage of economic development such as characterize western Europe and the northeastern quarter of the United States.

Although cities often have multiple functions, it is possible to divide them into several types on the basis of their respective major function. *Commercial* and *industrial* cities are the two most common types. The former is the older and may vary in size from a small agricultural market center to a large city such as New York or London. The size is directly related to the extent, richness and accessibility of the trade areas, and to location with respect to transportation routes. Since the Industrial Revolution and the development of machines and factory production, industrial centers have grown to dominate regions where the bases for manufacturing are favorable. Such is the case in the Ruhr District of Germany, the Donetz Basin of the U.S.S.R., and the Pittsburgh-Cleveland district of the United States. Many commercial cities also function as industrial centers, since the advantages of assembly and distribution are sometimes favorable to manufacturing.

There are several lesser categories into which cities may also be classed. Some, like Washington, D. C., are governmental; others, such as Miami, Florida, where climate or scenery is attractive, are recreational. Where resources exist, a city based upon their exploitation may develop, as the iron-mining center of Hibbing, Minnesota, or the fishing city of Gloucester, Massachusetts. Residential, educational, religious, and military functions may also result in city growth.

WORLD REGIONS

The earth's surface is characterized by a great variety of physical and cultural patterns. Few areas are homogeneous in all aspects; however, large segments of the earth are often similar in one or more distinctive features, either physical or man-made. A geographic study of the world is facilitated by classifying it into regions on the basis of one or more elements. These may be physical elements such as landforms, climate, vegetation or soil, or human elements such as land utilization patterns, economies, or cultures.

When an analysis is made of the interrelated factors of the man-nature complex, climate appears to play the dominant role. Man and nature everywhere feel its impact. Under given climatic conditions there are similarities in natural vegetation, soils, crop possibilities, and shelter needs, as well as other physical and human conditions. Broad areas exist with climatic homogeneity; this makes possible a simple classification as an aid to the study and understanding of the earth's lands and peoples.

This text presents a geographic appraisal of the world organized into 14 types of regions based on similarity of climatic characteristics. Study begins in the equatorial regions and progresses to the poles.

SELECTED REFERENCES

General texts

Blair, Thomas A., *Weather Elements,* Third Edition. New York: Prentice-Hall, Inc., 1948.

Brunhes, Jean, *Human Geography.* Chicago: Rand McNally and Company, 1920.

Davis, Darrell H., *The Earth and Man.* New York: The Macmillan Company, 1948.

Finch, Vernor C., and Glenn T. Trewartha, *Elements of Geography.* New York: McGraw-Hill Book Company, Inc., 1949.

James, Preston E., *A Geography of Man.* Boston: Ginn and Company, 1949.

Jones, Clarence F., and Gordon G. Darkenwald, *Economic Geography.* New York: The Macmillan Company, 1954.

Kendall, Henry M., Robert M. Glendinning, and Clifford H. MacFadden, *Introduction to Geography.* New York: Harcourt, Brace and Company, Inc., 1951.

Lobeck, A. K., *Geomorphology.* New York: McGraw-Hill Book Company, Inc., 1939.

Van Valkenburg, Samuel, and Carl L. Stotz, *Elements of Political Geography,* Second Edition. New York: Prentice-Hall, Inc., 1954.

Periodicals

Annals of the Association of American Geographers (Quarterly)

Economic Geography, Clark University, Worcester, Mass. (Quarterly)

Geographical Review, American Geographical Society, New York (Quarterly)

Journal of Geography, National Council of Geography Teachers (Monthly except June, July, and August)

Atlases

Bartholmew's Advanced Atlas of Modern Geography. New York: McGraw-Hill Book Company, Inc., 1950.

Goode's World Atlas. Chicago: Rand McNally and Company, 1953.

Van Royen, William, *Atlas of the World's Resources. Volume I: The Agricultural Resources of the World.* New York: Prentice-Hall, Inc., 1954.

Van Royen, William, and O. Bowles, *Atlas of the World's Resources. Volume II: The Mineral Resources of the World.* New York: Prentice-Hall, Inc., 1952.

CHAPTER 2

Rainy Tropics

THE RAINY TROPICS, VIEWED FROM space, appear as an irregular although broken ring of green encircling mid-earth. The world's densest vegetative cover masks the details of the landforms in this green girdle and man-made clearings are lost in the sea of forest. Warm, wet, and humid are the key words to the weather and climate. Temperatures are constantly high and showers drench the land almost daily. The Rainy Tropics cover about ten per cent of the earth's surface but contain only five per cent of the earth's population. However, surprising population paradoxes exist. The small island of Java teems with people, whereas the imprint of man is negligible in the vast basin of the Amazon. The Rainy Tropics are the principal strongholds of primitive tribes, but the demands

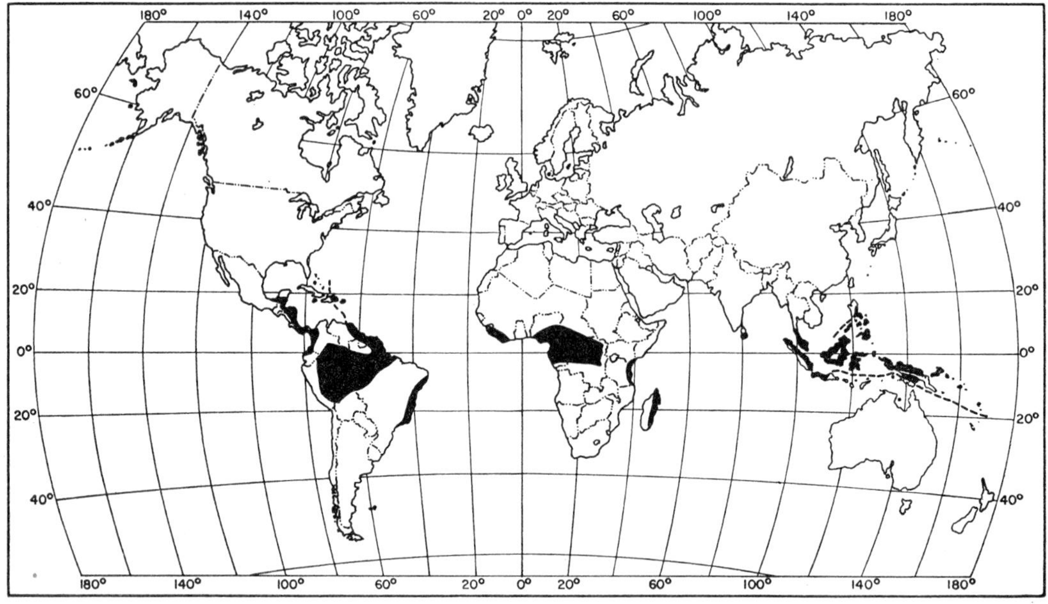

FIGURE 2-1. *The Rainy Tropics.*

for raw materials and foods have stimulated interest in these regions on the part of industrial nations and a veneer of western culture has been superimposed upon the peoples of those areas that favor development. Today these regions supply the world with the products of tropical agriculture, strategic minerals, and cabinet woods.

To many the Rainy Tropics conjure visions of mysterious jungles peopled by savages—lands of pleasant climate where nature is so lavish in her gifts that every need is easily supplied. In reality the majority of natives are farmers, forests dominate the vegetation, climate is monotonous, and nature in general presents many problems. Frontiers are gradually being invaded but great areas are still question marks on the map. The Rainy Tropics are lands of mystery; the veil is only partially lifted.

Location

The Rainy Tropics straddle the equator in an irregular latitudinal belt of from 5 to 10 degrees on either side with an extension of from 15 to 25 degrees on windward coasts. This places the major portion in the doldrums or belt of equatorial calms, a belt of low pressure that encircles the earth near the equator and where the noonday sun's rays are never far from vertical. The Rainy Tropics attain their greatest areal extent in the northern part of South America, the heart of Africa, and the islands of Southeast Asia. The regions are not continuous, as boundaries in all areas are often disrupted by highlands.

South America. The largest Rainy Tropics region is in the Amazon Basin, which lies mainly in Brazil but extends westward to include parts of Bolivia, Peru, Ecuador, Colombia, and Venezuela. On the northeast, the region extends along the coast of the Guianas. The Andes Mountains isolate a small part from the main body of the region on the west coast of northern Ecuador and Colombia. A narrow strip also extends along the trade wind coast of Brazil from south of Recife to the Tropic of Capricorn.

Middle America. The onshore trade winds cause the Rainy Tropics to extend into Caribbean America. The region is restricted to the eastern periphery of the mainland by a mountainous backbone, but it includes parts of all

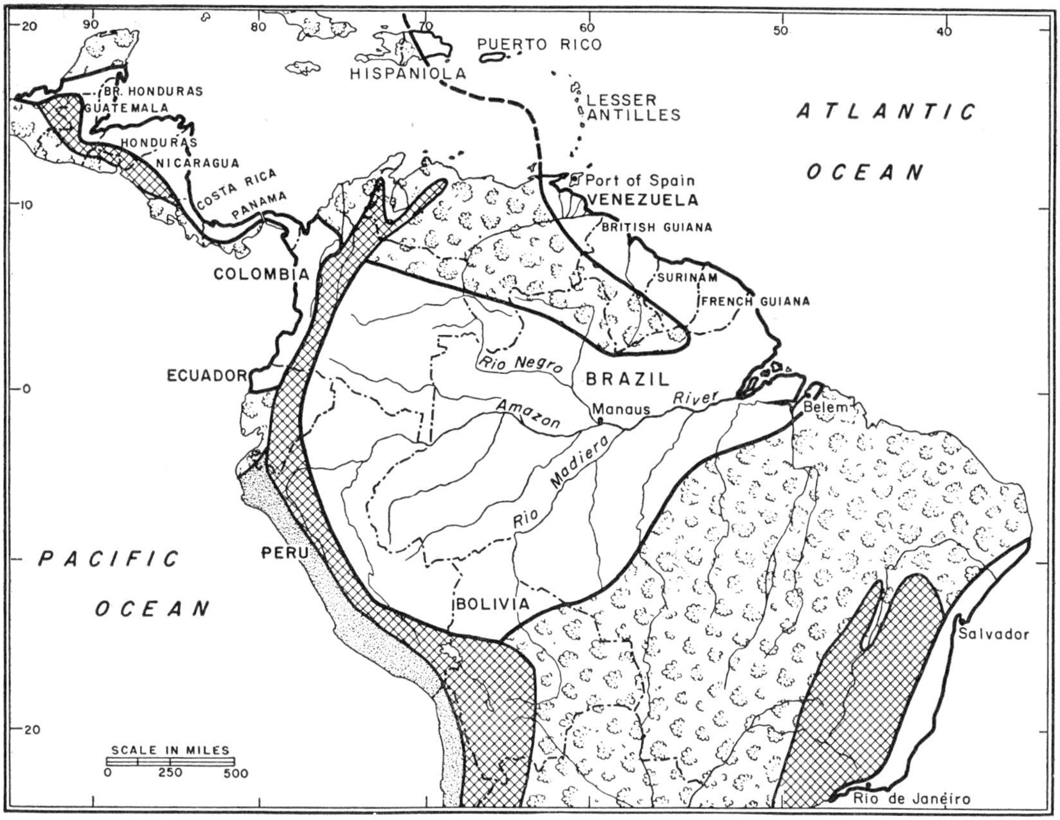

FIGURE 2-2. *The Rainy Tropics of Latin America.*

FIGURE 2-3. *The Rainy Tropics of Africa.*

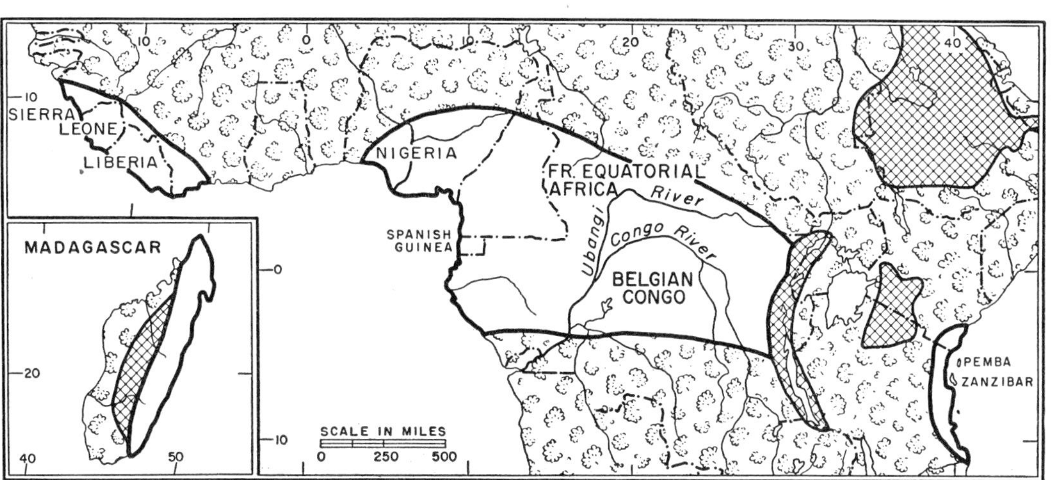

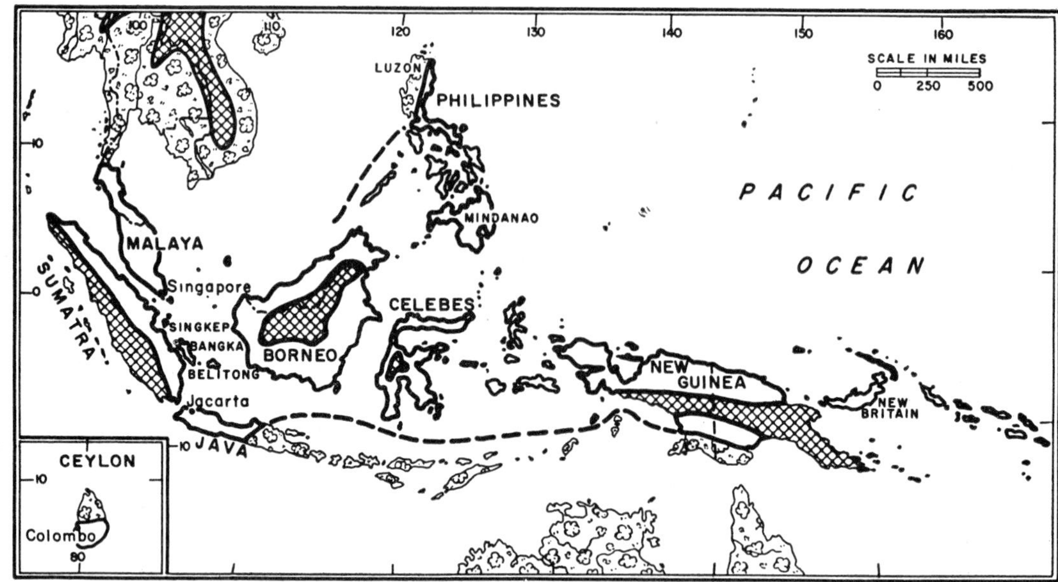

FIGURE 2-4. *The Rainy Tropics of Southeast Asia.*

the Central American republics plus the base of the Yucatan Peninsula. The Rainy Tropics also include the windward sides of many islands of the West Indies.

Africa. Like the South American region, the bulk of the Rainy Tropics in Africa lies chiefly in the basin of a large river, the Congo. Political units consist of Belgian Congo, part of the Anglo-Egyptian Sudan, and the southern fringes of French Equatorial Africa and Nigeria. A smaller section is located along the coast of the Gulf of Guinea and contains the countries of Liberia, Sierra Leone, and the Ivory Coast. On the east side of the continent a narrow strip of Rainy Tropics is found along the coast of Tanganyika and southern Kenya. The islands of Pemba and Zanzibar, offshore of Tanganyika, are also included. The last area of Rainy Tropics within the African realm is the windward coast of eastern Madagascar.

Southeast Asia and adjoining islands. The Malay Peninsula is the only section of the Asiatic mainland in the Rainy Tropics. Most of the region is contained in equatorial islands that include the eastern one-third of the Philippines, most of Indonesia, southwest Ceylon, and many islands of Oceania.

PHYSICAL ENVIRONMENT

Climate

The climate of the Rainy Tropics results chiefly from the combination of conditions produced by location in the belt of equatorial low pressure. In these low latitudes the sun's noonday rays are always nearly vertical. Consequently, insolation is uniformly high and days and nights are of approximately equal length the year around. The sun rises and sets at about the same time through the months and the periods of dusk and dawn are never prolonged. The alternation of a season of long summer days with a season of short winter days is lacking. January is quite like July—it is inappropriate to divide the year into seasons of summer, winter, spring, and fall. There may be a wet season and a less wet season, but throughout the year a uniformly warm temperature prevails.

The northeast and southeast trade wind air masses converge in the equatorial low, causing air to move upward from the earth. However, surface wind conditions are complex; squalls alternate with light variable winds and periods of dead calm. On the whole,

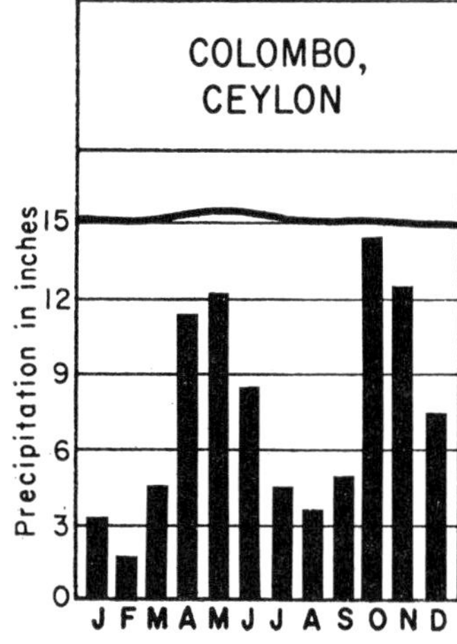

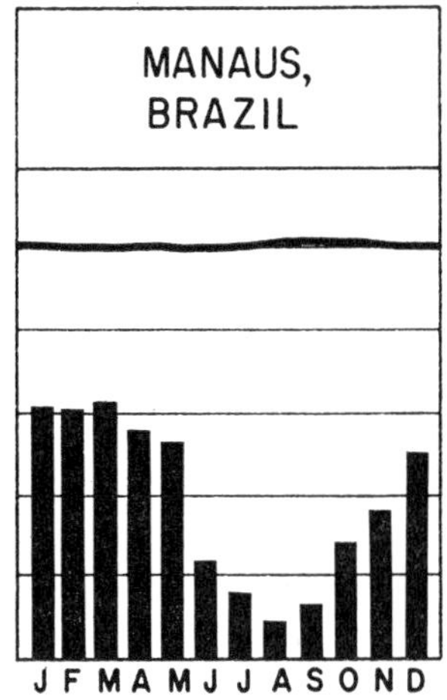

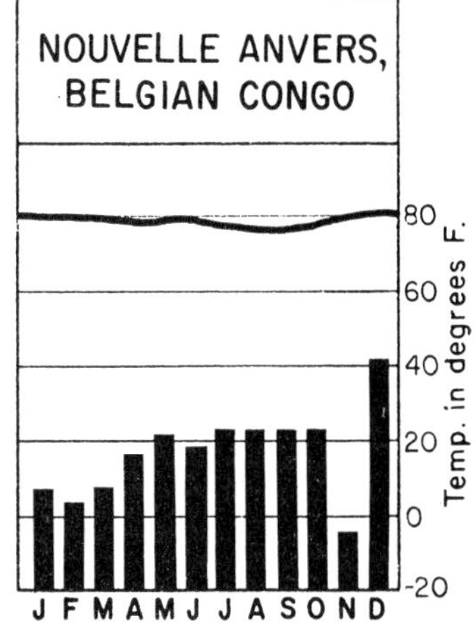

FIGURE 2-5. *Typical climatic graphs of Rainy Tropic stations.*

these regions are poorly ventilated. Clear days are rare, and billowy cumulus clouds have usually formed in the sky by noon. Thunderstorms are frequent and heavy showers a common occurrence. Relative humidity is constantly high. Each day is like the next; through the years, weather and climate are synonymous. The unvaried length of day and night, absence of seasons, tedious heat, and almost daily rain produce a monotonous day-to-day, month-to-month climatic environment.

Temperature. The vertical rays of the overhead sun which dominate the equatorial belt throughout the year produce a constant supply of heat—a year of continuous summer. Temperatures have three dominant characteristics: (*1*) they are uniformly high throughout the year, (*2*) there is a small range between coolest and warmest month, and (*3*) there are no great extremes. There is an unending procession of months with thermometer readings hovering between the high 70's and 90's; typical yearly averages are close to 80°. The difference between the average monthly temperatures of the warmest and coolest months seldom exceeds five degrees. Manaus in the interior of the Amazon Basin has a yearly average of 81.3°, ranging from a March average of 80.4° to an October average of 82.9°. Average monthly temperatures at New Antwerp in the Congo Basin range from 76.3° to 80° and at Singapore on the tip of Malaya from 79° to 81°. Daily extremes as high as 100° are exceptional. In contrast summer recordings in New York have reached 102°, in Chicago, 105°, and in Omaha, 114°. Although several other climatic regions have seasonally higher temperatures, no region can match the combination of consistently high temperatures and small yearly range of the Rainy Tropics. Temperature is not excessive, but the air is constantly charged with water vapor. The heat and the high humidity produce a high *sensible* temperature that creates considerably body discomfort.[1]

The diurnal range, or the difference between the warmest and coolest daily thermometer readings, averages about 15 degrees. Nighttime temperatures usually fall to around 70°. This has led some writers to speak of night as the "winter of the tropics." A high percentage of cloudiness prevents greater diurnal ranges; the cloud layer, plus humidity, retards heat radiation. However, during the less wet season, some areas experience clearer nights and temperatures may drop to 65°. Day temperatures tend to be higher during this period. Island or coastal locations have lower average temperatures than inland stations. Islands and coasts are favored by a cooling sea breeze (in

[1] Sensible temperature does not refer to thermometer readings, but to the heat or cold one actually feels.

places referred to as the "doctor") that tempers the heat of the day, causing these areas to be much more attractive for living than the interiors.

Frost is unknown, except in areas of higher altitude, and there is no cessation of growth. Harvest can occur at any time of the year, being determined by the time of sowing and length of period required for a crop to mature.

Precipitation. The average yearly amount of precipitation is from 60 to 120 inches; there is no definite dry season but there is often a less wet season, especially in those portions of the regions more distant from the equator. During the season of heaviest precipitation, rain falls almost every day, whereas in the less wet period showers are lighter and there are a few days with no rain.

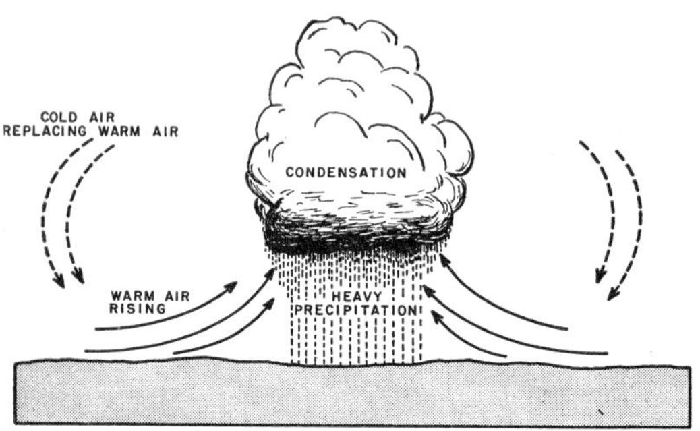

FIGURE 2-6. *The mechanics of convectional precipitation.*

The equatorial low, frequently known as the *convectional* belt, is an area of rising air currents where the resulting rain is seldom of long duration. This precipitation is chiefly the convectional type which is a result of the interaction of a set of physical laws.[2] The earth absorbs and is warmed by incoming solar radiation. The humid surface air becomes heated, causing a decrease in air pressure. The warm air, expanding and rising, is further lifted by an influx of cooler air into the low pressure area. The warm air, filled with water vapor, ascends, cools, and condenses in the upper altitudes, forming numerous billowy cumulus and cumulo-nimbus clouds with anvil-shaped crowns. The maximum of heating is usually in the early afternoon; at this time the cycle of convection is completed by the release from the cumulus clouds of torrential rain storms, often accompanied by thunder and lightning.

The convectional belt has an average of 75 to 150 thunderstorms a year. The islands of Southeast Asia are the most thundery parts of the world. Buitenzorg, Java, records 322 days a year with thunder. In some localities several thunderstorms occur during one day. Showers are usually of short duration and the sun often appears after the storm has passed. Sometimes rain continues to fall into the evening, but as the heat of the day diminishes, there is a tendency for skies to clear. There have been instances, however, when rain has continued for 24 hours or more. Besides the usual daily occurrence of the showers, there is also a somewhat clock-like regularity to their arrival. These precipitation conditions are usually associated with large land masses.

The daily rainfall regime over island areas or coastal fringes tends to reach its peak toward evening. Bodies of water heat more slowly than land and reach their maximum temperature later in the day, producing the convectional condition that causes showers to occur early in the evening or in the night.

The rainfall of the windward coasts is less influenced by the convectional belt. Heavy precipitation in these areas is due to the continuous trade winds rising along the highlands paralleling the coast. This precipitation is the *orographic* type. The steady trades, blowing over wide expanses of warm water, take up great quantities of water vapor. These winds, charged with vapor, rise along the windward slopes of the highland barriers. The forced ascent causes cooling in the higher altitudes and heavy precipitation falls on the windward sides. Leeward of the mountains where the air is descending and warming, there is less rain. The leeward side is known as the dry shadow (or *rainshadow*). The amount of precipitation received in the dry shadow area is dependent upon the altitude and the continuity of the mountain barrier. High, continuous mountains reduce the precipitation to

[2] Recent investigations indicate that weak cyclonic storms are also important sources of rain in the vicinity of the equator.

FIGURE 2-7. *Cumulo-nimbus clouds with partially forged anvil. The "cauliflower" swellings have dissolved in the upper portion of the cloud mass. Notice the heavy shower in progress.* (United States Weather Bureau.)

arid proportions in the lee areas. In contrast, orographic influences produce the highest precipitation in the Rainy Tropics as well as in the world as a whole.

Climate and white man

The impairment of energy resulting from the direct effects of Rainy Tropical climate on white man has been considered the major handicap to tropical development. Research, however, is proving that white man can work and live successfully in the Rainy Tropics if shelter, clothing, customs, and attitudes are fitted to the environment.[3] Indirectly, Rainy Tropical climate may have an adverse effect on white man. Proper vitamin requirements are not supplied to the body since crops are unable to derive nutrients from leached soils. The moisture and warmth favor the rapid growth of bacteria and disease-carrying insects. Poor health, lack of energy, and therefore initiative are usually due to an insufficient amount of proteins and vitamins, and to debilitating diseases. The lack of energy often characteristic of the indigenous peoples is attributed to the direct effect of climate,

[3] For a discussion of climate and man, see L. H. Newburgh, ed., *Physiology of Heat Regulation and Science of Clothing*. Philadelphia: W. B. Saunders Company, 1949.

FIGURE 2-8. *The mechanics of orographic precipitation.*

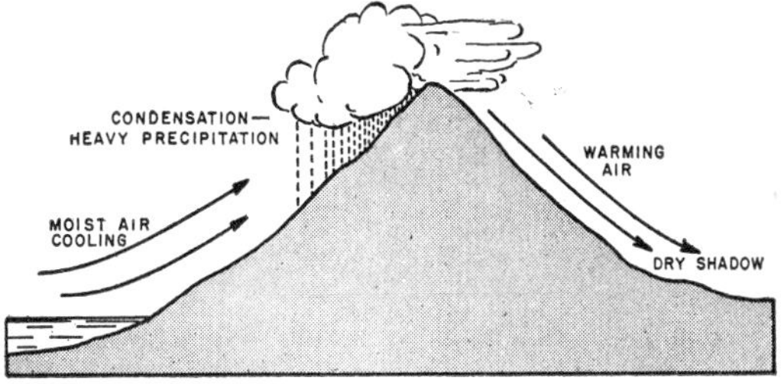

whereas this lethargy is actually caused by malnutrition and disease often brought about by low standards of living.

Experience and research show that the following facts are of value to tropical dwellers: (1) Consistent exercise is an aid in maintaining better physical condition. (2) Frequent visits to the highlands act as a tonic. (3) Plenty of salt in the diet replenishes loss through excessive perspiration. (4) Supplementary vitamins furnish the body with necessary elements lacking in the food. (5) Loose-fitting and light-colored clothing aids in combating heat and humidity. (6) Shaded and well-ventilated housing improves the comforts of living. (7) Proper sanitation procedures, including provision for safe water supply and adequate sewage, minimize the dangers of disease.

Surface features

Climate is one of several factors that influence the nature of landforms. Rocks are decomposed rapidly by the chemical action of the atmospheric elements. In the Rainy Tropics, prevailing high temperature, heavy rainfall, and organic acids generated by both living and decaying plants and animals combine to produce rapid chemical weathering. Thus, one of the characteristic features of these regions is a deep layer of *regolith* or weathered material overlaying the solid bedrock and completely obscuring it. The heavy mantle of vegetation tends to retain this unconsolidated mass and gives a rounded form to the land surface.

Numerous perennial streams result from the heavy and persistent rainfall. Two of the longest rivers in the world, the Amazon and the Congo, are found here. The concept of extensive swamps covering much of the area is erroneous. Rapid run-off and evaporation do not permit this condition, except along low-lying positions on flood plains, deltas, and coastal fringes.

Amazon Basin. The basin drained by the Amazon system is one of the major lowlands of the world. In an area so large it is apparent that there would be a variety of surface features, but away from the streams vast stretches are little known; accurate maps and information are lacking.

FIGURE 2-9. *River transportation in the Amazon Basin. Notice the string of small boats being towed. For a low fee, native boatmen can save themselves much labor in going upstream.* (Brazilian Government Trade Bureau.)

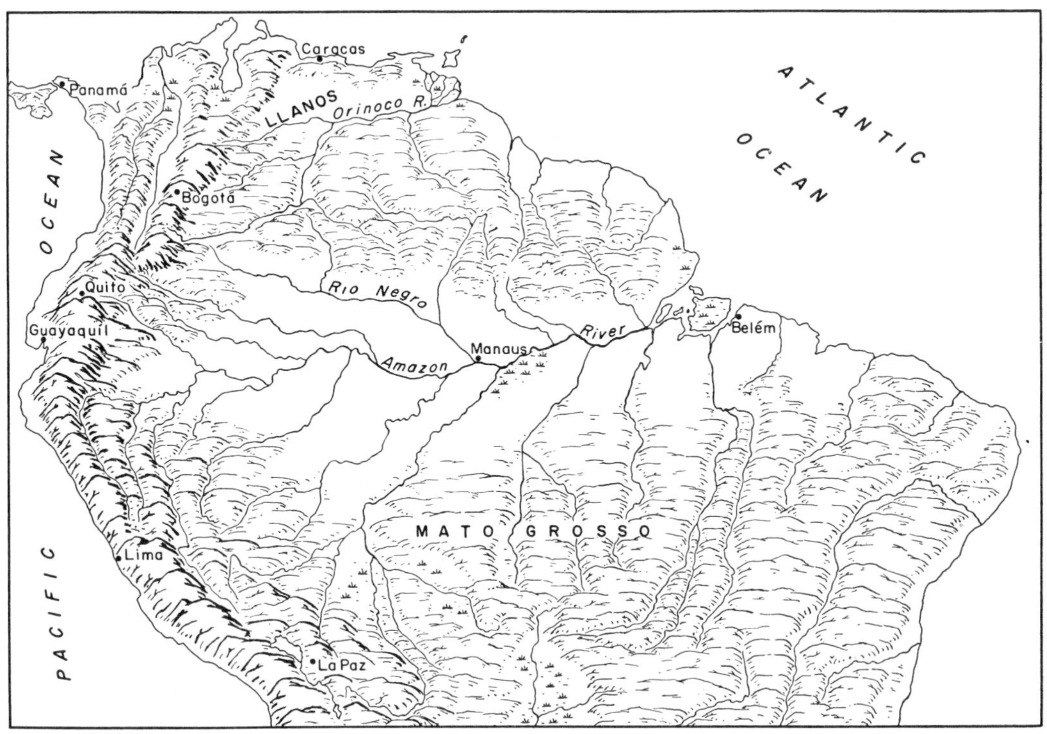

FIGURE 2-10. *Physiographic diagram of northern South America.*

The Amazon lowlands, which extend westward in a *dendritic* or tree-like pattern, have been formed by stream deposits and comprise one of the world's major alluvial plains. In the lower course of the main stem this flood plain is about 50 miles wide, but it decreases in width toward the headwaters. Narrower flood plains extend finger-like out from the Amazon and up the tributaries. The rise in elevation progressing up the river plain is slight and the river has a remarkably low gradient all the way from the mountain front to the sea; this is a major factor producing the seasonal widespread inundation. The flood plain is usually constricted by bluffs and the *interfluves,* or areas between the streams, are generally considered to be low, undulating uplands.

Since the earliest penetrations by man, the Amazon system has been the transport artery of this great basin. Rivers are still the most important means of access. The largest of ocean-going vessels can sail regularly to Manaus, about 1000 miles from the open sea, and smaller craft can go virtually to the foot of the Andes and hundreds of miles up many of the tributaries. The magnitude of this giant river is difficult to comprehend. Earl Parker Hanson in his *New Worlds Emerging* states:

> In length, the Amazon River is exceeded only by the Nile, and very little by it; in volume of water, by no three of the world's other rivers combined. Three thousand nine hundred miles long, it has its western-most sources high in the Andes, within a hundred miles of the Pacific Ocean, and its mouth in the Atlantic. It is estimated that one-fifth of all the world's running fresh water is carried by the Amazon; at low water its mouth, a hundred and fifty miles wide, pours some 60 billion gallons per hour into the sea to turn the ocean from salt to brackish for over a hundred miles from shore. It would take a score of Mississippi Rivers to equal that low-water flow, which is vastly exceeded in the rainy season.

Nobody has more than a vague idea of the Amazon's annual high-water flow. Near Manaus, a thousand miles upstream, it has a yearly rise, between the dry season and the rainy, of up to sixty feet. At its peak, the river increases hundreds of miles in width at several points, flooding thousands of square miles of forest-covered land.

There are some eleven hundred known tributaries of the Amazon, not counting thousands of brooks. Nine or ten of these tributaries exceed the Rhine in length, and carry more than double its volume of water. Seven of them are over a thousand miles long, and one, the Madeira, is nearly three thousand miles from source to mouth. Yet the main stream often receives the waters of these subject rivers without showing any appreciable increase in either width or current.[4]

Middle America. In Middle America, the Rainy Tropics occupy a relatively narrow coastal zone, backed by the slopes of the rugged cordillera which is part of a continuous belt of mountains stretching from Alaska to Tierra del Fuego. This coastal zone, largely an undulating plain and in proximity to United States markets, has been favored for the establishment of numerous banana plantations. Most of the islands of the West Indies included in this region have interior highlands with narrow coastal plains.

Congo Basin. In contrast to the lowland drained by the Amazon River, the basin drained by the second great river of the Rainy Tropics, the Congo, is 1000 feet and more above sea level. In fact, the entire continent of Africa may be thought of as a large plateau with steep edges bordered by a narrow coastal fringe of lowland of varying width. The Congo Basin is an immense shallow depression within the surface of this plateau. The rim of the plateau forms a highland border, which becomes more pronounced where the East African Highlands form a distinct barrier, displacing the Rainy Tropics climate with Tropical Highland climate. The lowest portion of the basin is in the north where the drainage divide between the Ubangi tributary of the Congo and the Shari River draining northward into Lake Chad is almost imperceptible. Drainage of the basin is provided by the Congo River system; the main stem enters in the southeast, swings in a broad curve through the basin, taking up tributaries from the north and south, and leaves via the southwest, where the Congo cuts through the rimming plateau and descends nearly 1000 feet to the coast in a series of wild rapids. Inability to navigate the lower Congo was a major factor retarding exploration of the heart of Africa. Above the falls the main stem is navigable for river steamers from Stanley Pool to Stanley Falls; many miles of the major tributaries are also navigable. The western slopes of the plateau are drained by many short, swift-flowing streams.

Southeast Asia and adjoining islands. The Southeast Asia realm comprises the southern two-thirds of the Malay Peninsula and several thousand islands of Indonesia and the eastern Philippines. The surface features are characterized by mountainous interiors and intricate patterns of lowlands and valleys. The major plains are coastal; many are deltaic, formed by the accumulation of sediments at the mouths of the short, swift streams draining the mountain slopes. Many of the Pacific islands display similar characteristics, although low, flat islands are also found; the nature of these will be discussed in the following chapter.

Natural vegetation

The high temperatures, heavy precipitation, and high humidities of the Rainy Tropics produce a climatic optimum for luxuriant vegetative growth. Few areas compare with its abundant plant life; the many varieties defy easy classification. Studies made in Malaya and the island of Trinidad indicated that several thousand different species may be found in a relatively small area. In all regions many botanical specimens still await scientific study and systematic nomenclature.

Natural vegetation of the Rainy Tropics is grouped into (*1*) the selva or rain forest, (*2*) jungle, and (*3*) coastal types. The *selva* is a broadleaf evergreen forest. The many varieties are mixed and do not grow in pure stands like the forests of Douglas fir in the North Amer-

---

[4] From Hanson, Earl Parker, *New Worlds Emerging.* New York: Duell, Sloan, and Pearce, Inc., 1949, 109-110. By permission of the publishers and author.

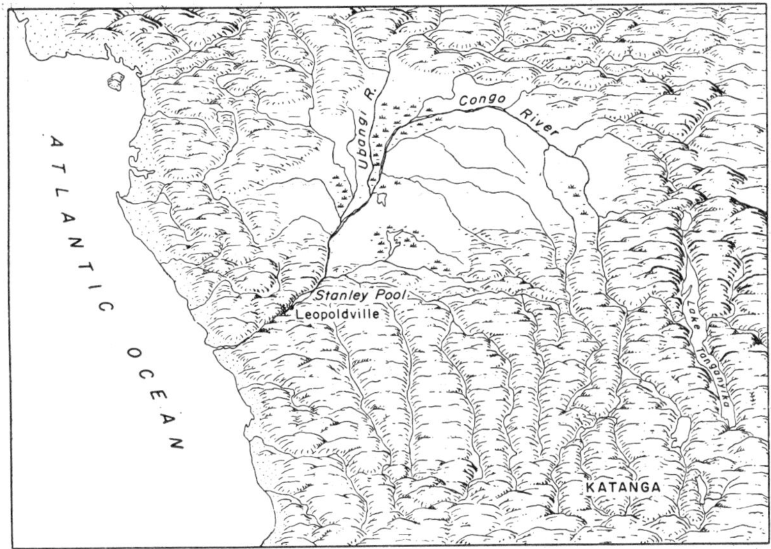

FIGURE 2-11. *Physiographic diagram of the Congo Basin.*

ican Pacific Northwest. The trunks, with little branch structure, stretch 100 to 150 feet into the air, bursting suddenly into branches and foliage. Each tree carries on a life-and-death struggle for light. The separate crowns coalesce and form a thick canopy above the forest floor. Weaving around the trunks and intermingled with the crowns is an intricate network of lianas, colorful orchids, and parasitic plants. The canopy prevents sunlight from reaching the forest floor; this limits the growth of grass and other low vegetative cover. The interior of the forest is gloomy and the light is subdued even at mid-day; the lianas hanging in garlands from the canopy give an eerie effect. Travel is not restricted, but it is easy to become lost. There is no guiding sun nor landmarks, only the tree columns and the green roof overhead.

On steep slopes, along drainage ways, and in other places where light can penetrate to the forest floor, the jungle, a dense thicket of low trees, shrubs, and vines, takes command. If a clearing has been made by man, storm or fire, it becomes a battleground with every green thing competing for the life-giving light. The jungle is an impenetrable barrier that hinders development and exploration and has relatively little economic value. Because waterways were the chief means of penetration, the heavy jungle growth overhanging these streams erroneously gave the early impression that vast areas consisted of nothing but jungle.

Heavy stands of mangroves fringe mud flats, lagoons, and marshes, and cluster around river mouths entering salt water. During high water, the mangroves appear as a thick wall of greenery; as the water subsides, their exposed stilt-like roots present a weird impenetrable maze. Coastlines with sandy shores are frequently rimmed with stately coconut palms. Coconut seeds are carried by ocean currents; the palm is found on nearly all islands of the humid tropics.

There is no holiday for vegetation in the Rainy Tropics—growth is rapid, uninterrupted, and continuous.

Native animal life

The native animal life matches the natural vegetation in abundance and variety. As yet man has little altered the virgin conditions. All the regions are characterized by: (*1*) an immense number and variety of insects, (*2*) a majority of arboreal fauna, (*3*) few grazing and carnivorous types, and (*4*) abundant aquatic life. Similarities, however, stop with these generalizations; each region has its own special species.

FIGURE 2-12. *Jungle scene near Belem in the Amazon Basin. Note the variety, luxuriance, and impenetrable character of the vegetation.* (Brazilian Government Trade Bureau.)

The count of insect life is endless. There are clouds of brilliant butterflies, endless termites, mosquitoes, spiders, ferocious driver ants, ticks, and gnats. Many are stinging, blood-sucking, and disease-carrying. The warm humid climate affords ideal breeding conditions for insects and the absence of frost prevents any interruption in their life cycle. Nature partly compensates for the gloom of the selva by the brilliant colors of its bird life, which varies from bee-like hummingbirds to gaudy parrots. Reptiles, camoufláged by color and resembling lianas, vary from deadly vipers to thirty-foot anacondas. Ranging through the canopy of foliage, which provides a variety of food such as fruit, nuts, sap, bark, and leaves, are monkeys, sloths, bats, and other arboreal creatures. There are few herbivorous animals in the selva, due to the lack of forage. The carnivores who prey on the grass-eaters are also uncommon. Characterizing the ground types are the anteaters with tongues nearly two feet long, ground cats, wild pigs, and (in Africa) lowland gorillas and the strange okapis. Occasionally animals from the bordering savannas penetrate the fringes of the selvas. Streams abound in fish and water fowl, and crocodiles are often seen dozing on the mud banks. Herds of hippopotami, found only in Africa, feed on aquatic plants in the quiet stretches of tropical rivers. In the warm ocean bodies of the tropics animal life is as abundant and varied as that found on the land.

Soil

Soils are generally low in fertility and removal of the natural vegetation soon exhausts the meager fertility available for crops. This situation appears anomalous in view of the vigorous vegetative cover, but the climatic conditions that produce the heavy vegetation also account for infertile soils. Soil fertility refers to the cultivated crop-producing capacity of soils rather than natural vegetative-producing capacity. The fertility elements most often needed for plant growth are nitrogen, phosphorus, and potash. Several additional elements are recognized as essential plant nutrients; calcium, magnesium, sulphur, and iron are supplied by the soil, and from the air and water come carbon, oxygen, and hydrogen. Various types of malnutrition in plants are corrected, and better yields sometimes are obtained, when small traces of minerals such as boron, copper, and magnesium are available.

In the Rainy Tropics four features tend to reduce the quantity of fertility elements in the soil. (*1*) Prevailingly high temperatures and heavy rainfall promote exceedingly rapid chemical decomposition. (*2*) Leaching is extreme and continuous as there is no frost season. Because of abundant rainfall, much water soaks into the ground. Water percolating

FIGURE 2-13. *A palm-rimmed bay on a Rainy Tropic island.* (Pan American World Airways.)

through the soil tends to dissolve the soluble minerals as well as silica, removing them in the drainage, and leaving mainly the insoluble residue which is largely iron and aluminum hydroxides. (*3*) The water soaking down through the soils tends to carry fine particles, concentrating them at lower levels out of the reach of plants. This process, *eluviation,* tends to form a soil with a coarse surface layer and a layer of fine accumulation at some depth. (*4*) The climate conditions favor the existence of an extremely active bacteria life on the forest floor; this rapidly destroys the limited organic matter and, as a result, soils are very low in organic content. The soil-forming process common to the Rainy Tropics is known as *laterization;* the soils, often reddish in color, are termed *lateritic*.

There are two significant exceptions to the general infertility of soils in the Rainy Tropics. The first, and most widespread, is the young alluvial soils found on the flood plains and deltas of streams, where they have been carried from all parts of the individual drainage basins and deposited during periods of flood. The alluviums are usually relatively productive and, moreover, their fertility is replenished by periodic flooding. The second exception is found where the soils have been derived from young volcanic materials, high in mineral-content. The most notable example is found on the island of Java, where rich young soils developed from volcanic materials are a large factor in the island's ability to support a dense population.

MAN IN THE RAINY TROPICS

On a population density map, the Rainy Tropics stand out as thinly settled regions of the world. Over extensive areas of the Amazon Basin, the population density is under two persons per square mile.

Similar conditions prevail over much of the Congo Basin as well as on many of the large islands of Indonesia and the Philippines. Throughout the major portion of the Rainy Tropics, man has yet failed to become the conqueror, and the native vegetation cover still dominates.

Somewhat denser populations tend to follow the pattern of the river valleys, where alluvial soils and transport possibilities are attractive. Coastal areas, too, sometimes provide these conditions as well as offering a more favorable climate. The trade wind coast of Brazil and the Guinea Coast illustrate these conditions.

A great contrast to these sparsely-populated regions of Africa and South America are the oriental lands of Southeast Asia, where, in some areas, man and his works dominate. The island of Java, 50,745 square miles in area, has a population of 50 million, one of the most densely populated lands in the world.

Native man in the Rainy Tropics

Among the native peoples that constitute the greater part of population of the Rainy Tropics, there exists great diversity in race, customs, and stage of development. However, in most cases native man would be classed near the bottom of modern industrial society's scale of culture. In contrast to man in the United States, Canada, or Europe, his living is primitive and his needs and wants are few. Work is performed by hand, dwellings are simple structures, clothing often satisfies only minimum requirements, and transportation is on foot or by crude river craft. Modern trappings of industrial societies would not, for the most part, fit into his present scheme of living nor be adaptable to his present mode of life. Many factors account for his simple scale of living and slight resource development. The year-round harvest season removes the necessity for storing food and tends to curb initiative for producing surplus. Owing to isolation and limited contact with the industrial world, his culture has been only slightly affected and his material needs have remained small. Where he has come in contact with European and American tropical exploiters, however, his mode of life has been altered and a veneer of their culture superimposed.

Concepts of the native living entirely upon wild game and fruits, roots, and nuts from the forest are erroneous. The pygmies of the Congo Basin, certain primitive Indians of the upper Amazon, and a few of the tribes in the selvas of Asia live by hunting and gathering. The Semang of Malaya present an example of this way of life. The Semang wander in bands of about 30 people, depending almost entirely upon edible roots, stalks, leaves, fruits, and larvae for nourishment. A little fishing is practiced and small game is hunted with blowguns, bows and poisoned arrows. After a forest area of approximately 20 square miles has been covered thoroughly and all sources of food depleted, the group moves to a new area. These are the true "jungle nomads." Altogether these people represent but a small segment of the total population of the Rainy Tropics. Most groups have advanced beyond this stage and such activities are only an adjunct to the basic means of support—farming.

Migratory agriculture. A migratory system of agriculture, variously known as *milpa* in Latin America, *fang* in parts of Africa, and *ladang* in Indonesia, as well as by many other local names, is practiced in the areas of sparse population. The natives usually supplement the food they grow and provide other necessities by gathering, hunting, and fishing. They often exchange products of the forest at trading posts for essentials such as cloth and metal equipment. Migratory agriculture varies only in detail from one area to another; the general characteristics are similar throughout the Rainy Tropics. With the aid of a machete, a long, thick-bladed knife, small islands are partially cleared in the selva by cutting down the smaller trees and girdling and trimming the limbs of the larger ones. The slash is burned and crops are planted among the stumps and charred logs. Normally this process involves the simple dropping of seeds into holes gouged with a pointed stick; following the planting, the crops are given little care until the harvest. Fortunately, under the reliable climatic conditions, crop failures are rare. Crop emphasis varies from place to place, but one of the main staples grown in these native patches is *plantain,* a member of the banana family. Plantain can be boiled, fried like potatoes, or ground and used as flour. Cloth may also be woven from the fibery parts of its leaves. Other crops may include cassava (manioc), yams, corn, and a variety of vegetables. The root of the taro is used extensively for food in many of the Pacific islands. As a rule, few domestic animals are kept, but some groups do have dogs, a small number of chickens and ducks, and perhaps a dozen or so sheep and goats that are reserved for payment of debts, purchase of wives, or sacrifices. Much of the farm work is done by the women while the men are hunting, fishing, and gathering. A clearing may be farmed for two or three years, at the end of which (*1*) soil fertility is virtually depleted because the land is exposed to leaching and the growing of crops is exhausting nutrients, and (*2*) coarse grasses and other vegetation are beginning to take over the clearing. Rather than attempt to cope with these conditions, the natives find it easier to abandon the clearing and make a new one—usually nearby, a short distance from their semi-permanent village.

The village is frequently located on a stream or within a short distance of a water supply. A stream not only furnishes domestic water, but also fish and a transport artery. The village consists of a small cluster of houses, often without plan; occasionally there is a linear pattern with houses lining a central street. Construction is simple, using natural materials at hand. A framework of poles support a thatch roof; walls are of woven grass, palm fronds, or bark. In some settlements the houses are elevated on poles—this provides better air circulation and some protection from insects, marauding animals, and the dangers of high water. Furnishings are simple. A household will usually have an iron kettle; other kitchen utensils are made of wood and coconut shells or sea shells. Bamboo is used extensively in Southeast Asia for construction, and also for making containers for cooking food and carrying water. Nothing indicates permanence in the village or the clearing. It is a relatively simple matter to abandon one site and move quickly to another.

FIGURE 2-14. *A native hut in the Philippines.* (G. Martin.)

Sedentary cultivation. Migratory agriculture may typify native activity scattered over the bulk of the area of the Rainy Tropics, but larger numbers of people are supported by sedentary or settled agriculture. Many groups remain permanently in one area, cultivating the same fields year after year. Several conditions seem to induce sedentary farming. (*1*) Population pressures have forced continuous use of the same land. (*2*) Settlement has been more common upon fertile soils whose enduring productiveness encouraged continuous use. (*3*) Techniques which have made possible the continuous use of the same land have been acquired, developed, or adapted from other cultures.

Sedentary agriculture is more advanced and the society practicing it more stable; however, not all groups are on the same level. In general, the crops are similar to those grown by migratory agriculturalists, but more stress is placed upon perennial crops such as coconuts and plantain. In some cases families live on isolated farms—this is especially true along the Amazon River, where they raise subsistence crops, keep livestock, and supplement their living by fishing. For cash income, wood is cut and sold for fuel to passing river steamers. Products are also gathered from the forest. Where people live in clusters the villages are permanent, but the houses, buildings, furnishings, and implements are of simple construction.

The imprint of western contact is often greater upon the sedentary farmer than upon the migratory groups. Many have developed

FIGURE 2-15. *Javanese farmers carrying their produce to market in Bandoeng. This is a typical mode of transporting goods in the Orient. The modern bridge and road are evidences of the former Dutch colonial administration.* (Standard Oil Company of New Jersey.)

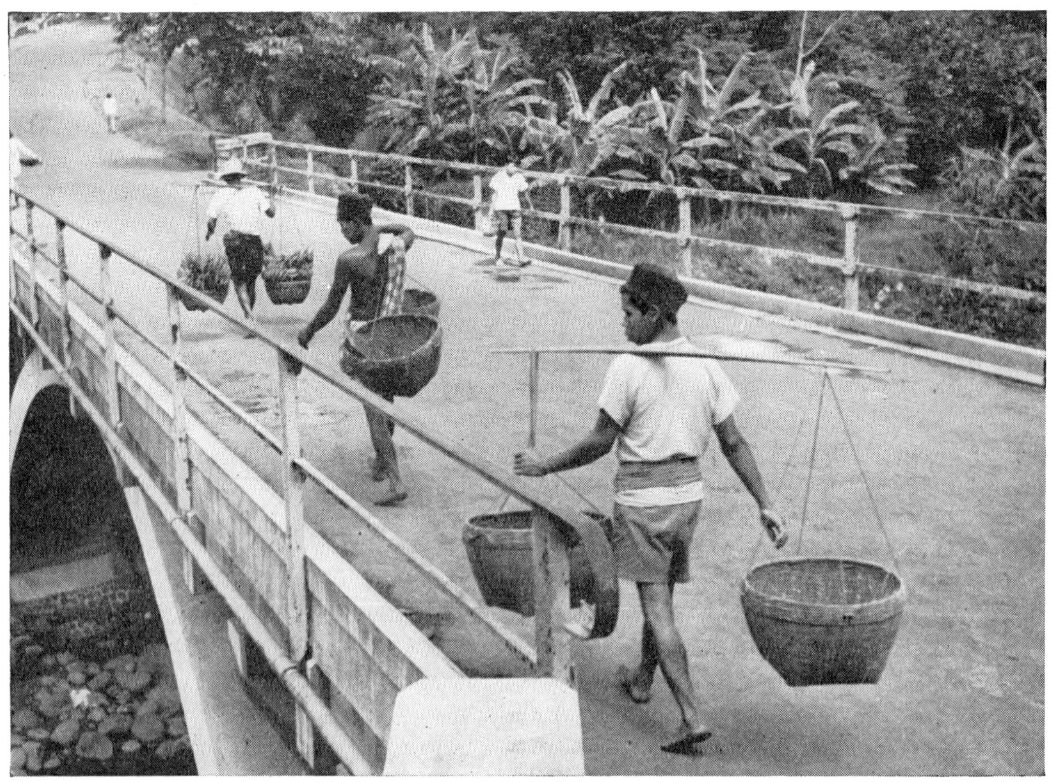

tastes for imported materials such as cloth and various items of manufactured equipment. Sewing machines may be found in many homes throughout the tropics. Cultures in these cases are definitely in transition; many of the traditional ways of life are fast disappearing.

The prime example of sedentary subsistence agriculture is found in Southeast Asia. Java is distinctive as one of the most densely populated lands of the world. Prior to the coming of white man to the area the fertility of the rich lava soils had been discovered by the natives of Java, who were largely permanently-established agriculturalists. Dutch colonization brought stability to government, provided agricultural guidance which developed an increased food supply, and improved sanitation and health, paving the way for great increases in population numbers. Today the Javanese are practicing an intensive subsistence agriculture in which rice, the highest yielding cereal, is the principal food crop. Farming is similar in other parts of the Orient which will be discussed in succeeding chapters.

Native commercial farming. Native commercial agriculture on a small scale existed in Southeast Asia before the Christian era and trade was carried on with merchants from India, China, and Arabia. Beginning with the fourteenth century, spices from Malaya and the East Indies became an attraction for European trade. These products, so important in Europe for preserving and flavoring food, were produced entirely in native gardens. In time, demands from western Europe and the United States encouraged the production of other crops, such as coconuts, palm oil, cacao, and rubber.

Native commercial agriculture in the modern era has been overshadowed by the plantation system; however, considerable amounts of commodities are produced on native plots and the trend in this direction is increasing. Most of the native commercial agriculture is found in the African and Asian regions. Along the Guinea Coast of Africa, most of the cacao production is in the hands of the natives. In Southeast Asia and adjoining islands much of the coconut production is in native hands, and the native output of natural rubber supplies nearly one-half of the total of the world. The native holdings are generally small; the average Malayan native rubber grove is about 4½ acres. Unscientific and lackadaisical methods often lower the quality of native production, but this is a peasant enterprise with little fixed cost, in contrast to the plantations. It is unlikely that small scale native commercial farming will soon entirely supplant the occidental plantation system in supplying tropical foods and raw materials, but it would appear that this phase will be accelerated by growing nationalism and increasing technical knowledge. Many small farmers of Middle America today are growing bananas for export. This

FIGURE 2-16. *A small native rubber producer in Malaya. Having no smoke house, he hangs his sheets of rubber on poles in the open air to dry. The coconut palms surrounding his stilted, wooden house furnish an integral part of his food supply.* (Natural Rubber Bureau.)

FIGURE 2-17. *Native cacao production in the Gold Coast. All the family take part in harvesting and marketing the crop.* (British Information Services.)

traditional plantation commercial crop is being grown on farms ranging from half an acre to 25 acres. The problems of controlling disease in the larger plantings and obtaining labor supply for the large operations have helped speed the trend toward the smaller production pattern. World War II provided a stimulus for the increase of rubber production in Latin America. Most of the larger countries, determined to be self-sufficient in rubber, have or are considering programs to encourage small-farm production.

White man in the Rainy Tropics

The exotic products of the Rainy Tropics have long been the lure attracting white man to these regions. Exploitation began with the Phoenicians, followed much later by the Portuguese, Spanish, Dutch, British, and other European nations, and finally the United States. Much of the area has been under the political domination of these nations and development has revolved around their economic activities. Early trade was chiefly in sugar, spices, gold, ivory, and slaves. Today's exploitation is concentrated on the products of tropical agriculture, tropical woods, and minerals.

With the rapid development of industry in western Europe and the United States in the latter part of the nineteenth century, native agriculture and gathering failed to supply the increasing needs for tropical foods and raw materials. This growing market, along with improvements in transportation, refrigeration, and tropical sanitation, gave impetus to the plantation system. Plantations have brought the products of the forest to cultivated fields to meet the needs of middle-latitude consumers.

FIGURE 2-18. *Homes of workers on a rubber plantation in Malaya. Workers live in neat, attractive villages furnished by the management. Families have their own individual garden plots, and grazing areas are provided for livestock.* (Natural Rubber Bureau.)

Plantation agriculture. The plantation system is commercial tropical agriculture specializing in particular crops to supply areas outside of the tropic regions. The system was developed during the early colonization of the humid tropical Americas. Today, its greatest development is in Malaya, Indonesia, and the Caribbean area.

Plantation locations are usually close to the sea—the islands of Indonesia and the Malay Peninsula have long been favored. Littorals provide the best sites—flood plains have rich alluvial soils; there is accessible water transportation; sea breezes tend to alleviate the heat and humidity. The Southeast Asia area has the further advantages of being located on one of the great world trade routes and near large population centers from which cheap, industrious labor is readily available. If plantations are inland, their sites are often contiguous to rivers or railroads for ease of transporting commodities.

Plantations vary from area to area and with different crops, but their general characteristics are similar. They are based on large land holdings, and because of capital risks involved, are usually corporate organizations. Units range in size from simple developments consisting of only the overseers' dwellings and outbuildings, with a few hundred acres of crop land, to the more elaborate plantations, with homes for workers and technicians, stores, hospitals, schools, and several thousand acres of crop land. The average size of a rubber plantation in Malaya is 1538 acres.

The region supplies the proper environment

FIGURE 2-19. *Latex collection center. Tappers converge at the loading stage to await the factory truck. Notice the orchard-like appearance of the rubber trees in the background.* (British Information Services.)

and usually the labor. Technicians, tools, capital, fertilizer, clothes, building materials, and even canned and refrigerated foods are imported. The work is largely performed by hand labor. In the past plantation owners found it cheaper to use native laborers instead of mechanical equipment. Now operators are beginning to use some machinery; the greatest advances in this trend are found on banana plantations of Middle America and rubber plantations of Southeast Asia. In some areas small herds of livestock are maintained to keep down the undergrowth.

The chief crops of the plantations in the Rainy Tropics are rubber, coconuts, bananas, palm oil, cacao, and abaca (manila hemp). The Malayan-Indonesian area provides over 90 per cent of the plantation rubber. Banana production centers around the Caribbean Sea. Cacao is grown on the Bahia Coast of Brazil and in Ecuador. Palm oil plantations are centered in Indonesia and Malaya, but much of the product is obtained from native plots in West Africa. About one-third of coconut production is in the Philippine Islands, another third in Indonesia, and the balance on scattered Pacific islands. Abaca is produced on both plantations and small holdings in the Philippines.

The development of the plantation system has accorded the world (*1*) a larger and more dependable supply of tropical products, (*2*) lower prices for the consumer, (*3*) a more uniform and a better quality of products, and (*4*) an introduction of scientific methods in the cultivation and production of tropical commodities.

The plantation system is not without problems. Growth in nationalism within the countries of the Rainy Tropics is resulting in policies which are not as favorable to foreign investors as previously. Regulations regarding benefits to native workers are more stringent, taxes are higher, and tropical countries are attempting to increase their own returns from foreign developments. Plant disease is a problem in the production of certain crops such as bananas, where control programs, including occasional abandonment of one area and reestablishment in another, leads to increased cost. Marketing is another problem. The huge areas available for the growth of commercial crops in the Rainy Tropics make the production of surpluses easily possible. Inability to maintain production volume in the proper relation to demand results in lowered prices and profits—this has been notably true regarding rubber, which has the further limitation of a synthetic competitor. Nevertheless the plantation system will undoubtedly continue and perhaps even increase in importance, but

FIGURE 2-20. *Cutting a road through a forest in New Guinea.* (Standard Oil Company of New Jersey.)

it may well be that the tropical countries will assume an expanded role in its management. There are many more species of vegetative life that thrive in this environment that could furnish food and raw materials. Commercial production awaits the development of tastes and markets.

Forest industries. The tropical selva is the most vigorous vegetative growth on earth and covers large areas, yet lumbering has been a secondary industry. The basic difficulty is found in the great variety of species coupled with the fact that many are at present of little economic importance. In contrast to lumbering in forest stands of the middle latitudes, where much of the cover can be used commercially, the valuable trees in the selva are widely scattered. Transportation is complicated by difficulties encountered in the movement of extremely heavy logs. Roads are hard to build and maintain on the rain-soaked terrain; proximity to water is one of the major considerations in forest exploitation. Streams are the main means of transport, but often the logs are too heavy to float and must be shipped on rafts. Labor is scarce, workers lack stamina and are unfavorably affected by disease. Modern logging equipment, especially Caterpillar tractors, is used in a few areas but the bulk of the labor is still performed by hand.

Despite the numerous limitations to the forest industry in the Rainy Tropics, certain hardwoods, especially mahoganies, are being exploited and have growing markets for furniture, veneering, decoration, and other special purposes. The South American selva contributes Brazilwood, mahoganies, rosewood, cedars, and Brazilian teakwood. Valuable commercial species from Middle America include dyewoods, mahogany, lignum vitae, and balsa. From Africa come rosewood, ebony, and African mahogany. Several hardwoods, but principally *lauan* (Philippine mahogany) are exported from the Philippines. The hardwoods are seldom prepared for consumer use in the region but are exported as logs or rough lumber for furthering processing.

Undoubtedly lumbering will take on greater significance as new uses are discovered for tropical woods, intermediate zone supplies are further exhausted, and mechanization in operations increases. The selva, furthermore, is a vast storehouse of cellulose raw material for the future. Forest plantations also offer possibilities since growth is rapid under the favorable climatic conditions. Balsa plantations in Latin America may be indicative of a trend.

The tropical forests provide many other products—fibers, gums, drugs, nuts, and saps—that enter the channels of trade through the native gathering industry. For example, chicle, the base for chewing gum, is the sap of the zapote tree of the Caribbean area; Brazil nuts, wild rubber, and balata are gathered in Amazonia, and palm nuts for vegetable oil, in Africa. Gathering is practiced by both the "jungle nomads" and the farmers who carry on the activity to either earn cash or have a medium for trade. The greater quantities are supplied by the latter group who, instead of wandering aimlessly through the forest, have somewhat systematized their activity. Sources of supply are well marked and definite routes are followed through the for-

FIGURE 2-21. *Hydraulic tin mining in Malaya. This is one of the many processes employed in tin mining. Powerful water jets cut and disintegrate the ground of the mine. A mixture of sand and clay, ore and water collects in the bottom of the mine whence it is pumped to the head of a flume. There the heavy tin ore is deposited while the lighter sand and clay are carried away with the stream of water.* (British Information Services.)

ests. Although the flow of products is often sporadic, the gathering industry makes valuable contributions of raw materials for which the demand is still too limited to make plantation production profitable.

Mining. The mineral wealth is not fully known. The remoteness of many areas and the heavy vegetative cover have made mineral surveys difficult. With the increasing needs of industrial nations, greater attention is being given to these regions for possible mineral resources.

Several areas are already prominent in mineral production. Much of the world's tin is mined on the Malay Peninsula and the Indonesian islands of Bangka, Belitong, and Singkep. Petroleum is produced on Sumatra, Borneo, and Java. Small deposits of iron are worked on a limited scale in Malaya and Mindanao. The Gold Coast is a leading producer of manganese, a metal vital in the steel industry. Bauxite is mined in large quantities in Surinam and British Guiana, which is also a producer of industrial diamonds.

Undoubtedly the Rainy Tropics will become more important sources of minerals as industrial demands multiply and stimulate further search. The control and exploitation of the mineral resources of the Rainy Tropics are largely in the hands of the United States and European interests.

Manufacturing. The bases for manufacturing are largely lacking under existing conditions. The normal procedure has been for the movement of raw materials to the industrial areas of western Europe and the United States. However, there is some semi-processing of certain agricultural products and tropical woods, oil refining, and tin smelting for ease and lower cost of shipment. On the windward coast of Brazil, Rio de Janeiro and Salvador have expanding industries based on raw materials from hinterlands beyond the Rainy Tropics to which they are connected by a net of railroad lines. Rio de Janeiro is a leading manufacturing city of the nation with products including cotton and wool textiles, leather goods, furniture, and flour. On the other hand, the natives who formerly provided their own requirements through handicrafts have in many cases become dependent upon imports for some of their necessities. The trading post is such an important factor in supplying native wants that often villages are built around them in some areas.

Urban centers

The lack of many urban centers in the Rainy Tropics reflects the limited commercial and industrial activities as well as the relatively small populations. Most cities of importance are commercial centers owing their development to favorable water transportation. Only two large urban centers of significance are found in the Amazon Basin. Manaus, 12 miles above the confluence of the Rio Negro and the main stream, is the central collecting point for the upper portion of the Basin. Belem, near the mouth, is the gateway city to the entire Amazon Basin. Rio de Janeiro and Salvador, the first and third largest cities of Brazil, are on the windward coast. Both are important commercial centers with rich agricultural hinterlands. Maceio, capital of the thriving sugar and cotton producing state of Alagoas, is also on this coast. Port of Spain is the chief city of Trinidad, serving as the seat of government and main port.

There are no important centers in the Rainy Tropic portion of the Congo Basin. Leopoldville on the southwest margin functions as the outlet for the entire basin. Situated 250 miles from the sea at the outlet of Stanley Pool on the Congo River, it serves as the breaking point where river traffic meets the rail line to Matadi, the ocean port on the Congo River.

Singapore is the master city of the Southeast Asia realm with a population of over three-fourths of a million. It owes its significance to several factors of location. One of the world's most important trade routes winds through the Straits of Malacca and bends around the Malay Peninsula. Singapore, a strategic port of call on a small island at the southern tip of the peninsula, has an excellent harbor and has become a notable collecting and distributing center, particularly for rubber and tin, due to its situation in the heart of

FIGURE 2-22. *Rio de Janeiro, Brazil, the largest city of the Rainy Tropics. Notice how the pattern of the city is rigidly controlled by the landforms and the sea. An excellent harbor was the attraction for city development.* (Pan American World Airways.)

the most highly developed tropical area. Singapore is also a British naval base. Jakarta, Java, is the main city, capital, and principal port of Indonesia, serving as the *entrepôt* for the entire archipelago. Farther east is Semarang, the fifth largest city and the port for north central Java.

OUTLOOK

With world population growing and food and industrial requirements multiplying, there appears to be little doubt of increasing development in the Rainy Tropics. The optimum climate for many plants and the enormous spaces devoid of people provide the regions with great argricultural potentialities, the development of which is dependent in part upon increased research in tropical soil management and a scientific approach to production. Acreage in crops currently grown on a commercial scale could be expanded many times, and the commercial production of other native plants usable for food, sap, or fiber awaits needs and markets. The rain forests offer one of the major hopes for filling the increasing wood demands of the world; utilization depends primarily upon the advancing field of wood technology to make practical the logging of the highly mixed stands. Mineral shortages in other regions have caused intensification of critical surveys; the list of strategic minerals supplied by tropical areas is growing. The hydroelectric potentials have been scarcely touched; Africa alone has almost four times the potential of North America. Although the industrial wave is just beginning to lap upon the Rainy Tropics, trends point to growing world significance of these regions.

Undoubtedly much capital and direction will come from Northern Hemisphere industrial nations, but there will also be greater local participation. Most of the countries with areas in the Rainy Tropics are awaking to their possibilities and beginning to move forward with scientific programs for development.

SELECTED REFERENCES

Bates, Marston, *Where Winter Never Comes, A Study of Man and Nature in the Tropics.* New York: Charles Scribner's Sons, 1952.

Dobby, E. H. G., "The Kelantan Delta," *Geographical Review,* XLI, No. 2, 1951, 226-255.

Forester, C. S., *The Sky and the Forest* (A novel). Boston: Little, Brown and Co., 1948.

Higbee, Edward C., "Of Man and the Amazon," *Geographical Review,* XLI, No. 3, 1951, 401-420.

Lawton, Graham H., "Recent Cultural Changes on the Islands of Nauru," *Journal of Geography,* L, No. 1, 1951, 12-20.

Metcalf, John E., "Decline of Plantation Agriculture in Indonesia," *Foreign Agriculture,* XVI, No. 4, 1952, 74-76.

Pelzer, Karl J., *Pioneer Settlement in the Asiatic Tropics, Studies in Land Utilization and Agricultural Colonization in Southeastern Asia.* New York: American Geographical Society, 1945.

Price, A. Grenfell, *White Settlers in the Tropics.* New York: American Geographical Society, 1939.

Spate, O. H. K., "Changing Native Agriculture in New Guinea," *Geographical Review,* XLIII, No. 2, 1953, 151-172.

Spencer, J. E., *Land and People in the Philippines.* Berkeley, Calif.: University of California Press, 1952.

Stamp, L. Dudley, *Africa, A Study in Tropical Development.* New York: John Wiley and Sons, Inc., 1953.

Wagley, Charles, *Amazon Town, A Study of Man in the Tropics.* New York: The Macmillan Company, 1953.

CHAPTER 3

Wet-Dry Tropics

THE WET-DRY TROPICS FORM ZONES of transition between regions of great contrast—the hot, wet lands of the Rainy Tropics and the hot, dry lands of the Tropical Deserts. From one border to the other there are marked changes in rainfall, vegetation, and agricultural potential. The unifying feature is a climatic rhythm, characterized by a season of rain and a season of drought, as distinguished from the sameness that prevails in the bordering lands. The heart of the Wet-Dry Tropics contains the great tropical grasslands, or savannas. The season of drought and the resource of grass provide the people of this realm with materially different conditions for living than are found in the Rainy Tropics or in the Tropical Deserts.

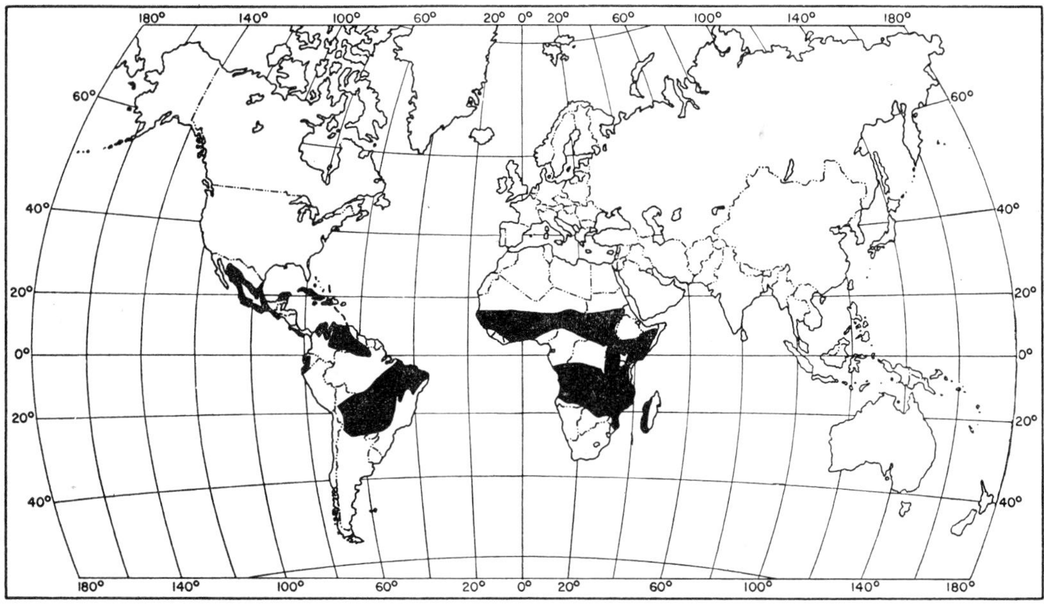

FIGURE 3-1. *The Wet-Dry Tropics.*

Location

The Wet-Dry Tropics lie on the poleward margins of the Rainy Tropics of Africa and Latin America—chiefly between 5° and 20° north and south latitude. A definite belt is formed only in Africa where the savanna lands extend across the continent; elsewhere highland barriers and continental configurations produce irregular shapes. Four major areas may be distinguished.

South America. The largest area in South America lies south of the equator. The greater portion is known as the Campos, the great grassland of Brazil; also included is the Gran Chaco of Bolivia, Paraguay, and Argentina. A second area comprises the basin of the Orinoco River, known as the Orinoco Llanos, and reaches northwestward to include the Maracaibo Basin of Venezuela and the Bolivar Savanna of northern Colombia. West of the Andes Mountains a smaller area of Wet-Dry Tropics is found on the coast of Ecuador.

Middle America. The Wet-Dry Tropics extend along the south and western coasts of Middle America, continuing through the Pacific and Caribbean lowlands of Mexico as far as the Tropic of Cancer. The major portion of the Yucatan Peninsula, Cuba, and other western islands of the West Indies are also included.

Africa. In Africa, Wet-Dry regions form a crescent partially encircling the Rainy Tropics. North of the equator the Sudan stretches from the Atlantic Ocean eastward to the highlands, including large portions of French West Africa, Anglo-Egyptian Sudan, the northern fringe of Ivory Coast, Gold Coast, and Dahomey, and a major share of Nigeria, where this climate type extends southward to the Gulf of Guinea. South of the equator the region reaches across the continent, including the northern and eastern portions of Angola, the southern edge of the Belgian Congo, all of Northern Rhodesia, part of Southern Rhodesia, and virtually all of Mozambique. The lower elevations of Tanganyika, Kenya, and Ethiopia in East Africa, as well as the west coast of Madagascar, also fall within this category.

Central Pacific Islands. Many islands in the Central Pacific between 5° and 20° north and south latitude may be classified in the Wet-Dry Tropics. They receive their rainfall principally as a result of shifting of the convectional belt and the trade winds.

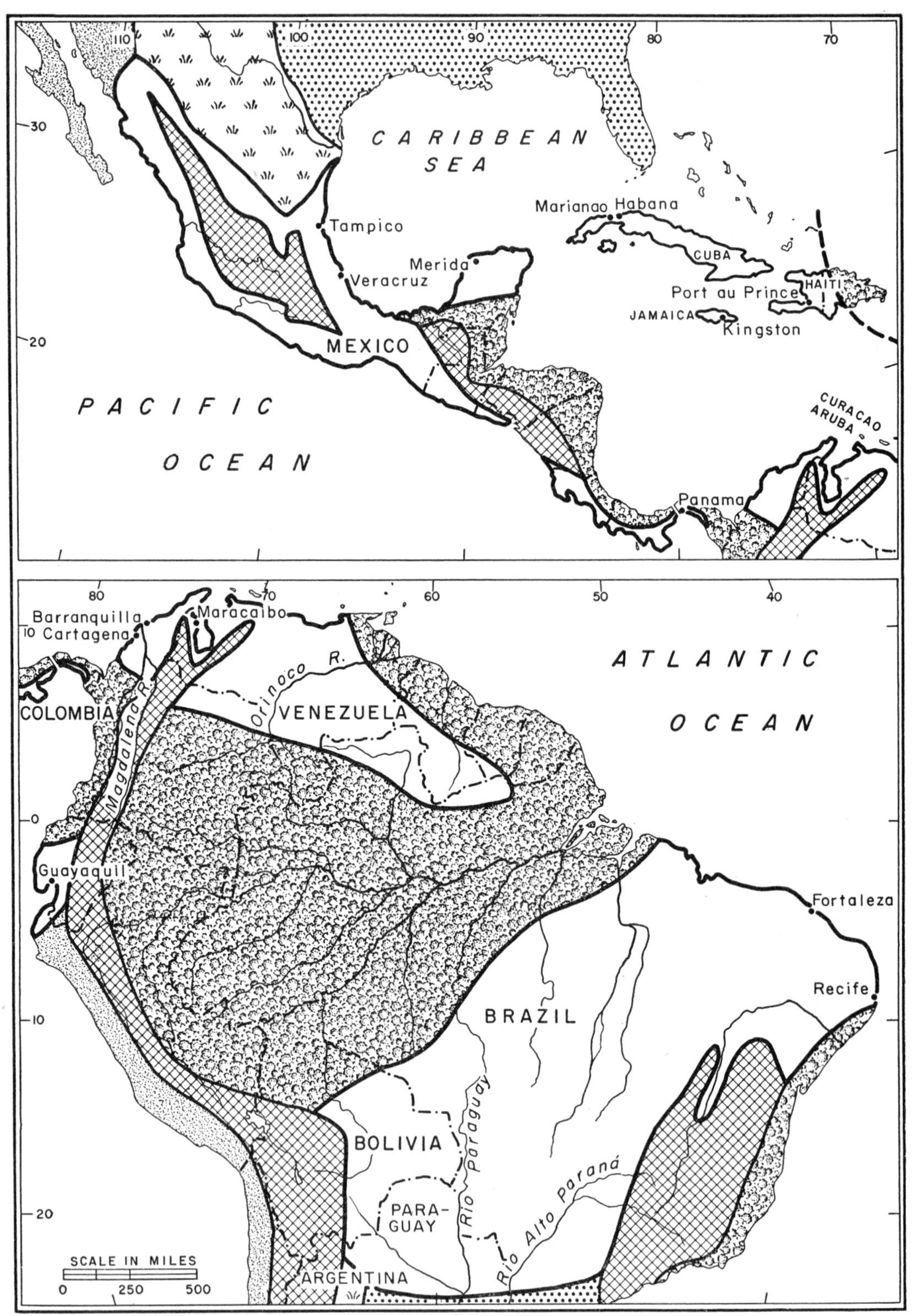

FIGURE 3-2. *The Wet-Dry Tropics of Latin America.*

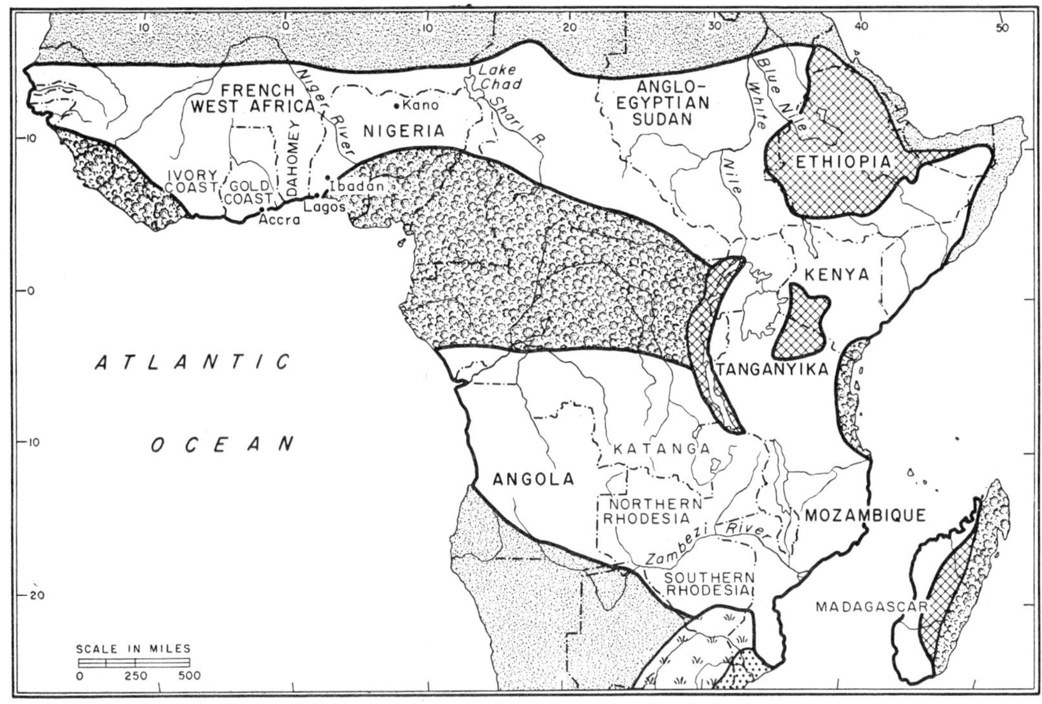

FIGURE 3-3. *The Wet-Dry Tropics of Africa.*

PHYSICAL ENVIRONMENT

Climate

The shifting of the sun's vertical rays rules the climate of the Wet-Dry Tropics. The equatorial low, or convectional belt, always dominant over the Rainy Tropics, migrates north and south with the movement of the sun's rays. The poleward extremes of this migration mark the outer boundaries of the Wet-Dry Tropics. Following the spring or vernal equinox in March, as the sun moves northward, areas bordering the Rainy Tropics in the Northern Hemisphere begin to acquire climatic conditions which are characterized by high humidities and thunder showers—similar conditions are present in the Southern Hemisphere following the autumnal equinox. When the convectional belt is in control, the climate of the region closely parallels that of the Rainy Tropics.

During the low sun period, the convectional belt is replaced by the trade winds or their source, the dry, settling air of the subtropical high. The low sun period is the dry season in each hemisphere; a blazing sun from an almost clear sky often raises temperatures to above 100°. Relatively clear night skies allow heat radiation, and diurnal ranges surpass those of the Rainy Tropics. The humidity is low and the air is hot, dry, and dusty. In some areas strong winds are characteristic; the Harmattan in the western Sudan blows directly from the Sahara Desert, lowering humidities and desiccating the ground and plant life. During the dry season, many small streams disappear and nature appears to be in hibernation. All this is changed when the high sun returns and the rains arrive. Rivers are transformed from sluggish streams to raging torrents, green shoots of grass appear, trees send out new leaves, and all nature is rejuvenated. The Wet-Dry Tropics are truly regions of marked seasonal contrast.

Temperatures. There is a constant supply of heat throughout the year and frost-free periods are continuous. The average monthly

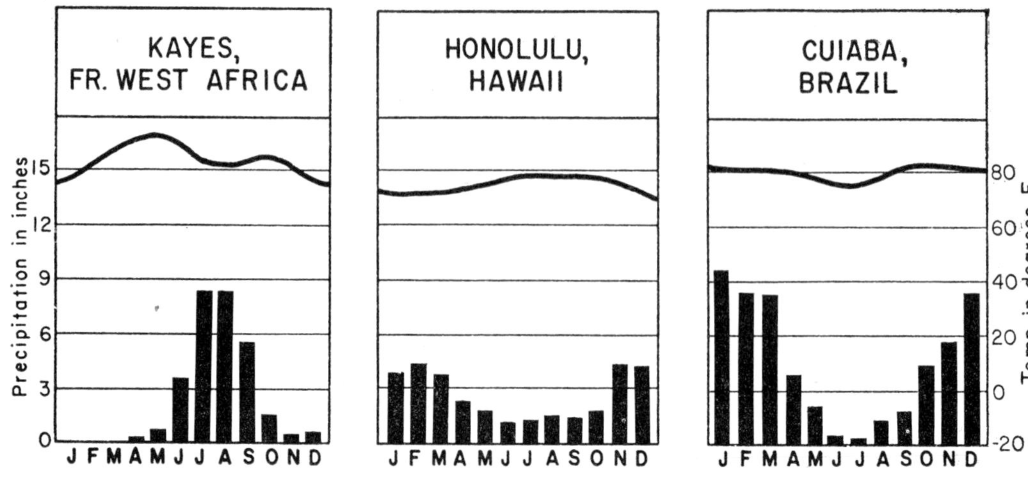

FIGURE 3-4. *Typical climatic graphs of Wet-Dry Tropic stations.*

temperatures during the dry season range between 90° and 100°, with highest recordings of the year occurring just prior to the rainy season when skies are clear and desert-like conditions prevail. There is a lowering of average monthly temperatures to 70° and 80° during the high sun period, due to the heavy rains and the associated cloud cover. Yearly average ranges are above five degrees, but seldom exceed 15 degrees of variation.

Precipitation. The seasonality and amounts of precipitation are the significant factors that set this climate apart from that of the Rainy Tropics. Concentrations occur during the season when the sun is overhead; average amounts range from 60 inches or more down to 10 inches. In general, rainfall decreases in amount progressing toward the desert margins as a result of shorter and shorter convectional belt control. On the basis of length of the wet season and total precipitation, these regions are frequently sub-divided into savannas with long wet seasons (with precipitation of 30 to 60 inches) and savannas with short wet seasons (with precipitation of 10 to 30 inches). Convectional precipitation or thunderstorms are characteristic, but in areas where mountain barriers interrupt moisture-bearing winds, orographic precipitation is prevalent and rainfall is often excessive. Mount Waialeale, on the Hawaiian Island of Kauai, has an annual rainfall of about 460 inches—on the leeside of the island the amount diminishes to about 20 inches annually. Rainfall is not reliable; the beginning of the rainy season is unpredictable, and there are wide variations in amounts from year to year. Generally the reliability of precipitation decreases as the annual totals decrease.

Surface features

South America. The Campos of Brazil, a west sloping plateau, gradually merges into the lowland of the Parana-Paraguay River system. Some diversity of surface is produced by the many headwater streams of the Amazon, Parana, and Paraguay Rivers, which rise in the tabular surface of the Mato Grosso Plateau and the rolling surface of the Goiaz Plateau. These streams have carved broad valleys radiating from the higher land (see Figure 2-10). In the southwest the level plain of the Paraguay River separates the Brazilian Highlands from the Andes Mountains.

The Orinoco Llanos, largely the alluvial plain of the Orinoco River, forms an elongated lowland, generally less than 1000 feet in elevation, between the plateau-like Guiana Highlands and the Venezuelan Andes. In the west it merges with the Andes through several terraces and in the east juts seaward in a large delta. The Orinoco is the principal river and transportation artery of the Llanos. This great stream and its tributaries can be navigated for a distance of 1500 miles by boats drawing 12 feet of water. During the wet season such boats can proceed up the main stem to the Colombia border.

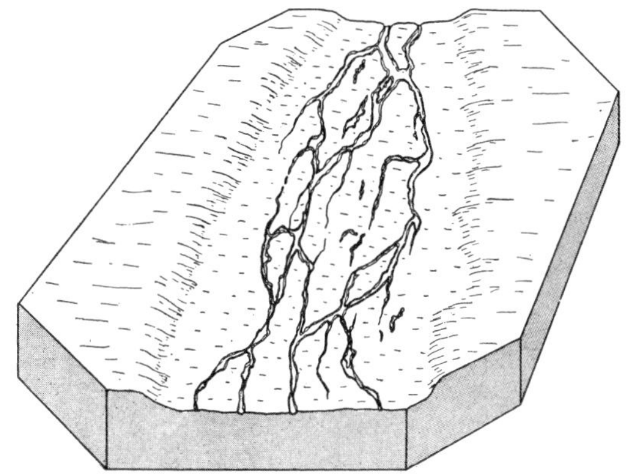

FIGURE 3-5. *Braided stream pattern.*

The Orinoco and other streams of the Wet-Dry Tropics have a marked yearly rise and fall. During the dry season they slowly lose volume and become unable to transport their load of silt; they then frequently deposit sediments in their beds. Often they split into a maze of channels forming a braided pattern through the alluvium. When the rainy season comes, the clogged channels of the plains often cannot carry the increased volumes and vast sections of the riverine areas may be inundated. Where rivers are incised in plateaus, seasonal flooding is restricted to the local valleys.

The Maracaibo Basin is a depression situated between two north-trending branches of the Venezuelan Andes. Lake Maracaibo, 120 miles long and 60 miles wide, occupies its central portion. A shallow river connects this fresh water lake with the Caribbean Sea. The Magdalena Valley of northern Colombia lies between the central and western ranges of the Northern Andes. Its surface is a low, flat plain mantled with stream-deposited materials.

The west coast Wet-Dry Tropics region is contained largely in the Guayas Lowland of Ecuador, an alluvial surface 40 or 50 miles wide extending north between the coastal hilly belt and the slopes of the Andes.

Middle America. The Wet-Dry Tropics of Middle America occupy the coastal lowlands and the lower slopes of the central mountains. The Yucatan Peninsula is an area of *karst* topography—unique to regions whose base is soluble limestone (see Figure 3-6). The undulating surfaces are usually characterized by numerous shallow depressions, sinks caused by subsidence of the roof of solution caverns, and the general absence of surface streams. Some areas are honey-combed with caverns. The Yucatan Peninsula receives moderate rainfall, but owing to the absorptive quality of limestone the landscape appears arid.

The smaller islands of the West Indies have central mountains and coastal fringing plains. Cuba, the largest island in the group, contains nearly half the land area of the West Indies, but lacks the high central mountain range. Distinctly mountainous country is found only in the eastern portion. The major share of the island is flat to gently rolling and the surface is suited to the use of modern farm machinery and the construction of transportation lines.

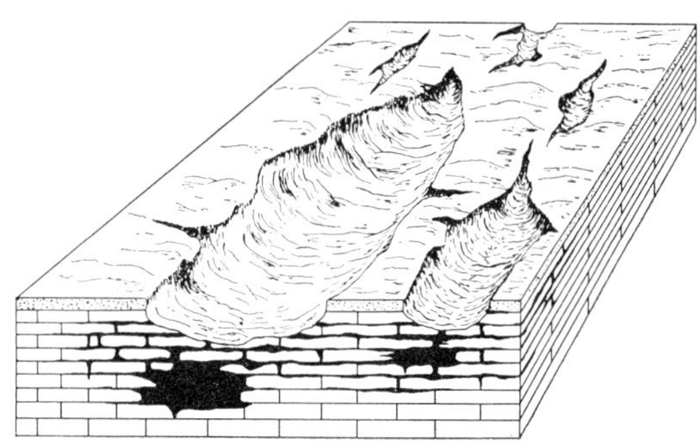

FIGURE 3-6. *Karst topography. Such landforms occur only in limestone areas.*

Africa. The two major areas of Wet-Dry Tropics in Africa are plateaus with broadly similar features. The average elevation of the Sudan is less than 1500 feet and the regional slope is northward. The most prominent relief features are isolated residual masses of harder rock which withstood the erosional forces that have worn down the surrounding country.

Three rivers—the Niger, the Shari, and the Nile—provide the drainage of the Sudan. The Niger River in the west rises in the highlands of French Guinea and flows northeast toward the Sahara. It is probable that the Niger once terminated in a vast area of inland drainage—this is evidenced by the remnants of a former great lake on the margins of the desert south of Timbuktu where the sluggish Upper Niger inundates vast areas during the rainy season. East from Timbuktu it bends southward, and here the more powerful Lower Niger has captured the drainage of the Saharan-bound Upper Niger by a process of gradual headward erosion and river piracy. The river then flows southeastward, sometimes through gorges, to the Gulf of Guinea.

The major drainage of the central Sudan is provided by the Shari River which rises on the northern rim of the Congo Basin and seasonally directs an abundance of tropical rain runoff toward the Sahara. This stream resembles the Upper Niger but terminates in Lake Chad, a great expanse of shallow water frequently under ten feet deep which covers an area of 10,400 square miles, nearly the size of Belgium. This island-strewn lake has no definite banks, often merging into swamps and varying in size and shape from season to season with fluctuations in precipitation. There is no visible outlet, but underground drainage to the lower basin in the north is probable.

The greatest river of the Sudan is the Nile. In contrast to the other streams, it succeeds in traversing the entire width of the Sahara Desert to empty into the Mediterranean Sea. Two Niles cross the Wet-Dry Tropics of Africa—the White or Clear Nile and the Blue or Muddy Nile. The White Nile, which resembles the Upper Niger and Shari Rivers, rises in the lakes south of the equator, flows northward and, upon reaching the Sahara, spreads out in an alluvial section of marshes around its confluence with the Bahr-el-Ghazal, and then bends toward the east for about 100 miles before continuing its northward course. The Blue Nile has its source in the highlands of Ethiopia, which provide an abundant supply of water. This river has great erosive power; the sediments gathered as it flows down the steep slopes account for its dark color.

The region south of the equator—the second major area under discussion here—has an average elevation approaching 3000 feet. Only near the narrow coastal plains do elevations decrease below 1000 feet. The Zambezi River is the main stream of the southern region. Fed by numerous tributaries originating from the drainage divide with the Congo System, it flows in a generally easterly direction and discharges into the Indian Ocean midway down the coast of Mozambique. The Victoria Falls on the Zambezi River—one of the most spectacular natural features in Africa—are over a mile wide and 360 to 400 feet high.

FIGURE 3-7. *Atolls. This diagram shows various stages of atoll development.*

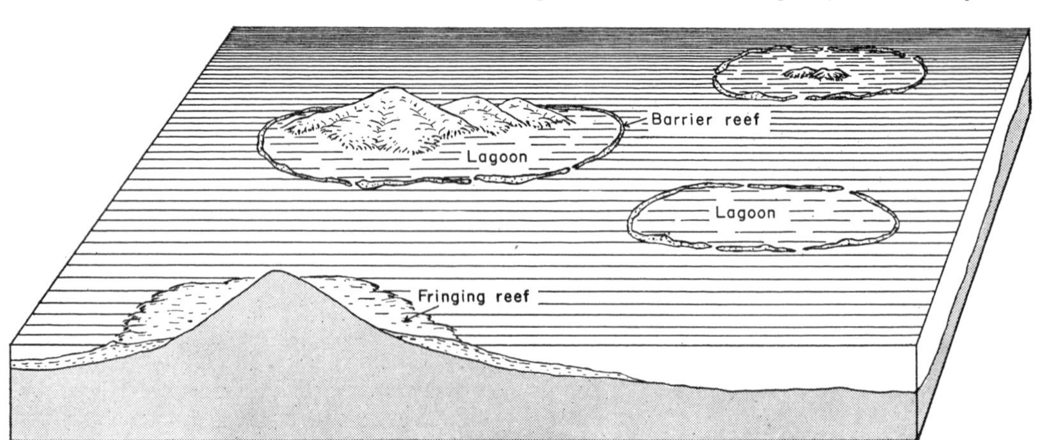

FIGURE 3-8. *A simplified cross-section of the natural vegetation of the Wet-Dry Tropics. The gradation from trees to grass parallels the decreasing rainfall.*

Central Pacific Islands. Based upon manner of formation and present surface, two principal types of islands may be distinguished in the mid-Pacific Ocean. These are the "high" islands of volcanic and diastrophic origin and the "low" islands built of reef limestone. The Hawaiian chain, representative of the former, owes its origin to flow after flow of volcanic material accumulated on the top of a submarine platform or ridge. Other "high" islands, especially in the western Pacific, are the summits of submarine mountain ranges. The "low" or coral islands have been constructed by lime-secreting organisms which thrive in the warm, shallow, tropical waters. Coral reefs frequently form offshore and with emergence may be added to the land. In other cases small reef-encircled islands, perhaps of volcanic origin, appear to have slowly submerged while the coral reef continued to grow. Such reefs now appear as more or less complete coral rings, called atolls, which encircle a central lagoon.

Natural vegetation

The intermediate position of the Wet-Dry Tropics between two areas of climatic extremes results in a vegetative zone of transition from tropical selva through woodlands, then from grasslands to almost barren desert. There are no sharp boundaries between grass and forest. The forest continues from the equator side of the region and slowly loses its identity poleward. The merging of forest and grass is imperceptible; the forest continuity is gradually broken by low bushes and patches of grass. The savanna soon governs the vegetation, with occasional trees dotting the landscape to give it a parkland appearance. The forest remnants are low, with umbrella-shaped crowns. In the African savanna an occasional baobab tree appears with its scraggly branches drooped over a huge bottle-like trunk. Bordering the banks of streams entering or emerging from the Rainy

FIGURE 3-9. *A giraffe in his native habitat. This is park savanna with trees found in isolation and in clumps rising above the thick grass cover.* (Union of South Africa Government Information Office.)

FIGURE 3-10. *Animal life in the African Wet-Dry Tropics: a lioness.* (Union of South Africa Government Information Office.)

Tropic regions are *galeria* forests, long tongues of the jungle or selva that penetrate into the savanna. Approaching the desert margins the grass becomes shorter and the cover less continuous, finally giving way to scattered scrub growth.

The heart of the Wet-Dry Tropics is dominated by seas of grass broken only by isolated trees. The grasslands often present a nearly impenetrable wall of rank vegetation making travel on foot difficult unless wild game, cattle, or native trails are available. The seasonality of the rainfall is reflected in the colors of the landscape; a monotonous vista of brown during the dry season is replaced by pleasing successions of greens following the rains. In some of the grazing areas, the end of the drought is marked by dense clouds of smoke filling the skies when the parched grass is burned to make way for the new growth. The savanna grass usually grows as individual stalks and attains heights ranging from four to occasionally twenty feet. The first early shoots are tender and palatable to the grazing herds but the grasses later turn coarse and stiff.

Native animal life

The distribution of animals in the Wet-Dry Tropical regions is uneven. The savannas of Africa, in general, have greater numbers and varieties of species than their counterparts in the Americas. An abundance of insect life is common to all but few large animals are present in the tropical savannas of the Americas. In Africa the great grasslands support vast numbers of herbivorous animals. Herds contain thousands of antelopes of various species such as the kudu, hartebeest, and gnu. Striped zebras blend with the grassy background. Towering giraffes browse on isolated tree groups. Flesh-eating carnivores such as lions and the scavenging jackals and hyenas prey on the grass-eaters. The savanna is also the habitat of the fierce

African buffalo, one of the most dangerous of all game animals, and the home of the rhinoceros and the African elephant. Hippopotami sport in the streams and crocodiles bask on the muddy banks. Monkeys and baboons inhabit the tree islands and surrounding areas. Snakes and lizards are common. Great ant nests serve as landmarks on the plain; some even provide shade for solitary animals. Many types of birds, including the swift-footed ostrich, live on the grasshoppers, locusts, and enormous numbers of other insects swarming through the air. In no other region does the animal life form such a colorful pattern in the panorama of the landscape.

The advent of the dry season places restrictions on the activity of the animals on the African savanna. Large herds of grass-eaters, followed by the lions, leopards, and hyenas,

FIGURE 3-11. *An elephant in the African Wet-Dry Tropics.* (Union of South Africa Government Information Office.)

FIGURE 3-12. *Animal life in the African Wet-Dry Tropics: zebras and gnus converging at a waterhole.* (Union of South Africa Government Information Office.)

must leave the dry areas and migrate to places where water is available. Elephants seek the galeria forests or climb the slopes of mountains to the higher forests. Insects and many animals become inactive during the dry season. When the rains begin, the savanna comes to life. Herds disperse from the waterholes and divide into smaller groups. The air is soon filled with winged ants, termites, and newly-emerged butterflies. All animal life responds to the termination of the drought!

Soils

Owing to the transitional nature of climate and vegetation, and to the diversity of parent material, it is difficult to make generalizations concerning the soils of the Wet-Dry Tropics. The soils have greater general fertility and better structure than those of the Rainy Tropics because of less rainfall and the dry season. They do show transitional characteristics paralleling the climatic change. On the wetter margins, soils are leached and are classed as lateritic. Toward the drier margins the soils have developed under conditions of high evaporation, low rainfall, and grass vegetation—they thus contain more fertility elements. The primary agricultural problem on the dry margins results from the limited and unreliable rainfall. Throughout the areas where rainfall is sufficient for crop production, natural soil-degrading processes operate on the cultivated land and permanent agriculture requires fertilizers and care in management.

MAN IN THE WET-DRY TROPICS

Immense spaces in the Wet-Dry Tropics remain virtually unoccupied. These regions, up to the present time, have discouraged widespread settlement for many of the same reasons as the Rainy Tropics. Only the most favorable areas have been developed, and for the most part population densities are below 15 persons per square mile. Notable concentrations are found in the West Indies, where Jamaica has 300 persons and Cuba 110 persons per square mile. In Mexico and along the west coast of Middle America several prominent areas of concentration are found; in South America the major distribution is in eastern Brazil. The greatest densities in the African regions are in the Sudan, especially in Nigeria. In recent years several nations have been placing considerable emphasis upon development in these regions. Many of the problems which have so long deterred progress and settlement are being met with new technology. Although advances are yet small, there appears to be little doubt that the future will bring greater utilization of the Wet-Dry Tropics.

Native man

Some of the native peoples are in a primitive stage of development, while others are rather advanced. As a general rule all are more advanced than is average for the Rainy Tropics. The intermittency of plant growth resulting from the seasonality of rainfall eliminates the possibility of obtaining a yearly food supply by simple gathering and continuous crop production; thus the people of the Wet-Dry Tropics must plan and provide for the dry season.

Few peoples are exclusively hunters, although game is abundant in Africa. Hunting is carried on in a primitive manner; weapons usually consist of bows and arrows, spears, and occasionally blowguns. Some tribes smear poison on the tips of their weapons—this may either paralyze or kill the game in a few minutes. Pits, excavated and carefully concealed along game trails, are used to trap animals.

Where lakes, streams, and the sea are available, fishing may become an important means of livelihood. This activity is especially noteworthy in the Bangweulu Swamps of Northern Rhodesia. In a few areas, especially the West Indies, some people are commercial fishermen. Hunting and fishing are usually more for the purpose of augmenting food supplies; native man is dependent upon either livestock grazing or agriculture for his primary livelihood.

Native agriculture. On the equatorial side of the Wet-Dry Tropics, where the forests occur, the natives practice migratory agriculture. The tribes use similar methods and are faced with the same problems common to primitive farmers in the Rainy Tropics. Here, too, is the need for crudely-cleared patches in the forest and the abandonment and rotation of fields owing to short duration of soil fertility. The old plots revert under favorable conditions to second-growth forest, and are not cleared again for a period which may vary from eight to fifteen years or more, depending upon population density and need. Soil fertility thus has an opportunity to regenerate. Unfortunately, conditions sometimes are not sufficiently favorable to allow the development of a good second-growth. Over large sections of the tropical forests there are extensive open grasslands, resulting from the too-frequent employment of fire-clearing the fields. In some areas pressure on the land has led to such a shortening of the period of rest from the traditional system of cultivation as to induce serious soil erosion.

Progressing away from the equatorial margins of the Wet-Dry Tropics, the dry season lengthens, grass replaces forest, and soils undergo less leaching. The farming possibilities are materially improved with the land easier to clear, the soil fertility more enduring, and the dry season favorable for land preparation, planting, and the complete maturing of crops such as grains. Under these conditions, it is not surprising that some groups have developed a rudimentary agriculture of the sedentary type in the savanna lands. The fields are cleared by burning the grass during the dry season. The degree and manner of tillage varies from group to group. Some use hoes or mattocks to work the soil, while others simply use sharpened sticks. The rainy season is the growing period and the dry season the ripening and harvesting period. Principal crops include millet, corn, wheat, peas, beans, sweet potatoes, and pumpkins, and in some African regions peanuts and cotton are also important.

Regular trading with the grazing tribes is frequently carried on by the farming groups. Even though these tribes are more advanced than the migratory farmers, individual ownership is not common. The farmers live mainly in communal villages. Houses are simple and often constructed with mud walls and grass-thatched roofs. Toward the drier margins farming becomes precarious as the result of less rainfall and the dangers of drought—here agriculture gives way almost entirely to grazing.

In the areas where there is contact with foreign settlement, the natives frequently produce agricultural products for sale. The British and French have developmental programs under way in Africa. These are designed to lift the level of living of the natives as well as to increase exports and open new markets. Assistance comes in the form of technical advice, machinery, capital, plans, and guidance. Complete subsistence farming is gradually giving way to farming where subsistence crops are combined with one or more cash crops. One of the most significant developments in agriculture is in Anglo-Egyptian Sudan, where the British have sponsored several irrigation projects. The largest takes water from the Sennar Dam constructed across the Blue Nile to irrigate a portion of the Plain of Gezira between the two Niles. The dam was completed in 1925 and the canal system in 1929. The project, covering close to a million acres, has been a successful cooperative venture between European management and African cultivators. The area has changed from a land of marginal agriculture limited by uncertain rain to one of a stable agrarian economy based upon a certain water supply and improved farming techniques. Today, it is a major producer of cotton, with nearly a quarter-million acres devoted to the crop. Cotton is systematically rotated with *dura* (millet) for food and *lubia,* a leguminous fodder for workstock and other animals.

In Latin America considerable portions of the export products are grown by non-white tenants [1] and small land-owners. Their econ-

[1] The Negroes are native to the tropics but not to the Latin American region.

FIGURE 3-13. *Sennar Dam on the Blue Nile. This dam stores flood-waters for use in the Sudan's long dry season. The canal on the left carries water to the irrigated fields of the plain of Gezira.* (British Information Services.)

omy and way of life has long been influenced by association with white men and their techniques, and by the nearness of American markets.

Native grazing. Many of the native African tribes of the savannas depend chiefly on cattle for subsistence. The native breeds are able to withstand the heat, penetrate through the high grass, and defend themselves against wild animals. They are used chiefly for milk and are seldom butchered.

In addition to their use as a source of food or as beasts of burden, ownership of many animals elevates a man's social position—they are often traded for wives! Among these tribes, animals are the chief source of wealth and the medium for barter; a man's social position often depends upon the size of his herd. Around settlements located near a source of water, natives sow millet at the beginning of the rainy season. When the crop is in, the younger and more able-bodied members of the tribe move their herds in search of grass while those who are unable to follow remain at home to care for the fields. The tribe returns during the dry season to harvest and store the grain.

White man

The presence of white man in the Wet-Dry Tropics is explained largely in terms of commercial products. Up to the present at least, he has been in these regions to manage the exploitation of climatic advantages for agriculture or to exploit the grasslands, forests, and mineral resources. In the African savannas, much of the development has been and is on a colonial basis and white man is there as an administrator or technician. In Latin America, where white man came from western Europe as a conqueror and exploiter, foreign political ties have been largely broken. Descendants of the Spanish and Portuguese are the dominating elements in many Latin American countries, but they have preferred to settle in the higher altitudes where climate is more moderate. The long period of their occupance has had profound effects on the population make-up, owing to

FIGURE 3-14. *Sugar cane harvest in Cuba. A variety of conveyances, from the traditional bullock carts to modern twenty-ton trucks, are used to bring sugar from the fields to the central grinding mills.* (Sugar Research Foundation.)

the mixing of Europeans with the indigenous Indians and the African Negroes brought in during the colonial period as slave labor. Pure whites are in the minority.

Commercial agriculture. The establishment of commercial agriculture followed almost on the wake of the first European conquests in Latin America. The Portuguese developed important sugar colonies in northeast Brazil as early as the mid-sixteenth century, and that area continued as the world's chief source of sugar during most of the seventeenth century.

Late in the seventeenth century the West Indies' advantages for sugar production were recognized. These included the favorable climate, an abundance of suitable land, and accessibility to water transportation and markets. Slave labor was brought in from Africa and soon a flourishing sugar production was established under European management. The political status of the West Indies has changed, but commercial agriculture remains the major component of the economy. Other crops are produced but sugar persists as the leading enterprise with Cuba the principal world exporter.

Important quantities of sugar cane are also produced in other portions of the Wet-Dry Tropics, including Brazil, the Middle American countries, and the Hawaiian Islands, where irrigation is necessary to compensate for the short wet season and dry shadow locations. The Hawaiian Islands are also the leading world producer of pineapples. Improved varieties, fertilizers, mechanization, and chemical control of pests have made commercial agriculture here more advanced than elsewhere in the humid tropics. Cotton is a significant crop under lower rainfall inland from the sugar-producing area of northeast Brazil as well as in northern Argentina. The northern portion of the Yucatan Peninsula is the major producer of a cheap twine plant, henequen, which is a xerophyte structurally adapted to growing with a scarce water supply. The same area is a leading source of supply for sisal, a related plant whose fibers are used for higher quality cordage.

Commercial agriculture in the African realm, less developed than in Latin America, is found mainly along the rivers of the Sudan. As noted earlier, the French and British have concentrated considerable effort in these areas in recent years and some irrigation has been developed. In several sections cotton, sugar cane, and rice are produced in commercial quantities.

In the African regions it is difficult to separate Wet-Dry Tropics from the cool tropical highlands. Local differences are common because higher elevation produces more favorable temperatures for white settlers. These areas will be discussed in the chapter dealing specifically with the Tropical Highlands.

Commercial grazing. Despite the tremendous expanses of grasslands, the Wet-Dry Tropics produce relatively few livestock for commercial purposes. The grazing industry is confronted by a number of handicaps and problems: (*1*) During the dry season water is scarce, grass becomes harsh and dry and is poor forage for fattening cattle. (*2*) Floods, in the rainy season, inundate many acres of grazing land, especially in the Orinoco Llanos. (*3*) Cattle are subject to many diseases due to the prevalence of ticks and other insects. In Africa snakes and predatory animals take a toll of livestock, but the most serious problem is the tsetse fly. This pest, found throughout the Wet-Dry Tropical regions of Africa, accounts for a high death rate among the cattle population. Cattle raising is practically impossible in areas of heavy tsetse-fly infestation. (*4*) Productive beef breeds do not thrive under the high temperatures. (*5*) Marketing is difficult due to inadequate transportation and refrigeration—cattle are usually driven to the slaughter houses and arrive in poor condition. In addition there is sharp competition on the part of higher quality beef from more favorable producing areas.

The American savannas, due to early start, better transportation, and fewer wild animals, are utilized more for commercial grazing than the larger African grasslands. Much of the grazing industry in the Latin American savannas stems from hardy stock, descendants of cattle brought from Spain over 400 years ago. The industry is not based entirely on meat and hides since milk for cheese is also significant in the local economy. In the Orinoco Basin, herds are maintained on large cattle ranches by the *llaneros* or Venezuelan cowboys. The llanero lives on the plain in a simple mud hut with a thatched roof. His costume consists of a short-sleeved shirt and short breeches, and his equipment is the machete and a 60 to 75 foot rawhide rope. His chief activities are herding and, unlike the North American cowboy, milking, and cheesemaking. The llanero is a man on horseback—he scorns any activity associated with crop production.

Forest industries. Lumbering is not a widespread activity since climatic conditions impose numerical limits on trees of commercial significance. Only on the equatorward margins, the hill slopes which receive heavy orographic precipitation, and in the galerias do we find forests comparable to the selva. One of the outstanding forest products comes from the quebracho tree, which grows in the open forest of the Gran Chaco in South America and forms the greatest single source of tannin in the world. Quebracho logs are assembled along river banks where processing plants chip the extremely hard wood and extract the tannin. In the African countries, particularly in the Rhodesias, the governments are aware of the potential value of the trees of the woodland savannas. Teak and mahogany are presently being logged. Hardwoods have long been commercial products of the West Indies.

Mining. Minerals were the first lure that attracted white man to the Wet-Dry Tropics. The European conquistadors were spurred by the legends of hidden Indian accumulations of gold in Latin America. Extensive searches for natural deposits were made later, but in both cases the sources discovered were soon exhausted.

In the modern era, petroleum and rich deposits of iron and copper have contributed to the importance of these regions. Development has been largely by foreign interests and a relatively small segment of the benefits of exploitation has accrued to native inhabitants. Venezuela ranks second only to the United States in petroleum production, with major fields around the east shore of Lake Maracaibo, in the north central area, and west of the Lower Orinoco River. Across the Andes, Colombia has an important field in the central portion of the Magdalena Valley. Mexico also has a significant oil production on the east coast, with the principal field near Tampico. A major portion of the petroleum from the Latin American countries moves into world commerce—for example, about 90 per cent of Venezuelan production is exported, nearly half coming to the United States. Latin America today is exercising more rigid control over development than was formerly true. Colombia and Venezuela have divided their oil areas into reserves; they are controlling concessions and requiring that foreign developers carry on the refining within the country. Greater benefits are thus resulting, with larger numbers employed and the life of the reserves lengthened. Concentrations of workers in the oil fields and refining areas is encouraging the establishment of agriculture to provide the necessary food supplies. Development of rich iron reserves in the Guiana Highlands south of the Orinoco River by United States interests is bringing added importance to the South American country of Venezuela.

One of the major copper-producing areas of the world is found in Africa, extending from the Katanga District of southeast Belgian Congo into the adjacent portion of Northern Rhodesia. These rich deposits, the ores of which have a very high percentage of copper, are being exploited by Belgian and British interests. Copper mining, smelting, transportation, and the production of food for workers have stimulated a concentration of population. This same region is one of the world's principal uranium sources, with the mine at Shinkolobwe the leading producer. About three-quarters of the world's supply of cobalt is also mined in Katanga. Tin and coal, mined in Nigeria, are the most notable mineral products of the Wet-Dry Tropics north of the equator in Africa.

FIGURE 3-15. *Irrigation pipeline in the Hawaiian Islands. Here, through the engineering works of man, dry shadow locations have become productive commercial agricultural areas.* (Sugar Research Foundation.)

Manufacturing. Manufacturing is concerned mainly with the products of agriculture. Sugar is processed in numerous mills (called *centrals*) with cane by-products of molasses, rum, and bagasse, the residue fiber. Tobacco factories in Cuba produce cigars for export, pineapple is canned in Hawaii, and a few tannin extraction mills operate in the Chaco. Much of our cheap binding twine comes from Yucatan; and Recife, Brazil, has significant textile mills. A few South American slaughter

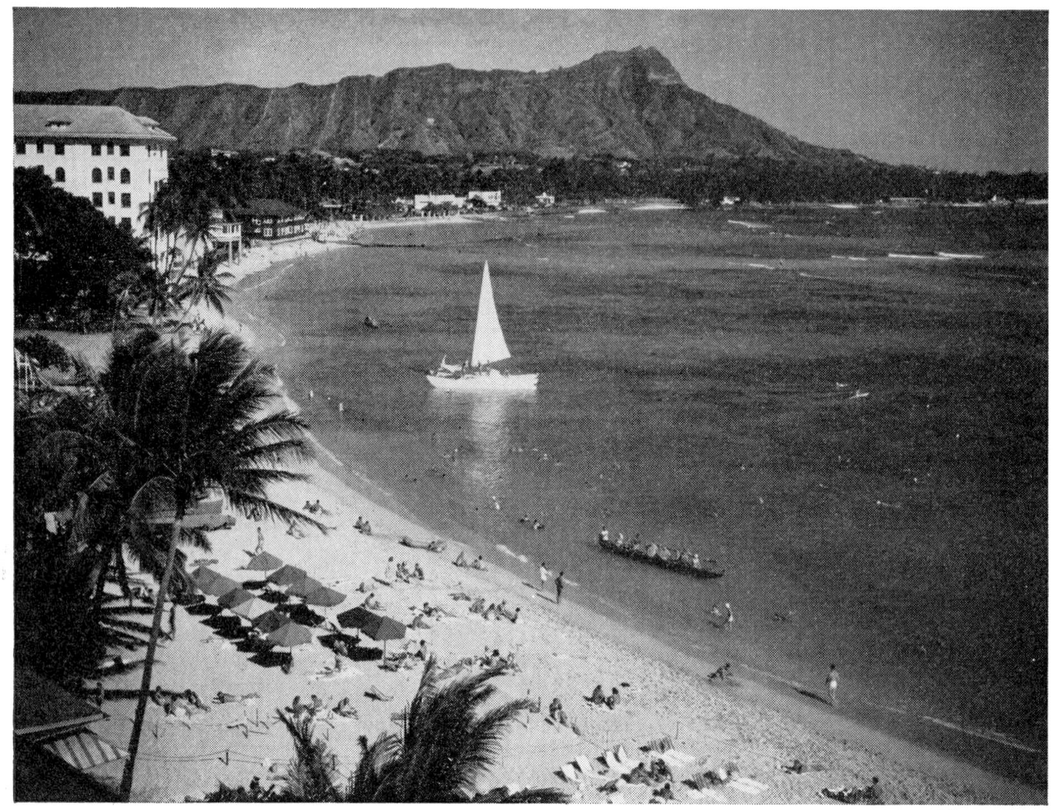

FIGURE 3-16. *The beach at Waikiki, Honolulu, Oahu Island, Hawaii. This is one of the outstanding attractions of the Wet-Dry Tropics. Sun bathing, swimming, boating, and surfboard riding can be noted. Diamond Head is in the background.* (Pan American World Airways.)

houses process the tough beef of the savannas. Venezuela and the offshore Dutch islands of Curacao and Aruba refine Maracaibo Basin oil.

Tourism. The Wet-Dry Tropics contain two groups of islands, the Hawaiians and the West Indies, in which the tourist trade is becoming increasingly important. The West Indies, favored by proximity to the populated eastern section of the United States, are invaded by tourists during the winter season.[2] The remoteness of the Hawaiian group has been broken by regularly-scheduled passenger service by sea and air. "Packaged tours" are making island vacations possible for people in low and medium income brackets. These tours include standard transportation, food, lodging, and directed scenic tours at one price. Tourist attractions are climate, sea and mountain scenery, exotic vegetation and animal life, fishing, and sandy ocean beaches with warm sea water.

[2] See "West Indies Escape," *Life,* January 11, 1954, XXXVI, No. 2, 76-89.

Urban centers

There are more community and village settlements in the Wet-Dry Tropics than in the Rainy Tropics. This is particularly true in Caribbean America and the Sudan of Africa. Few large urban centers again reflect the general absence of city-forming factors of commerce, industry, and large populations. Many of the large cities that do serve these areas are found in the highlands and will be discussed in the Tropical Highland chapter.

In the Wet-Dry Tropics proper, most of the major centers are located near the coast at favorable assembly and shipping points. The greatest concentration is found in the Caribbean area. Habana, Cuba's capital, chief port, and tourist attraction, is nearing a one-million population. Port au Prince, Haiti, and Kingston, Jamaica, both capitals and commercial centers, exceed 100,000 each. Veracruz, Tampico, and Merida are the main east coast centers of Mexico. Panama, with about 100,000 people, located on the south end of the canal, is the major city and capital of the Republic of Panama.

Barranquilla and Cartagena are large lowland cities, and the principal ports of Colombia; the former is situated at the main mouth of the Magdalena River and the latter at the mouth of a distributary. In Venezuela, oil development is responsible for the growth of Maracaibo, the only large lowland city in that country. The northeast coast supports the significant cities of Wet-Dry Tropical Brazil. Recife, railroad terminal and chief outlet for an important agriculture area, has a population of over 500,000. Fortaleza, with over 200,000, serves similar functions for an area farther north. On the west side of the continent, Guayaquil is the port and leading city of Ecuador.

The major city of the mid-Pacific Ocean is Honolulu, in Hawaii. Chief port and commercial center, it contains about half the population of the island group.

In Wet-Dry Tropical Africa there are but four centers above 100,000. Three of these, Ibadan, Lagos, and Kano, are in Nigeria and the other, Accra, is in the neighboring Gold Coast.

OUTLOOK

The Wet-Dry Tropics will undoubtedly play a more important role in future world affairs as suppliers of agricultural raw materials. Large available areas should make extensive mechanized farming feasible. Irrigation, possibly by pump and sprinkler method as well as diversion, could extend the agricultural potential of many sectors. Grazing has possibilities, but success hinges upon improved range management, better quality stock, scientific disease and pest control, and more efficient handling and shipping facilities.

The realm will continue to be a producer of sugar, cotton, sisal, and other established crops requiring tropical temperatures and wet and dry seasons. With sensible management oil and copper should continue to be significant and new discoveries are likely to expand the importance of these lands to the industrial world.

Greater changes can be expected to take place in native economies and growth in native populations will undoubtedly occur. At the same time there may arise problems of unbalance in the shift from subsistence farming to economies in which commercial production is emphasized. The danger lies in moving too rapidly.

Political changes can also be expected, particularly in Africa. The British colonial system today envisions the development of their territories gradually to the point when they can govern themselves and remain only, if they so elect, members of the British Commonwealth of Nations. The reorganization of the former French Empire into the French Union has had and will have more important effects in West Africa. The seven former French Colonies became territories within the Federation of French West Africa. They have been given greater voice in their home rule as well as in that of the French Union. The French system is designed to make the African a better citizen of Greater France.

SELECTED REFERENCES

Buchanan, Keith, "Nigeria, Largest Remaining British Colony," *Economic Geography,* XXVIII, No. 41, 1952, 302-322.

Carlson, Fred A., *Geography of Latin America,* Third Edition. New York: Prentice-Hall, Inc., 1952.

Freeman, Otis W., ed., *Geography of the Pacific*. New York: John Wiley and Sons, Inc., 1951.

James, Preston E., *Latin America*. New York: Odyssey Press, 1950.

James, Preston E., "Trends in Brazilian Agricultural Development," *Geographical Review*, XLIII, No. 3, 1953, 301-328.

Light, Richard Upjohn, *Focus on Africa*. New York: American Geographical Society, 1941.

Parson, James J., "The Settlement of the Sinu Valley of Colombia," *Geographical Review*, XLII, No. 1, 1952, 67-86.

Taylor, Griffith, "Fiji: A Study of Tropical Settlement," *Economic Geography*, XXVII, No. 2, 1951, 148-162.

Tuthill, R. L., "An Independent Farm in Cuba," *Economic Geography*, XXV, No. 3, 1949, 201-210.

CHAPTER 4

Monsoon Tropics

THE MONSOON TROPICS ARE SPECIAL wet-dry climatic regions. The seasonal pattern of rain and drought is the same as that of the Wet-Dry Tropics, but results from the climatic influences of the great Asiatic land mass, the continent of Australia, and the wide expanses of tropical ocean waters. The Monsoon region of Asia is *the* populated land of the tropics—the good areas teem with millions of people. The press of population stimulates a continual quest for food, and the imprint of intensive agriculture is deeply imbedded in the land; the soil has long been the intimate of generations of toilers. The land receives little rest, for the threat of famine makes farming an essential activity in dry as well as wet seasons. These are regions with sharp cultural contrasts, ranging

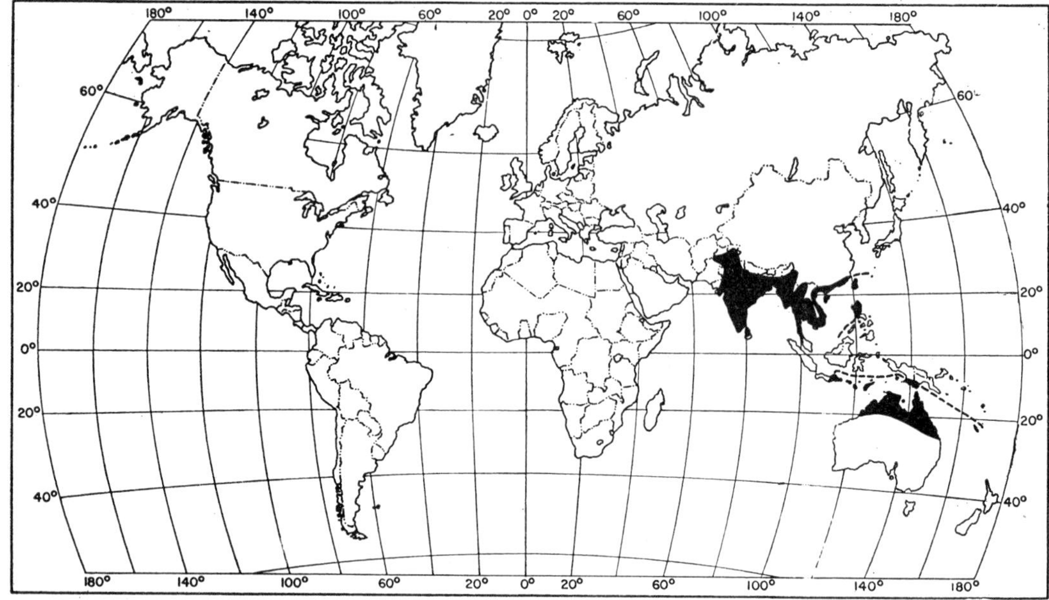

FIGURE 4-1. *The Monsoon Tropics.*

FIGURE 4-2. *The Monsoon Tropics of south and southeast Asia.*

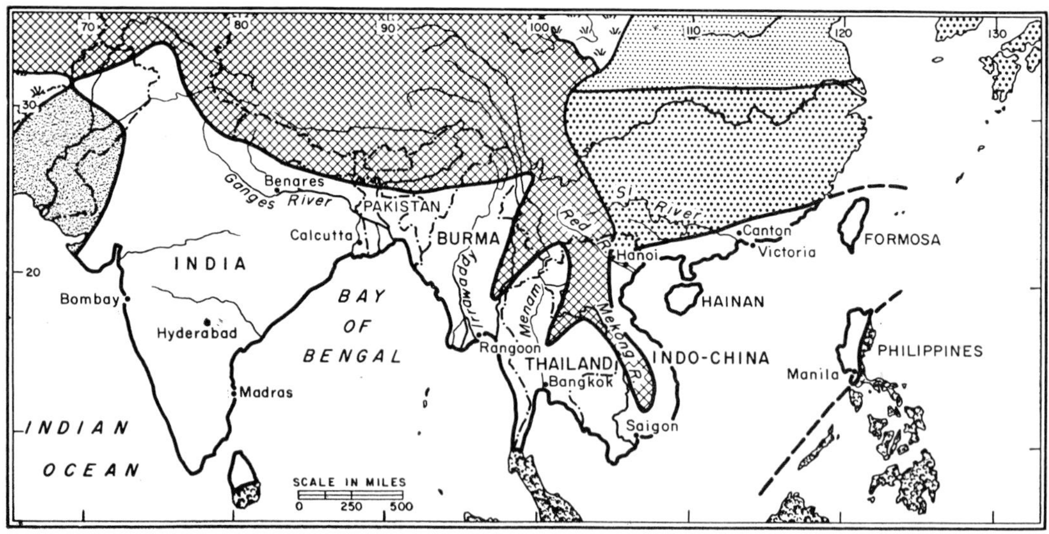

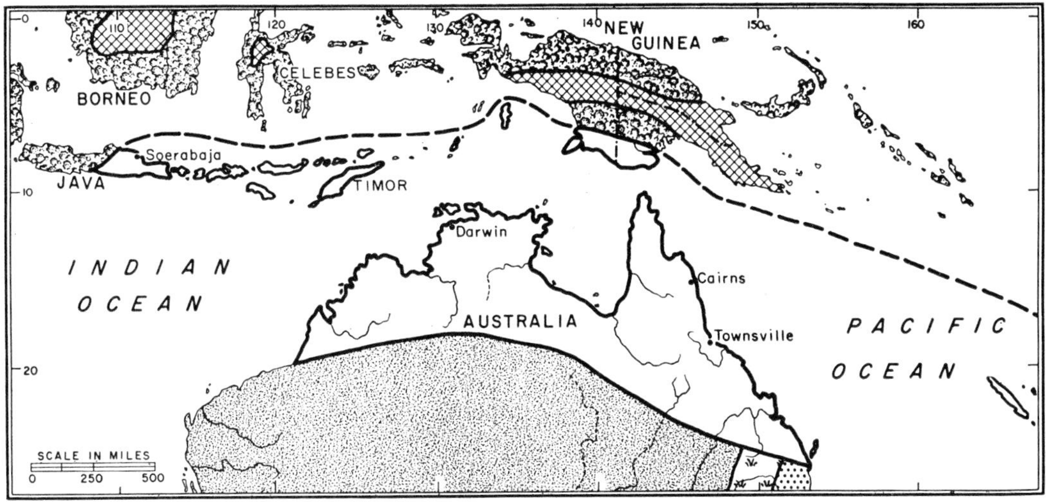

FIGURE 4-3. *The Monsoon Tropics of northern Australia and neighboring islands.*

from the mature civilizations of Asian peoples to that of the primitive aborigines in Monsoon Australia.

Location

In Asia and Australia the Monsoon Tropics are found in the same latitudes that the Wet-Dry Tropics occupy in Latin America and Africa. Due to the influence of the Monsoons, however, this climatic type extends further poleward in Asia, reaching 30° N in Pakistan and India.

Asia. The greatest extent of the Monsoon Tropics is in south and southeast Asia, where it includes virtually all of the area between 10° N and the Tropic of Cancer (23½° N), excepting the Himalaya Mountains and the highlands in Southeast Asia. The region stretches from the margins of the Thar Desert and the mountains in the northwest through West Pakistan, India, East Pakistan, Burma, Thailand (Siam), Indochina, and into south China. The islands of Hainan, Formosa, and the western Philippines are also included.

Australia and Indonesia. South of the equator the Monsoon lands embrace the northern portion of Australia and the southern fringe of Indonesia from east Java through the south-central lobe of New Guinea.

PHYSICAL ENVIRONMENT

Climate

Monsoon is an Arabian word meaning "season," but to the millions of people living in India and Southeast Asia it is synonymous with life-giving rain. Nowhere in the world do so many people antici-

FIGURE 4-4. *The sea and land breezes.*

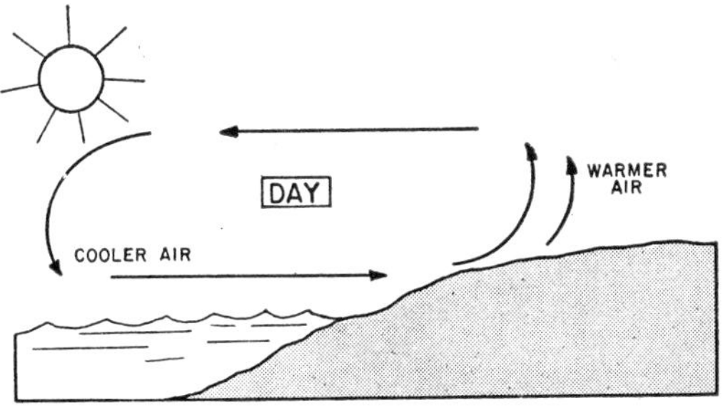

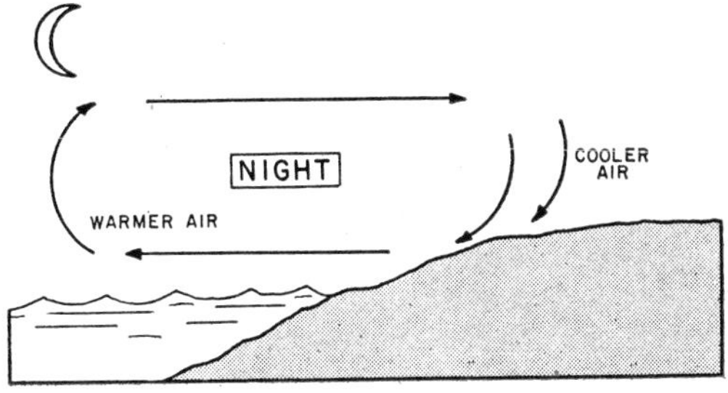

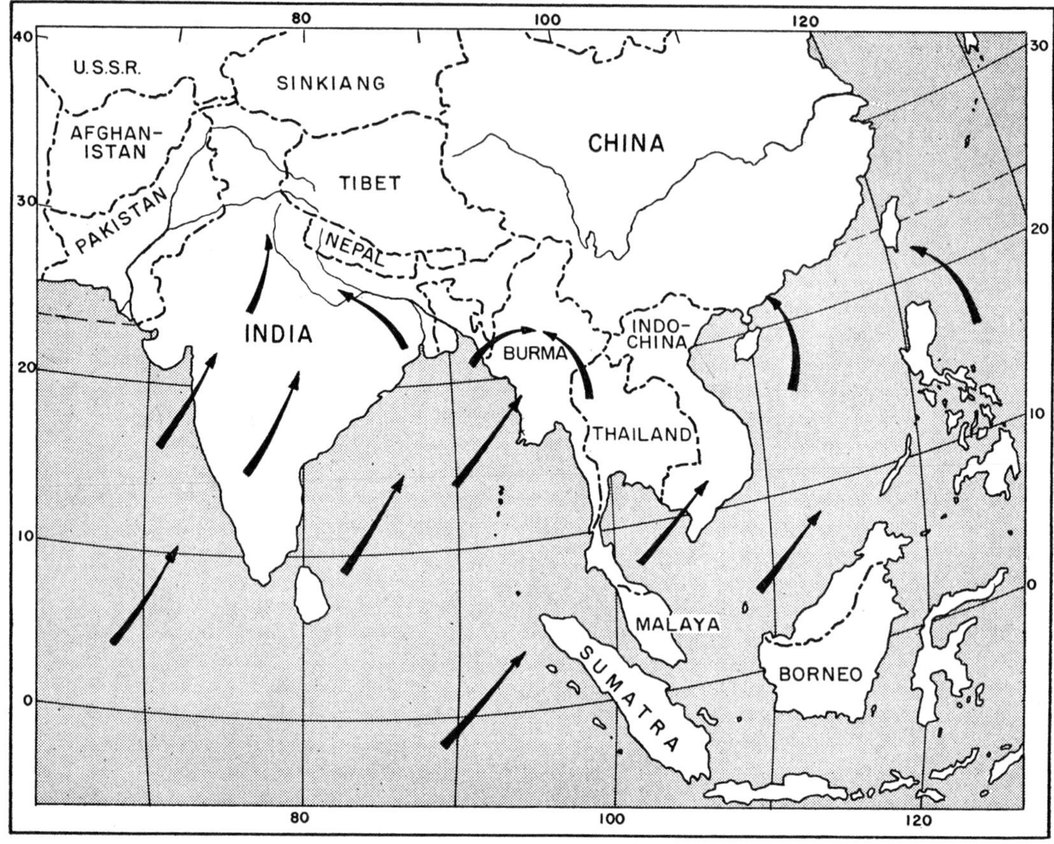

FIGURE 4-5. *The Asian Monsoon. The map on the left shows the generalized movement of air from the tropical seas toward the lower pressures of the Asiatic land*

pate and depend so much upon a phenomenon of nature.[1]

The mechanics of the monsoon are based on the differential heating of land and water which can be partially explained by the chain of developments producing a land and sea breeze (see Figure 4-4). During the day the littoral and the sea are heated by the sun. Since land heats faster, a lower pressure is developed toward which the cooler air from the sea moves, causing the sea breeze. During the night when the cool land develops a higher pressure than the sea, the air flows seaward as the land breeze. These daily winds are actually diurnal monsoons.

The Monsoon may be thought of as a seasonal land and sea breeze. During late May and early June, the low pressures that have been created over the Asiatic land mass induce a flow of warm tropical air from the sea toward the continent. The air has passed over warm ocean water and is laden with water vapor—this becomes the source of generous precipitation. In the winter months the winds are reversed, since the air from the cooled continent and its high pressures streams toward the lower pressures of the warm ocean. The dry season occurs in the Monsoon Tropics when the winds blow from the land. If the winds pass over water, areas such as

[1] The phenomenon of the monsoon is found in other continents, especially North America, but the greatest development is in Asia.

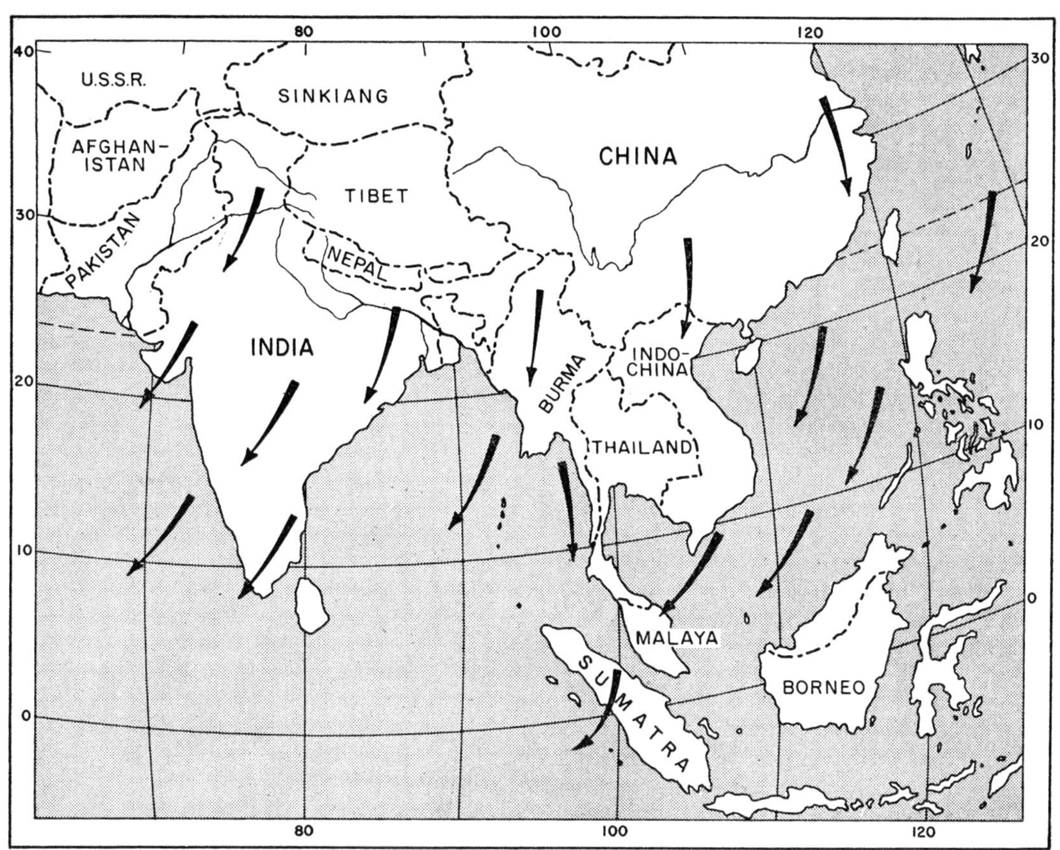

mass during summer. The map on the right shows the reverse in winter, when air moves from the higher pressures of the continent toward the lower pressures of the warmer seas.

Formosa and the east coast of peninsular India receive a second season of rain in winter.

The climate of northern Australia results from a similar monsoon development but, due to location south of the equator, the seasons are reversed. Australia's "winter" or dry season starts in June when the southeast trades blow out of the sub-tropical high that spreads across the island continent. The summer wet season is from December to April, when the high pressure belt migrates southward and the low pressures formed in its wake permit moisture-laden winds from the bordering seas on the north to flow toward the land.

The Monsoon Tropics, demonstrated by the climate of India, have three seasonal divisions: the cool season from October through February, the hot season from March through May, and the season of the rains from June through September. During the cool season, the sky is nearly free of clouds and there is little rain. Temperatures hover in the mid 60°'s on the northern margins of the country and increase to about 75° in the south. Humidity is low, but increases southward with higher temperatures. There are steady, though relatively weak, winds blowing from different quarters of the north. The cool season is generally the most pleasant time of the year, although lower temperatures occasionally cause discomfort. In March, a rise in temperature begins, skies remain clear, and there is little rain. The heat of the day becomes intense, with thermometer readings rising well over the

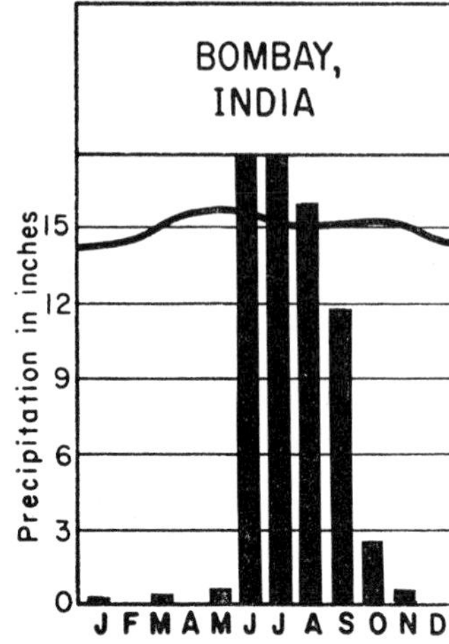

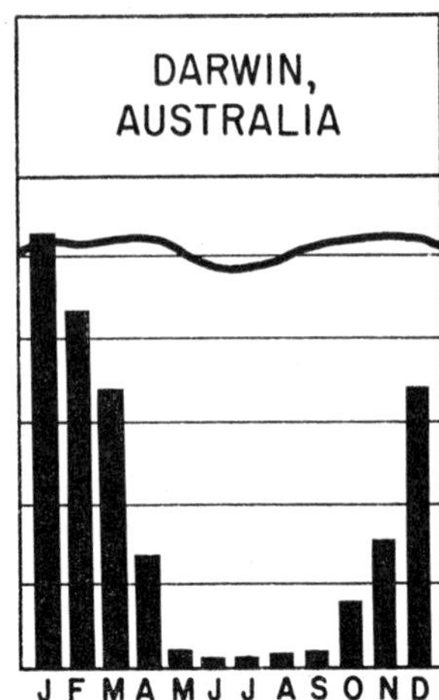

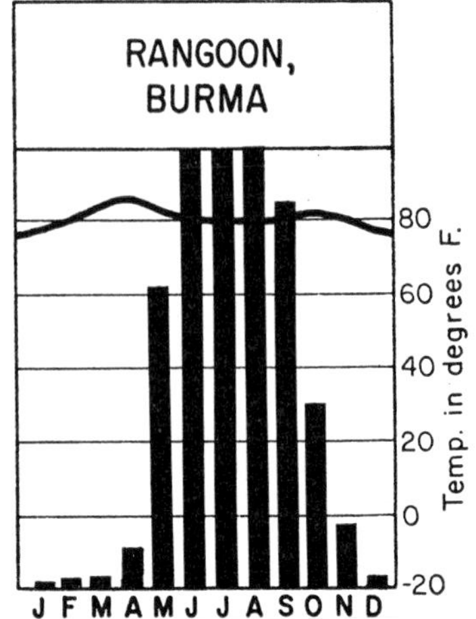

FIGURE 4-6. *Typical climatic graphs of Monsoon Tropic stations.*

100° mark. Hot winds desiccate the vegetation and often fill the air with dust. The heat continues to increase and reaches its maximum just before the "bursting" of the onshore monsoon. June heralds the beginning of the wet season—thick clouds cover the sky, humidities rise, and daily convectional storms send down heavy showers. Plants send forth their foliage and everywhere the earth is mantled in green. There is a marching effect to the sweep of the monsoon across India. The monsoon first strikes the tip of the Indian peninsula in early June and gradually sweeps up the country, reaching the north areas later in the month.

Temperature. Monsoon Tropic temperatures follow almost the same patterns as those of the Wet-Dry Tropics. The highest readings are recorded prior to the beginning of the rainy season. A majority of Monsoon Tropic stations have their highest temperatures in May and early June, with hottest month temperatures averaging 85° to 90°. January is the coolest month, with a 65° to 70° average.

Precipitation. Approximately sixty per cent of the rain comes during the summer months of June, July, and August. Stations, unless subject to heavy orographic rainfall, receive amounts ranging from thirty to eighty inches depending upon distance inland and exposure. Convectional storms account for much of the rainfall, but the rising of moist air along various mountain barriers also provides orographic precipitation. Cherrapunji, for example, located on the south slopes of the Khasi Hills in northeast India, is one of the wettest spots in the world, with a yearly average of about 450 inches. One year the station received a high of 905 inches; 41 inches have been recorded in one day, and 366 inches in a single month! Cherrapunji exemplifies the wet-dry regime at its extreme—the July average is 109 inches while December's is but 0.2 inches.

There are a few exceptions to the general rule of summer rainfall. Most notable are the southeast portion of the peninsula of India and the Annam Coast of Indochina, which receive winter maxima as the result of the winds blowing out from the continent, crossing the water, and again moving onshore.

Monsoon precipitation is unreliable in character; as in the Wet-Dry Tropics, amounts fluctuate greatly from year to year, especially along the drier margins. The impact of drought and flood is far-reaching, since either may bring famine to the crowded farm villages.

Surface features

Asia. Landforms in the Monsoon Tropics are a significant factor in the production of climatic differences and in the limitation of land-use possibilities. Since

FIGURE 4-7. *Physiographic diagram of India-Pakistan.*

this is a land of wet-crop farming, it can be readily understood that landforms are also a main control of population distribution. The plains are densely peopled, but the highlands (which repel agriculture) have few permanent inhabitants. Although there are no large structural plains, several sizeable river valleys are distinctive for their intensive settlement and are equally easy to locate on a physical or population map.

Two great peninsulas comprise the bulk of the Asian realm: India-Pakistan and Southeast Asia. Three major physical divisions are easily recognized in the India-Pakistan peninsula. The Himalayas in the north, the greatest mountains in the world, together with associated ranges in the west and east, effectively isolate India and Pakistan from central Asia. Inside this mountain wall the Ganges Plain, the depositional product of the Ganges River and its tributaries, sweeps 1500 miles in a broad arc from the northwest mountains to the Bay of Bengal, forming the largest lowland in the Monsoon Tropics. The Brahmaputra, an important river in the northeast, rises in Tibet and flows parallel to the Himalaya Mountains many miles; it breaks around the eastern end of these highlands, creating an important valley in Assam before turning southward to join the Ganges. Together these streams have built a large and complex delta at the head of the Bay of Bengal.

South India is primarily a plateau, the third major division, rising abruptly on the west coast. This mountain wall is called the Western Ghats; the land slopes rather gently eastward from it, terminating in the Eastern Ghats, a lower and less continuous line of hills. The plateau, sometimes called the Deccan,[2] has an undulating surface with an elevation of about 2000 feet. It has had a complicated geological history. Much of the plateau is

[2] The term *Deccan* is variously used; some restrict its usage to the area of lava flows; some apply it to the area south of the Narbada River; others use it to embrace all areas south of the Indo-Gangetic Plain.

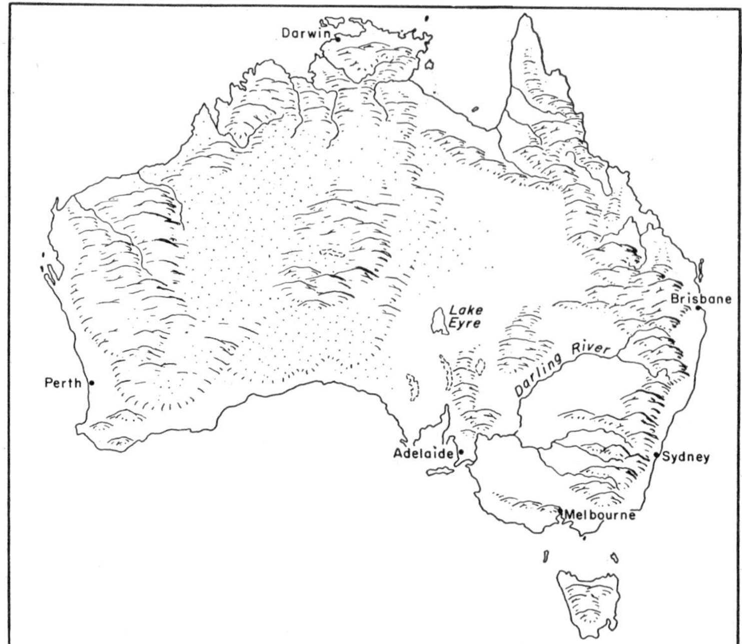

FIGURE 4-8. *Physiographic diagram of Australia.*

composed of very ancient crystalline rocks, but in the hinterland of Bombay enormous lava flows have buried these, and today an area of 200,000 square miles is still covered by volcanic deposits. The narrow plains bordering the peninsula are known as the Malabar Coast on the west and the Coromandel Coast on the east.

Forested mountains dominate the landscapes of Southeast Asia. From the lofty heights of eastern Tibet, many ranges spread fan-wise toward the sea. Several extend through Burma, one forms the backbone of the Malay Peninsula, and the Annam Mountains fill most of northwestern and eastern Indochina. The mountainous interior, characterized by sharp ridges and deep gorges, is largely inaccessible except from the south. Toward the coast several aggrading rivers have built flood plains by deposition and are projecting their deltas seaward. Five river valleys are the major lands of settlement: the Irrawaddy, including the Mandalay Basin in Burma, the Menam [3] in Thailand, the Mekong and Red in Indochina, and the Si in China.

Australia and Indonesia. The Monsoon Tropics cut latitudinally through the three major physical provinces of Australia—the western plateau, elevated about 1250 feet above sea level, the central lowland which here is drained into the Gulf of Carpentaria, and the Eastern Highlands which in northeast Queensland are usually under 3000 feet elevation.

Across the Arafura Sea, the largest lowland of New Guinea is also included within the Monsoon Tropics. This is essentially a deltaic plain formed by the Fly, the Digul, and other streams. Much of eastern Java and the Lesser Sunda Islands are comprised of mountains that are continuations of the mainland systems of Asia. Plains are usually associated with streams and border the coasts.

Natural vegetation

Natural vegetation reflects the pattern of wet and dry seasons. Forests dominate on the wetter margins and are replaced by scrub thorn forest and savanna where drier conditions prevail. Vegetation pat-

[3] The full name of this river is Menam Chao Bhraya, which westerners usually shorten to Menam.

FIGURE 4-9. *Elephant at work clearing land for establishment of a plantation.* (Natural Rubber Bureau.)

terns are quite similar to those found in the Wet-Dry Tropics; several factors account for some differences, however. Land suitable for wet-crop agriculture in the populated Monsoon regions has been cleared of its natural cover and planted. Only in the more inaccessible and non-arable areas are typical vegetative communities represented. The Ganges Plain of India is devoid of trees in many places due to extensive cultivation; the resulting lack of wood for fuel leads millions of people to burn dried cow dung, thus preventing its use as a fertilizer. The Ghats, Himalayas, and the numerous highlands that fan out into Southeast Asia receive heavy precipitation on their windward slopes and support Monsoon rain forests. In contrast to the selvas of the Rainy Tropics, these forests have fewer species and the trees are smaller in girth. Broadleaf deciduous trees, which lose their leaves during the dry season, are prevalent, and pure stands are common. Several species, such as the teak tree and multiple-use bamboo,[4] are typical of the Asian realm. Monsoon forests have wide tree spacing, resulting in little interlocking of crowns, as is characteristic of the selva, and therefore the penetration of light to the forest floor stimulates the growth of dense jungle understories. Thick tidal forests of mangroves flourish on the low deltaic plains of the rivers along the coasts. An example is the Sunderbans, a thick wall of stilted mangroves along the complex system of channels in the mouths of the Ganges-Brahmaputra.

---

[4] Bamboo is botanically classed as a grass although it often grows to heights of 60 or 70 feet.

Natural vegetation in Monsoon Australia, consisting of a selva coastal fringe, scrub thorn forests, and tall, coarse grasses, has a close resemblance to the vegetation landscapes of the Wet-Dry Regions of Africa and South America. The rapid-growing gray-green eucalypti are distinctive, being indigenous to Australia and Tasmania. There are numerous species—about 150 in all. Some rival the redwoods of California in size.

Native animal life

The Monsoon lands of Asia have a surprising number of wild animals despite the heavy concentrations of population. The forest and savanna are the habitat of a great variety of species, and animal life is comparable to that of the African Wet-Dry Regions, except for the absence of the vast herds of grass-eaters. Insects, birds, and reptiles are common. Poisonous snakes are especially prevalent and each year in India thousands of deaths are attributed to the king cobra and to small, deadly vipers. There are several species of monkeys; colonies inhabit the fringes of cultivated land and often make raids on fields and orchards, where they are usually left unmolested by the pious Hindu farmers. The rhinoceros and elephant represent the larger vertebrates. Although elephants have been domesticated and are the beasts of all work, many wild herds still exist. Asia is the only habitat of the tiger, king of the cat family. In their old age they often become man-eaters preying upon the inhabitants of the outlying villages.

In Australia animal life is less varied than in Asia. Insects, birds, crocodiles, and reptiles are common, but the unique feature of this continent, which has been long isolated from other land masses, is its archaic types; here live the greater part of the world's surviving marsupials, the most famous of which is the kangaroo. Australia is known as "the land of living fossils." [5]

[5] Allee, W. C., and Karl P. Schmidt, *Ecological Animal Geography*. New York: John Wiley and Sons, Inc., 1951, 112.

Soils

The mature soils of the Monsoon Tropics, having developed under similar conditions of temperature, rainfall, and vegetation, display characteristics much like those discussed for the Wet-Dry Tropics. Paralleling the diminishing precipitation and the change from forest to grassland vegetation, there is gradation from red and yellow lateritic soils of low fertility to the better quality chestnut and brown groups of the pedocals. Black soils, known as *regur,* occur over a wide area in the western portion of the Deccan. They have developed, largely upon lava, under modest rainfall and grassy vegetation. The regur have an excellent water-holding capacity, and in opposition to other plateau soils, are high in fertility. Much of the agriculture is found on alluvial soils of river floodplains and deltas which, owing to relative youth and diversity of source, are usually highly productive. This is particularly true in the Asiatic portion.

MAN IN THE MONSOON TROPICS

In contrast to the other regions of the tropics, which are thinly populated, the Monsoon lands stand out with one of the truly dense population blocks of the world. Over one-quarter of mankind is concentrated in south and southeast Asia. However, much of Monsoon Australia is relatively unpopulated.

The densities are so great in the lowlands of the Indian Peninsula and the river valleys of Southeast Asia that 600 to 700 persons per square mile are usual and concentrations of over 1500 are not uncommon. The majority live in farm villages, over 600,000 of which are found in India and Pakistan.

The land capable of supporting people under existing conditions is almost fully occupied in India and Pakistan, but in Southeast Asia there is an incomplete development of crop land. There is extreme crowding in the best lands of the river plains, while large upland areas that could be brought into use with clearing, irrigation, or transportation development are now only sparsely populated with primitive tribes.

Southeast Asia, along with adjoining mainland areas and the islands to the south and east, is one of the most fascinating centers of cultural contact and movement on earth. A distinguished geographer has recently claimed Southeast Asia as the probable "culture hearth" of agriculture where man first practiced plant cultivation. Over thousands of years peoples have mingled here, drifting south through the passes and down the great valley trenches, mixing with or driving older groups before them.

The invasions of northwest India by Aryans between 3000-2000 B.C. led to Hinduism, which overflowed India to the coasts of Southeast Asia about the time of Christ. This colonization was matched by migrations of Chinese merchants and the establishment of Chinese rule on the east coasts of the region. From the ninth to the fourteenth centuries, Moslems (Moguls) spread over India and beyond, and were reinforced in the fifteenth century by Moslem traders from Arabia who controlled and converted large groups in Malaya and the East Indies. Beginning in the fifteenth and sixteenth centuries, Europeans carried western political and economic systems and Christianity into India and Southeast Asia. More recently a strong Chinese cultural overlay has been added to many areas in Southeast Asia.

These waves of penetration have influenced every aspect of life in the Asian Monsoon Tropics. Cultural clashes between Hindus and Moslems were the principal reason for the division of India and Pakistan. In addition to the two great religions, there are seven others, plus more than two hundred languages in the Indo-Pakistan realm. Language, religion, and other cultural differences have tended to separate groups into communities—a condition which has been detrimental to economic development and political unification. Racial and cultural diversity also characterize Southeast Asia; there are five major races and at least a score of lesser races in Burma, and four major and several lesser races in Indochina.

Today the region is one of the world's centers of change. Differences are beginning to be compromised. Following World War II Burma, Indonesia, India, Pakistan, Ceylon, and the Philippines emerged as independent states.[6] All of these are now engaged in programs to elevate the level of living of their people in terms of education as well as material well-being through fuller resource development and improved technology. At the same time, their voices in world affairs are rapidly gaining importance.

The Monsoon Tropics of Australia support only a few people. Most of the remaining 75,000 aborigines are scattered through the area; their sparse density is indicated by the fact that only about 4000 occupy the 31,200 square mile Arnheim Aboriginal Reserve in the Northern Territory. These people, the vanishing remnant of an ancient stock, hunt, fish, and gather nuts, roots, and seeds for their sustenance, using largely the primitive weapons and implements of their ancestors. Only about 200,000 white people live in the entire northern third of the continent. They are concentrated mainly on the Queensland Coast, where they engage in commercial agriculture. There are scattered stock stations on the savanna, and a few small towns along the north coast; the inhabitants of some are employed in pearl shell fisheries.

Subsistence agriculture

The people of the Asian region are dominantly subsistence farmers whose destinies are controlled by the Monsoons. The productivity and supporting capacity of any given area are determined by the amount and regularity of the rains brought by the summer winds. Great contrasts are found, as illustrated by the differences between East and West Pakistan. The former, with high rainfall, is a rice-growing area and has

[6] The Indian Union is now a republic loosely tied to the British Commonwealth of Nations but without allegiance to the British crown; Pakistan and Ceylon now have dominion status.

FIGURE 4-10. *Threshing scenes in India: oxen and buffaloes treading out rice. These are typical work animals and share most of the duties connected with the rice crop.* (Government of India Information Services.)

an average population density of nearly 800 per square mile; the latter, a wheat-producing area far inland, receives much less precipitation and supports an average of but 90 persons per square mile.

Throughout the agricultural lands of south and southeast Asia, great population densities cause farm holdings to be small, seldom over five acres, and these are generally sub-divided into several plots scattered about the owner's village. Production from these small holdings provides the sole source of livelihood—thus they must be farmed intensively. Where the water supply permits, two or even three crops a year are common. In southern China the rainy season is of sufficient length to allow production of two successive crops of rice. This multiple-cropping greatly extends the supporting capacity of a farm holding.

In India and Pakistan irrigation development has increased the cropping possibilities and added stability to agriculture in many sections where uncertainty and irregularity of rainfall restricts normal production. Over most of the area irrigation is necessary for crops during the dry season of off-shore winds. The type of irrigation practiced varies with the source and supply of water. Canals are the most important, providing water for at least half the irrigated acreage. The major development is in the middle Ganges Valley and the Punjab, Land of Five Rivers, where rainfall is low and undependable and perennial streams are available. Wells provide the source of water in many districts, but especially in the Ganges Valley where the water table is high. Tanks are the principal means of providing water for irrigation on the plateau; by this

FIGURE 4-11. *Threshing scenes in India: women winnowing grain in the traditional manner, using the wind as an aid.* (Government of India Information Services.)

system the rain run-off of the wet monsoon is impounded in drainage channels by simple dams for diversion to the fields at the end of the rainy season.

The farmer's equipment is simple: a light wooden plow, sometimes with a metal tip, a crude wooden harrow, and various hand tools such as a hoe, sickle, and flail. Bullocks in India and water buffalo in Southeast Asia are used to plow and harrow, but most of the work of planting, cultivating, harvesting, and threshing is performed by hand.

The complete food supply must be produced on the farm. Crops grown are selected with a view to giving balance as well as greatest possible yields. Rice, the highest yielding member of the small grains, is the favorite. In areas receiving over 80 inches of rainfall it is the main crop, but where rainfall is below 40 inches rice can be grown only with irrigation; it remains an important crop in the intermediate areas. On millions of acres of the plateau of India, in northwest Pakistan, and the Mandalay Basin of Burma, farmers must grow wheat, sorghum, millets, or barley instead of rice. Grains dominate, but each farmer produces a variety of other items such as sugar cane, beans, peas, tropical fruits, and oil seeds, notably sesame, rape, and peanuts.

Commercial agriculture

Although it is primarily a land of subsistence agriculture, many Asian products find their way to city markets and some into channels of world trade. The aggregate is large. Many farmers are tenants and must share the harvest with their landlords, who in turn sell surpluses. Even the poorest farmers require certain essentials such as clothing, salt, and matches—they must sell produce to provide the cash for these purchases. In the rich black soils area inland from Bombay, many farmers grow a marketable crop of cotton. Most of the world's jute, a coarse fiber used for making burlap and gunny sacks, is produced on the wet delta lands of the Ganges and Brahmaputra Rivers.

Some commercial agriculture has been developed under European management and capital. The British were responsible for the tea industry of India, establishing plantations in the hills of central Ceylon (now independent of India), the Assam Province, the Himalayan slopes, and the hills at the southern end of the peninsula. The British also sponsored commercial rice production in the Irrawaddy Delta of Burma, the French developed some plantation agriculture in Indochina, while native landlords spread into the rich delta lands of Thailand. Burma, Indochina, and Thailand are the principal surplus-rice producers and exporters of Asia, since the local populations are not sufficiently large to consume their crops.

The Queensland Coast of Australia is unique among the developed areas of the tropics; sugar cane is produced by white farmers on relatively small holdings averaging about forty-five acres. This activity was first organized as a plantation enterprise based on labor recruited from the southwest Pacific islands. When this *Kanaka* labor was prohibited early in the twentieth century, sugar production was reorganized on a small farm basis with white ownership and labor, largely Italian.

Grazing

There has been little development of a commercial grazing economy in the Monsoon lands. This statement appears as a paradox since the Asiatic region raises two-fifths of the world's goats and India alone has over 200 million cattle and approximately 50 million sheep. Goats are hardy animals needing little care and are reared principally for milk and hides as part of the subsistence agriculture pattern. The humped cattle of India have a religious significance and hence play a very limited role as a source of food supply; they are used, however, for pulling carts and plows, and to supply hides and meager amounts of milk. Sheep are raised principally for wool. The Indian Government has recognized the seriousness of the livestock problem and is attempting to improve the situation through such measures as the introduction of better breeding stock, sterilization of low-quality male animals, and encouragement of the use of dairy products.[7]

The fringe of northern Australia contains the only commercial grazing economy in the Monsoon region. Cattle, rather than sheep or goats, utilize the natural savanna, since they are more able to survive on the coarse forage, to withstand the wet season climate, and to bear the long drives to north-coast slaughtering houses. Stations on the Australian savanna are large; some in Northern Territory measure their herds in tens of thousands and land leases in hundreds of thousands of acres. In Queensland, particularly on the coast, the operations are usually on a smaller scale. A better grade of beef is raised here than that produced in the Llanos or Campos of South America. Australian stockmen, however, are faced with problems similar to those encountered by the South Americans—seasonal drought, lack of supplemental feed, pests, and long distances to markets. Some advancements, yet minor in extent, are being made; these include the introduction of improved stock and the production of dry season feed by irrigation in some of the stream valleys. To avoid long drives, aircraft are coming into use for the transport of prime carcasses to the north-coast freezing plants.

Forest industries

Teak in the forests of Burma, Thailand, and Indochina is the leading commercial tree species of the region. Other important forest products include sal, bamboo, and rattan. Teak is used chiefly in ship construction; it resists salt water and contains an oil preservative which prevents iron from corroding when in contact with the wood. Resistance to termites and fire also favors its

[7] For a description of a new dairy development in the city of Bombay, see Spielman, Henry W., "World's Largest Dairy," *Foreign Agriculture,* XIV, No. 4, 1950, 75-76.

use as a cabinet and construction wood. Teak logging is complicated by the rugged terrain, dense vegetation, and heavy rains. The tree, too heavy to transport when green, must be girdled and allowed to dry for three years before felling. Cutting is done in the dry season and the logs are hauled by elephants to be floated down the swollen rivers during the wet season to Rangoon, Saigon, and Bangkok, the concentration ports.

Mining

The most significant mineral-producing area in the Monsoon Tropics is situated in the uplands of India 200 miles west of Calcutta. The country's most important reserves of iron and coal, along with deposits of manganese, mica, and limestone, are concentrated here. The iron belt contains one of the largest and best stores of iron in Asia. Manganese is widely scattered, with the largest deposits in the central portion of the plateau. India is one of the major world producers of manganese and is the leading supplier of mica.

The mineral wealth of Southeast Asia is varied and large, but inadequate transportation has limited development to only the most accessible and valuable deposits. Tin, tungsten, lead, zinc, copper, coal, petroleum, and gem minerals are mined in Burma; tin, tungsten, lead, zinc, iron, and phosphate are mined in Indochina; tin is the only mineral produced in noteworthy quantities in Thailand. The major portion of these minerals move out to European and American markets, much in semi-processed form or as ores. However, owing to the increasing world demand, the nations of Southeast Asia can be expected to increase their incomes from minerals by further processing as well as through increased mining development.

Manufacturing

The Monsoon Tropics—with greater and more diversified amounts of raw material as well as millions of consumers—lead the tropical areas in manufacturing activities. India, as a nation, leads in industrial development. Handicrafts characterize a large portion of manufacturing, with goods produced in small home workshops for local consumption. The country is making rapid strides toward modern industrialization and a number of factories are processing the products of field, forest, and mine. There are three distinct manufacturing regions in India: (*1*) the Bombay district on the margin of the cotton-growing area is the leader in cotton textile manufacturing; (*2*) the Calcutta region is more diversified with jute, rice and flour mills, wool and silk weaving, wood products industries, and sugar and oil refineries; and (*3*) Jamshedpur, in the northeast part of the plateau where coal and iron occur close together, is the iron and steel center. Although

FIGURE 4-12. *Indian industry: a worker operating a modern machine tool—a sharp contrast to the traditional village handicrafts.* (Government of India Information Services.)

far behind India in industrial progress, Pakistan, in the few years since the partition, has been rapidly constructing textile mills, machine shops, and other manufacturing facilities to improve the standard of living.

Under the colonial systems Southeast Asia functioned as a supplier of raw material much the same way as did India, but manufacturing was even more retarded. Industries in Burma are concerned almost entirely with rice, petroleum, and timber; in Thailand, with rice and timber; and in Indochina, with rice, other agricultural products, and timber. The people of all three countries are skilled in a variety of native crafts. Some of their products, such as the lacquer wares and ivory and wood carvings of Burma, have found exclusive markets abroad.

More industrial development can be expected in Monsoon Asia with growth in technology. The raw materials are available and there exists a market and a need for expanded production.

Urban centers

There are more cities in this climatic region than in any other within the tropics. Although they represent a small portion of the population, there are over 50 cities of the 100,000 class in India. Calcutta is the greatest city of that country, with nearly 4.5 million. With a port stretching 20 miles along the Hooghly River, a Ganges distributary, it occupies a strategic position for serving the commercial needs of the rich northern plain. Bombay, gateway and industrial center on the west, has about 3.5 million people; and Madras, principal city and port on the east coast, and Hyderabad, the main city on the Plateau, have passed one million. Most of the large cities of India are commercial centers, some derive additional importance from being provincial capitals, others have developed handicrafts, a few have become industrial, and a number, such as Benares in the middle Ganges plain, are religious centers. Growing cities of Pakistan are Lahore, the great educational and agricultural center of the Punjab, Dacca, the new capital, and Chittagong, its expanding port in East Pakistan.

Five notable cities are delta gateways to the river valleys of Southeast Asia, and each tends to dominate the trade of its respective valley. *Rangoon* on the Irrawaddy Delta is the trade center of Burma; *Bangkok,* near the sea on the Menam, serves Thailand; *Saigon,* on the Mekong River delta, and *Hanoi* with its port, Haiphong, on the Red River, are the chief commercial centers of Indochina. *Canton,* leading city of south China, occupies a delta position with the Si Valley as its hinterland. Victoria on the island of Hong Kong also lives largely by commercial activity with south China.

Jokjakarta and Soerabaja, the second and third cities of Java, are situated in the eastern or Monsoon Tropic portion of that island. Manila, chief port and city of the Philippines, is located on Manila Bay on the west coast of Luzon. This center is the hub of transportation for the island group and, with a population nearing 1.5 million, ranks as one of the great cities of the world.

The underdeveloped character of northern Australia is indicated by the fact that Darwin, the largest center on the north coast, has a population of only 4000. Somewhat greater activity on the east coast of Queensland has resulted in several small centers, of which Townsville, with about 35,000, and Cairns, with 17,000, are the largest.

OUTLOOK

It is obvious that over the world there exist great gaps between technical and scientific knowledge and actual practices. Such a condition exists in the Monsoon Tropics. Neither natural nor technical resources are being used anywhere near their potentials. Throughout the Asian region there are possibilities for increasing agricultural as well as other productions. In those areas of India where the two potentials have been brought together, farm productivity has increased from 60 to 400 per cent; a 10 per cent overall increase should permit India to become nearly

FIGURE 4-13. *The Tilaiya Dam. This dam, which went into operation in 1953, is part of a multiple-purpose project called the Damodar Valley Project, which is expected to provide irrigation for 800,000 acres and generate a peak load of 300,000 kilowatts. When completed, barges will reach the Ranigunj coal fields. The Damodar Valley Project is modeled after the American Tennessee Valley Authority, and is one of several such projects now under construction.* (Government of India Information Services.)

self-sufficient under present standards.[8] American and European technology is making inroads. Agricultural experiment stations have been established in most of the countries; the local scientists now have the knowledge for solving food and production problems. There is a vast gap, however, between the scientists of experiment stations and the farmers. Extension services, bringing the information and guidance to the man on the land, must be expanded. Although industrialization offers some hopes for improving living conditions in the Asian region, it has definite limitations and cannot be considered a panacea for all the problems. Agriculture will undoubtedly remain the key element in the economy of these nations; thus their well-being is closely tied to improving the use of the land.

Changes are occurring, with governments taking active roles, but there are many aspects of life in south and Southeast Asia, some rooted deep in religious beliefs and traditions, which will slow the process of education. An Indian professor has summarized the time requirement somewhat like this: "Give us two generations—one to arouse the people to the responsibilities of freedom, and a second to do some real spade work."

[8] Spielman, Henry W., "India Can Feed Itself," *Foreign Agriculture,* XIV, No. 5, 1950, 95-98.

SELECTED REFERENCES

Brush, John E., "The Iron and Steel Industry in India," *Geographical Review,* XLII, No. 1, 1952, 37-55.

Dobby, E. H. G., *Southeast Asia.* New York: John Wiley and Sons, Inc., 1951.

Fryer, D. W., "The 'Million City' in Southeast Asia," *Geographical Review,* XLIII, No. 4, 1953, 474-494.

Kirk, William, "The Damador Valley—*Valles Opima,*" *Geographical Review,* XL, No. 3, 1950, 415-443.

Roughley, T. C., *Wonders of the Great Barrier Reef.* New York: Charles Scribner's Sons, 1947.

Shen, T. H., "Food Production and Administration on Taiwan," *Scientific Monthly,* LXXIV, No. 5, 1952, 338-345.

Spate, O. H. K., *India and Pakistan, A General and Regional Geography.* New York: E. P. Dutton and Co., Inc., 1954.

Spate, O. H. K. and Enayat Ahmad, "Five Cities on the Gangetic Plain: A Cross Section of Indian Cultural History," *Geographical Review,* XL, No. 2, 1950, 260-278.

Wickizer, V. D., and M. K. Bennett, *Rice Economy of Monsoon Asia.* Stanford University, Calif.: Stanford University Press, 1941.

Wood, G. L., ed., *Australia, Its Resources and Development.* New York: The Macmillan Company, 1947.

CHAPTER 5

Tropical Deserts

THE TROPICAL DESERTS ARE LANDS so hostile that life scarcely exists over vast areas. Sunshine, heat, and wind comprise the climate with rain only a whim of nature, having little annual or seasonal pattern. In no other regions are life and water so intimately related. The meager vegetation and the limited animal life must make special adjustments to the heat, aridity, and excessive evaporation in order to live. Homes are constructed with thick walls for insulation, and light-colored clothing is often worn to reflect the daily stream of the sun's rays. There is no semblance of evenness in the distribution of the scanty population. The location of agriculture is strictly determined by the presence of water. Subsistence grazing exists only through a constant nomadic quest for forage and

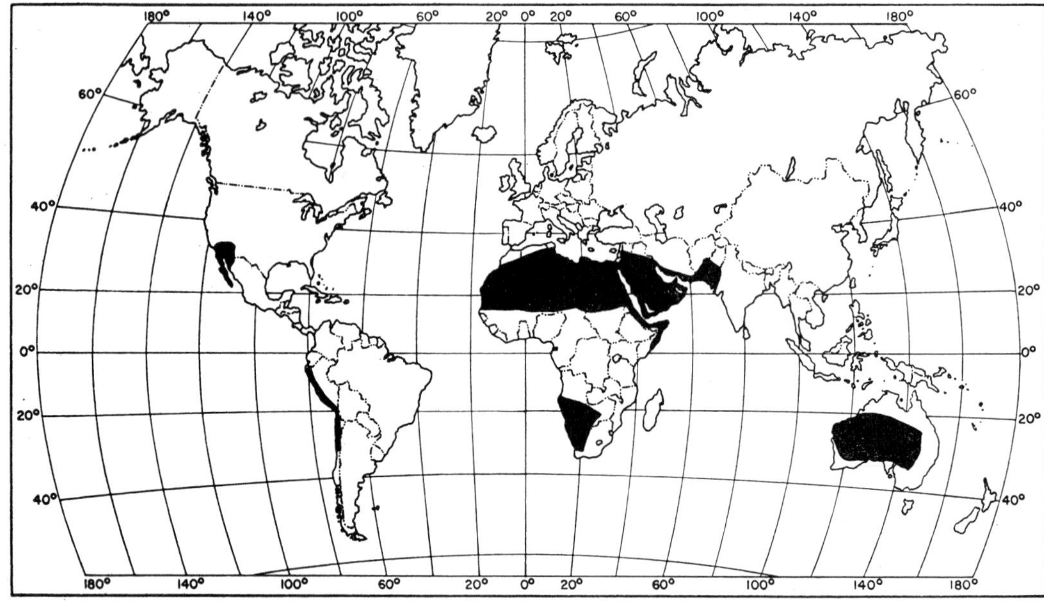

FIGURE 5-1. *The Tropical Deserts.*

water. Dependence on animals and crops from oases has dominated desert livelihood for centuries. Other economies were lacking until mineral discoveries, especially that of petroleum in the Middle East, stimulated mining activities. Oil development is having a significant impact upon the Arab way of life.

Desert causes

Deserts occur as the result of one or several of the following: (*1*) location in areas dominated by the subtropical high pressure belt of settling, therefore dry, air; (*2*) location in the belt of the persistent trades, whose drying action gives rise to the term "Trade Wind Deserts"; (*3*) a dry shadow location on the leeward side of high mountains where the barriers effectively block out moisture-laden air; (*4*) location in the interior of continents far removed from sources of oceanic moisture; and (*5*) the presence of offshore cold water due to cold ocean currents, such as the Benguela Current paralleling the coast of the Kalahari and the Humboldt Current offshore of the Atacama, and the upwelling of cold water from ocean depths. Winds which have passed over these cold waters reach the land with lowered temperatures, but become warmed as they pass over the land, and act as drying agents inland.

General location

The Tropical Deserts are usually situated between 15° and 30° north and south latitude. However, the latitudinal extent varies from one desert to another as the result of differences in surfaces, continental size, and configuration. They seldom extend to the east coasts because of rain resulting from onshore winds, but are deep in the continental interiors or in the lee of mountains. Only the Sahara of Africa spans the width of a continent, and in this case the Arabian peninsula and the land mass of Asia prohibit the trades from crossing an ocean. The western margins of deserts usually reach the sea; in South America and South Africa they are extended equatorward by the effects of bordering cold currents.

Major deserts. There are seven major tropical deserts. The Sahara (*1*) is the "Great Desert" filling the northern portion of Africa, stretching 3500 miles from the Atlantic Ocean to the Red Sea and 1200 miles from the Sudan

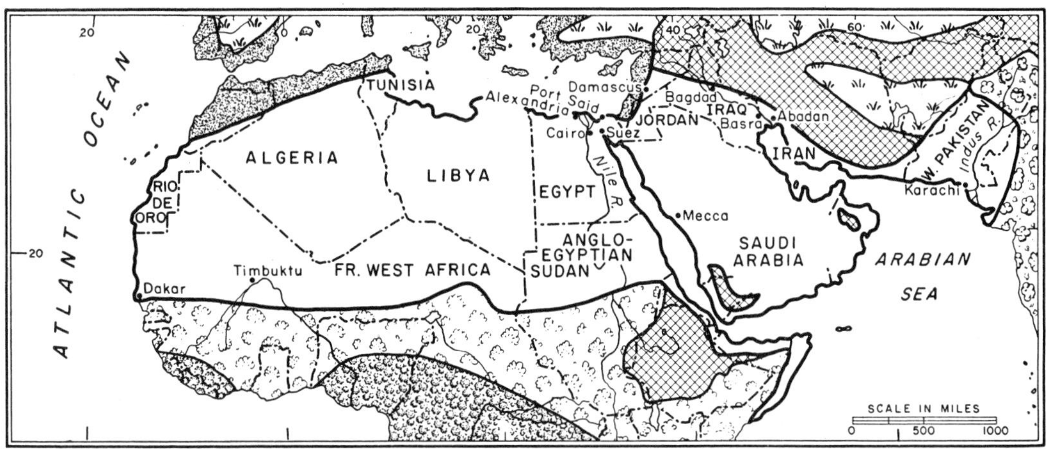

FIGURE 5-2. *The Sahara and the deserts of southwest Asia.*

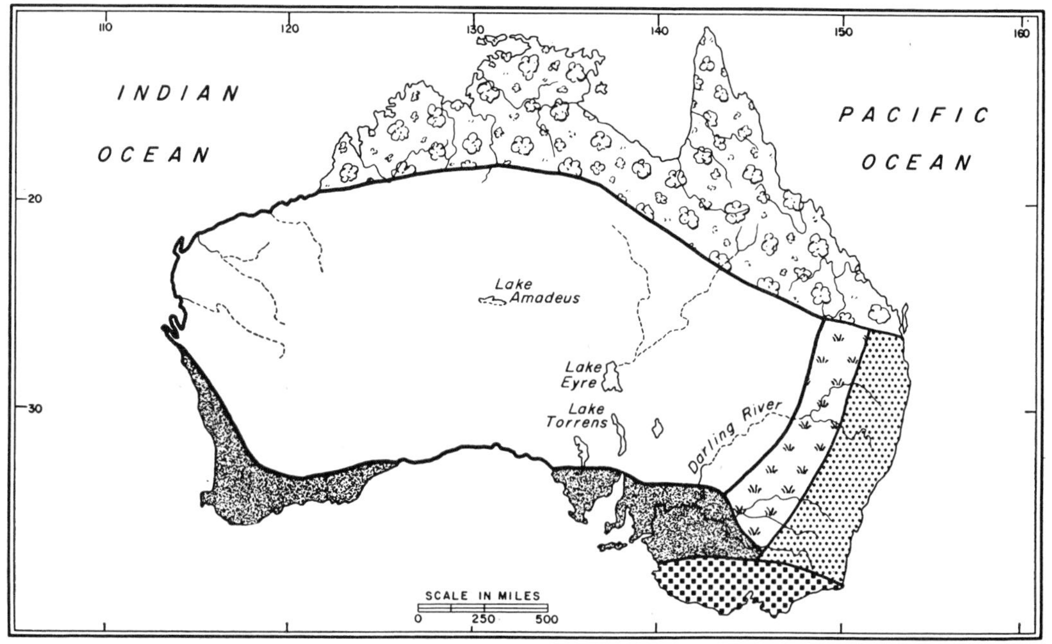

FIGURE 5-3. *The Australian Desert.*

to the Mediterranean Sea and the Atlas Mountains. Contained in this vast and often sterile expanse, which exceeds the size of the United States, are all or portions of Rio De Oro, French West Africa, Morocco, Tunisia, Algeria, Libya, Egypt, Anglo-Egyptian Sudan, Ethiopia, Eritrea, and British, French, and Italian Somaliland.

The desert of southwest Asia (*2*) contains an area at least half the size of the Sahara. All of the Arabian Peninsula is included, except for the highland corners in the south, southern Israel, Jordan, and most of central and southern Syria, Iraq, and Iran.[1] This broad, continuous tropical dryland which

[1] The northern fringes of the desert of southwest Asia could be classed as subtropical, but they are included in this classification because the physical character and human development are so closely related to tropical areas to the south.

comprises most of the Middle East joins the Thar Desert (*3*) which centers upon the middle and lower parts of the Indus Valley of West Pakistan and the adjoining area of India.

The Australian Desert (*4*) is the largest in the southern hemisphere, comprising some 40 per cent of the continent. The Kalahari (*5*) of South Africa includes, in a half-million square mile expanse, southwest Angola, southwest Africa, Bechuanaland, and the neighboring fringes of the Union of South Africa. In South America the Atacama Desert (*6*) is restricted by the Andes Mountains to a long, narrow belt fringing the continent from 4° S to 31° S latitude. It includes all of coastal Peru and the northern third of Chile.

North America has only limited land area in the latitudes of the Tropical Deserts, but this climatic type is represented by the Sonoran Desert (7) which includes Lower California, the northwest coast of the Mexican mainland, and a portion of California, Arizona, and New Mexico within its boundaries.

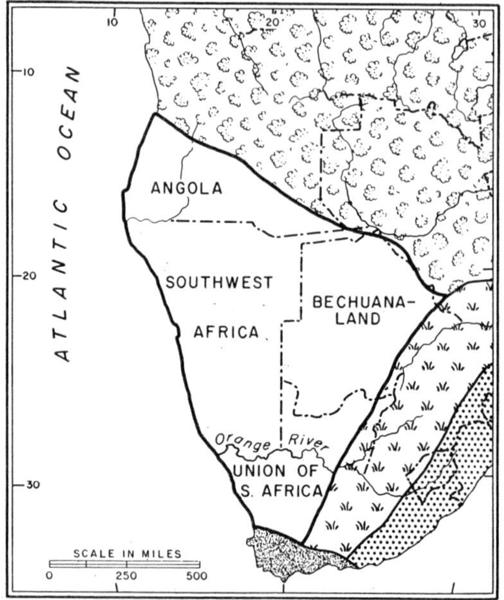

FIGURE 5-4. *The Kalhari.*

FIGURE 5-5. *The Sonoran Desert.*

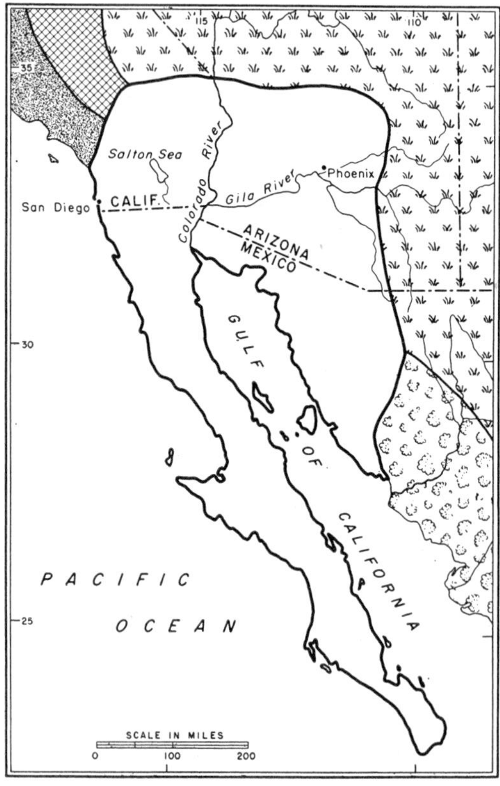

FIGURE 5-6. *The Atacama Desert.*

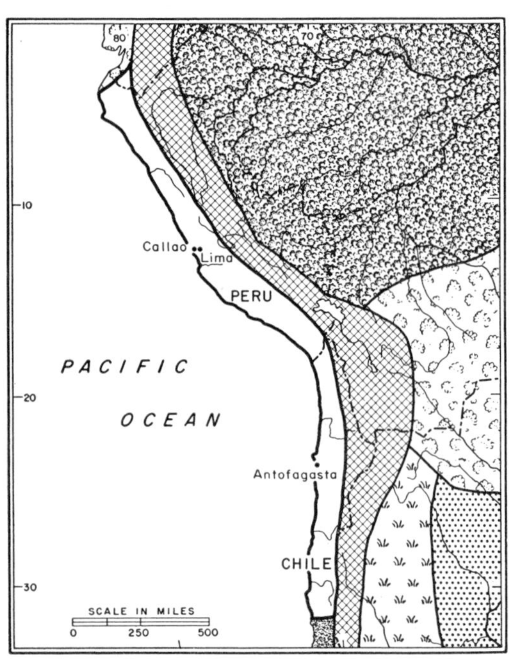

PHYSICAL ENVIRONMENT

Climate

The climate of the Tropical Deserts is one of extremes; superlatives characterize the weather elements. Temperatures are the highest on earth and precipitation is the lowest. The air is so warm and dry that rain is often evaporated before it reaches the ground. The desert can be a fiery furnace by day and uncomfortably cool at night. Each day the sun blazes down from usually cloudless skies and the heat shimmers from the rocks and dunes. Seasons have little meaning—the months pass in a monotonous succession. Where highlands are absent, winds sweep unhampered across the open spaces; with even a slight breeze the air is filled with sand and dust. The burning winds of the Sahara are so unpleasant that they are known by special names, such as the *Simoon, shahali,* and *khamsin.*

Temperatures. Average temperatures are always high. Averages in high sun periods range from 85° to 95° and over; noon readings of 105° to 110° are common. The highest shade temperature ever recorded was 136.4°, at Azizia in the Sahara.[2] The heat continues during the low sun period and average temperatures range from 60° upward and often reach 80°. Yearly annual ranges are from 20° to 30°. The clear skies at night promote rapid radiation of heat and diurnal ranges fluctuate from 25° to 50° with extremes as high as 60° and 70°. Surface heating is rapid; temperatures soar as soon as the sun rises and cool just as rapidly when the sun sets. Frost may even form during the cool season of the year. The character of the surface also affects heating and cooling. Sandy areas have more rapid temperature changes than rocky areas since the rocks absorb more heat during the day and consequently cool more slowly at night. Sands become abnormally hot during the day. Emile Gautier, in his book, *Sahara, the Great Desert,* mentions that in the battle of Metarfa, fought in the sand dunes of the Sahara, the lightly-clad native foot soldiers, unable to hold a prone position because of the intense heat of the sand, remained standing in spite of orders and were all killed.

Except in certain coastal areas, the air is very dry and relative humidities are extremely low, with daytime averaging approximately 25 per cent during the hotter season. Despite the high temperatures, however, man is less enervated by the dry heat of the desert when water is available than by the extreme humid heat of the Humid Tropics.

Precipitation. Desert precipitation can be characterized as low and erratic. Yearly totals

[2] Death Valley in California with a reading of 134° has the record in the United States.

FIGURE 5-7. *Typical climatic graphs of Tropical Desert stations.*

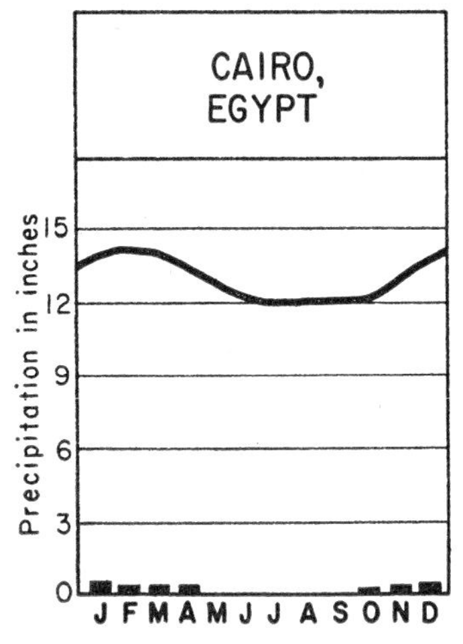

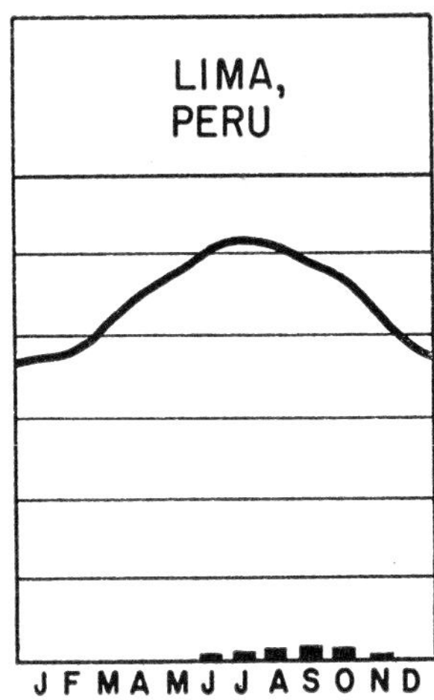

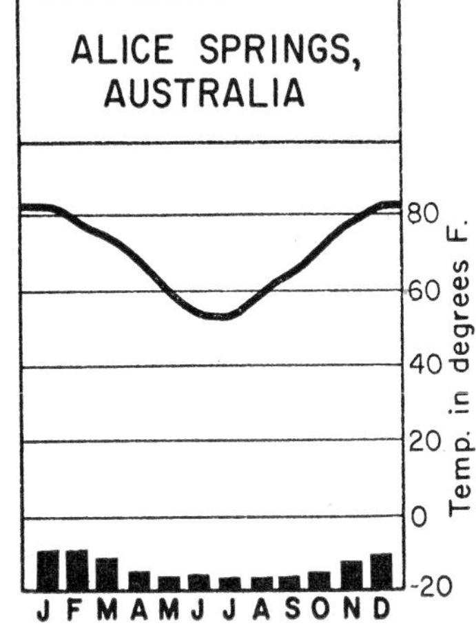

are under ten inches and, except on the margins, it is difficult to indicate any season of maximum. The great expanse of the Sahara has an average under five inches, but averages have little meaning since some years or series of years may be entirely dry; on the other hand, several inches may fall in a single day. Rain often occurs as short, violent convectional showers which may create more damage than benefit. Light showers are not too effective because the moisture is soon returned to the air by the excessive rate of evaporation.

Along the desert coasts of the Atacama and Kalahari, where upwelling and cool currents chill incoming air, dense mists are common. Fog banks form offshore over the cold water and are blown to the land. The persistent mist in some cases provides enough moisture for a green cover on the coast hills.

Surface features

To the observer from humid lands the desert is a world apart; landscapes and surface features are entirely different. The gradational forces work under conditions of slow and predominantly mechanical weathering, meager vegetation, low average but high intensity rainfall, and intermittent but rapid runoff. The characteristics of the landforms produced are thus unique to the drylands. Several distinctive features and types can be recognized.

Perhaps the most apparent is the fresh appearance of the landforms. Slow weathering and erosion result in widespread rock features in bold outline. Scanty vegetation makes visible the minute detail; rock debris mantles the base of every cliff and sharp rise. Deserts give the impression of youth!

An outstanding characteristic of the topography is the prevalence of closed basins, large and small. Many deserts have great areas with interior drainage with the erratic runoff directed toward the center of basins. Only a few streams succeed in transversing the entire width of the major deserts; these include the Nile of the Sahara, the Tigris-Euphrates of southwest Asia, the Indus of the Thar, the Orange of southwest Africa, and the Colorado of the Sonoran. In addition many smaller streams rising in the Andes Mountains flow across the Peruvian portion of the Atacama Desert to the Pacific Ocean. In all cases these exotic rivers rise in well-watered highlands from which they derive sufficient volume to carry across the drylands to the sea. Most other streams are intermittent, flowing only during and for a short time after a rainstorm. When volume is sufficient, water may be carried to the center of the basin, forming a *playa* or temporary lake. These stream beds, called *wadis* in the Old World Deserts and *arroyos* in the Americas, are characteristic features even in the driest deserts. Their banks are commonly perpendicular and their flat beds are rocky and sediment-covered. For a short time during a rainstorm they may be brimming full with raging torrents having tremendous erosive power; obstructed by their own deposition, they constantly shift their courses.

Although rains are few and far between, water action is the main force shaping the desert surface. During a storm water hurriedly moves over the land, down the slopes, some in definite channels and some in sheet floods, carrying sediments into the basin. Lack of volume and velocity causes much water to reach only the margins before dwindling and sinking beneath the surface. Thus the greatest deposition is at the basin margins where the streams form alluvial fans which coalesce and build inward toward the center. In time the basin becomes filled, forming a flat plain or *reg*. Often the wind alters the surface by removing fine materials, leaving a pebble desert.

As the bordering highlands are worn back, rock plains called pediments develop between the base and the alluvial fill. In some cases entire mountains apparently have been worn away, forming larger rock plains characterized by a thin and discontinuous mantle of rock fragments. This landform, termed *hamada*, has its largest expanse in the Sahara.

Most deserts have some sand-covered portions. Large areas of sandy or *erg* deserts occur in the Saharan, Arabian, Thar, Australian, and American drylands. Here the work of the wind is most apparent as frequently the surface is a billowing sea of dunes.

The large deserts display all the features mentioned, with many variations. It should be clearly understood that for drylands as a whole, features other than sand are usually dominant.

Water supply

Water means life in the desert. Knowledge of where and how a continuous supply can be found is of utmost concern to the desert dwellers. These drylands can be inhabited only so far as this great limiting factor will permit.

Exotic river. The most significant water source is the exotic river that rises in rainy areas beyond the margins and carries a good and manageable volume across the desert where it can be utilized even by the lesser-developed people. Utilization of many such streams for irrigation agriculture began in the early history of man. The Nile is the classic example, with its irrigated valley supporting the bulk of the Egyptians since the beginning of settlement. Like most of the exotic rivers, the Nile has a season of flood during which its waters, if uncontrolled, inundate riverine areas and deposit loads of silt to revitalize the soils of the valley floor. For the many centuries prior to 1900 the farmers along the Nile practiced a basin type of irrigation—fields surrounded by dikes acted as a reservoir, taking in water during the seasonal overflow. Water was thus held until the flood flow subsided and the fields were soaked; then the dikes were opened, fields drained, and the crops planted. The width of the agricultural belt paralleling the river depended upon the size of the yearly flood. Since 1900 the Aswan Dam and other engineering works have been constructed on the Nile; flood control has been effected and a more uniform yearly flow of the river maintained. Water is now distributed to the fields at all seasons through a system of irrigation canals and ditches. The area under irrigation has been increased and the cropping season lengthened, but the fertilizing silt has been lost.

Irrigation works also date back to the beginning of settlement in Iraq, where water is taken from the Tigris and Euphrates Rivers as well as from their combined channel, the Shatt al Arab, which flows from their confluence above Basra 120 miles to the Persian Gulf. The Indus River, which crosses the Thar Desert, has had a similar history and today supports very large irrigation works. Desert irrigation with water supply taken from the Peruvian streams had reached a high degree of development before the Spanish era. Today irrigation agriculture is practiced in many of the fifty-odd river valleys which cross the narrow coastal lowland. Irrigation in the Imperial Valley of California is based upon water diverted from the Colorado River.

FIGURE 5-8. *Erg desert. The sand dune scene is in Saudi Arabia. Notice the wind-made ripple marks on the dunes and the wadi bed in the mid-portion of the picture.* (Standard Oil Company of New Jersey.)

Wadi bottoms. In the Sahara and southwest Asian deserts, the seepage ground water below the bed of a *wadi* is sometimes reached through wells. A more or less continuous string of settlements may develop where the sub-surface water is abundant and easily tapped. For example, the great Wadi Dawasir with its extensive branches in southwest Saudi Arabia has several such stretches.

Springs. A natural spring may occur even in the desert land. These concentrated natural outflows from underground may result from a variety of conditions involving the position of the groundwater table, the rock structure, and the configuration of the land. In many cases they are caused by the local groundwater table being exposed on the side of a valley.

Artesian water. An artesian water supply depends upon the existence of a certain type of geologic structure (see Figure 5-9). In this structure an inclined pervious layer, or *aquifer stratum,* such as sandstone, is trapped between impervious layers. The aquifer exposed in an area of sufficient precipitation fills with water. Having no outlet the water in the lower portion of the incline is under pressure. A fissure in the overlying strata will result in a flowing spring, or water will rise in a well bore or even flow from it as long as head or pressure is maintained. The greatest development of artesian water occurs in the eastern part of Saudi Arabia where a number of wells have been drilled by the Arabian American Oil Company.

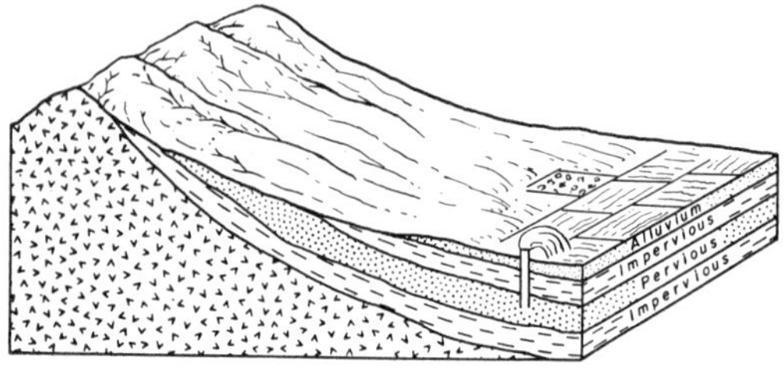

FIGURE 5-9. *Artesian structure.*

Kanats. In southwest Asia, particularly in Iran, the *kanat* is an important system used to tap the water table and collect sub-surface seepage in mountain valleys. Diversion channels direct the water into a central underground tunnel which conducts it to better soils fringing alluvial fans or to the plains. Water may be transported as far as 25 miles. The kanats are not lined and thus are subject to obstruction by caving; openings are provided at intervals along the course so that workmen can enter the channels to clear them. This ancient system has the unique advantage of radically reducing evaporation. Kanats are also used in North Africa; in the oases of Marrakech, for example, they are of basic importance, even in city water supply.

Natural vegetation

Few places in the desert are entirely devoid of plants and even in the most barren areas there may be a host of dormant seeds which will spring into life at the first sign of moisture. Carpets of vegetation are rare and plants are scattered as if they have been carelessly sown. Growth is low; however, a tall saguaro cactus occasionally towers over the lower shrubs. At certain seasons many plants produce delicate blooms in various shades of red and yellow, making the desert appear as fertile and colorful as any garden.

Desert plants are *xerophytes,* species adapted to drought and high rates of evaporation. Xerophytes show a remarkable adjustment to harsh environment; their methods of defense against adverse conditions are extremely interesting. Root systems are well-developed. Some plants have tap roots which go deep in search of water, while others have amazing lateral systems many times the size of the plant. Water is stored inside stems and roots; a thick bark, narrow leaves with waxy or hairy surfaces, or the complete absence of leaves retard evaporation. Some plants are equipped with sharp spines or have unpalatable flavors that discourage grazing animals. There are annuals whose seeds can wait years for a rain—when enough moisture is present, they sprout, flower, and go to seed in an in-incredibly short time. Perennials will remain brown and appear lifeless until rain stimulates new green growth.

Many types of grasses are found in most deserts, usually present in solitary tufts. Areas that appear barren may show, on closer inspection, large varieties of pigmy plants. Thorn bushes, especially the acacia, are common in the Old World Deserts. The highly alkali-impregnated soils of the Atacama probably make it the barest of all the tropical deserts and only a few scattered mesquite and sagebrush grow near the coast. The Sonoran is noted for its great variety of succulents—fleshy and thorny plants such as giant saguaro, cholla, other cacti, and yuccas. Their shapes give a weird appearance to this desert's landscape.

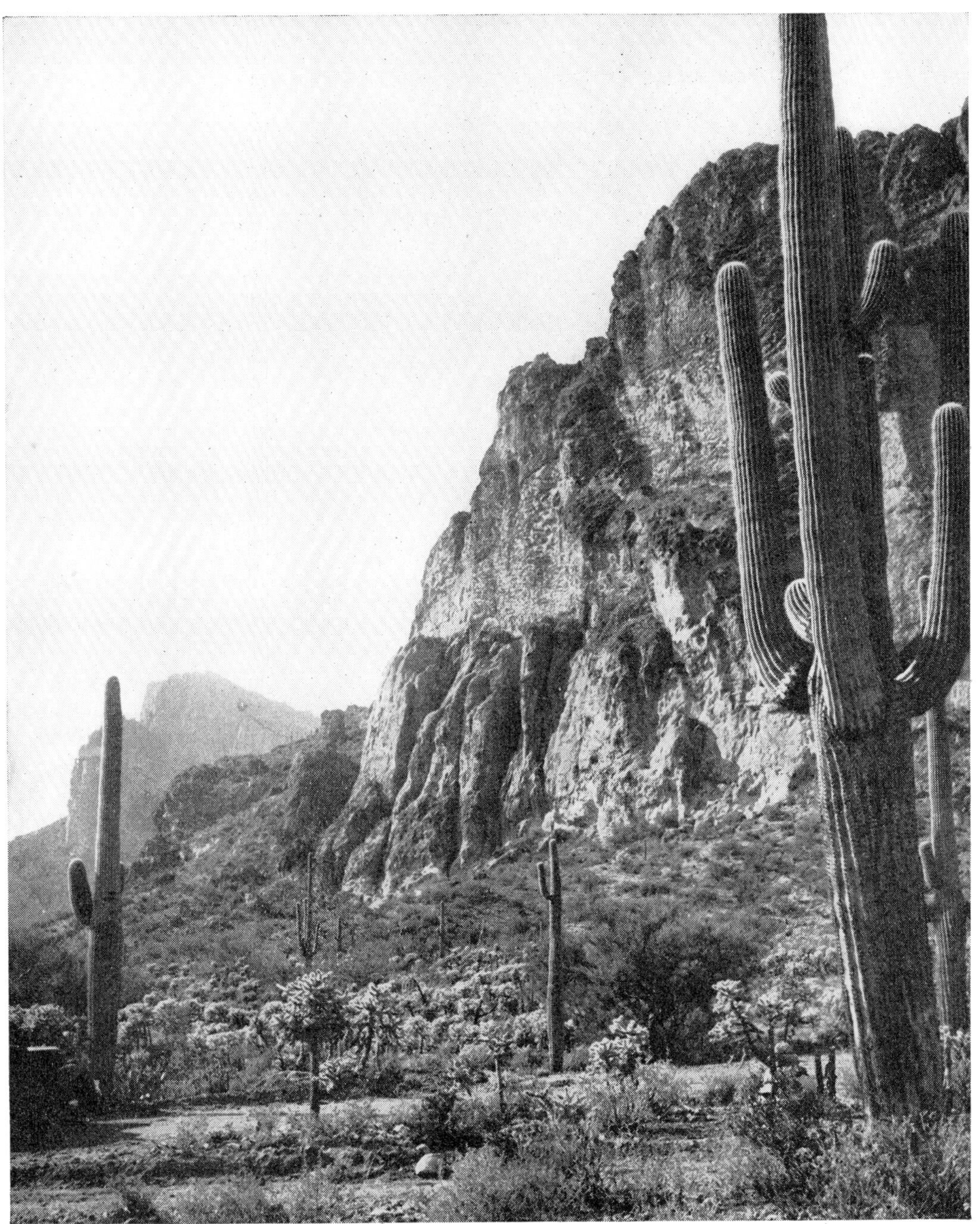

FIGURE 5-10. *Desert vegetation in the American Southwest. The giant saguaro cacti tower above the cholla cacti and lower shrubs. The cacti store water in their thick stems and are able to withstand long dry periods.* (United States Forest Service.)

Native animal life

Desert animal life is sparse and restricted to species capable of making adjustments to the arid environment—namely, the ability to subsist on the scanty vegetation and to survive with a minimum of water. Dew, in some cases, is the only water source. Desert animals tend to acquire camouflaging colors ranging from pale yellow to red. The majority are small; the desert fox and a species of antelope are the largest in the Sahara. Burrowing, running, and jumping animals are common. There are few birds, and even insects are scarce except around oases or animal habitats.

The camel is the animal most often associated with deserts. Domesticated for a beast of burden, his use is chiefly confined to the African and Asian deserts. The Romans introduced the camel from Asia to North Africa about 200 A.D., making nomadism possible for the first time; this stimulated an activity that has continued. Camels were introduced into Australia in the 1860's and were used to carry mail and supplies to ranchers and miners. The United States Army experimented with this animal in the Southwest during the mid-19th century, but the War Between the States disrupted the continuance of the project.

The camel is especially well-adapted to an arid environment and his ability to withstand heat and go for many days without water has made him invaluable for caravan traffic. The hump, erroneously considered as storage for water, is really a device for storing fat. Water is stored in a series of sacs in the walls of the stomach. The feet and knees are padded against the friction of rock and sand and the nostrils can be closed during sand storms. The nose is tough enough to browse among the coarse desert forage.

Soils

Desert soils have evolved under conditions of low rainfall, high evaporation, and sparse vegetation. They have been subjected to little leaching and are rich in soluble mineral nutrients which in places have concentrated in excessive amounts in the surface layer. With little or no plant life cover, these soils are low in organic matter; moreover, they have retained largely the color of their parent material and range from gray to red. With good management they can be made fruitful.

Under irrigation, desert soils will produce a wide range of crops, since the application of water can be adjusted to the length of the growing and maturing periods. The principal needs are organic material to improve soil structure and the elements nitrogen and phosphorus, which may be added through fertilization or the growth of legumes and the plowing under of green manure crops.

MAN IN THE TROPICAL DESERTS

Immense stretches of the Tropical Deserts are entirely without human life, yet within these seas of waste there are scattered islands, many too small to appear on a world map, where a permanent water supply has favored settlement. In these oases densities often rival those of the Monsoon Lands. For example, the 21.7 million people of Egypt are mainly crowded into the narrow belt, usually not over 14 miles wide, which extends the length of the country along the Nile River; within this fertile ribbon rural populations average nearly 2000 persons per square mile. Within the remainder of the Great Sahara, the total population does not exceed two or three million people.

Throughout the drylands the presence of man is determined chiefly by the availability of a permanent water supply, and numbers depend upon the amount. The great bulk of the people are oasis agriculturalists, small groups are nomads depending upon their small herds, and lesser numbers are engaged in mining or commercial activity in the "Ports of the Desert." It bears repeating that life of all kinds is found on the desert in direct proportion to water supply.

Nomadic hunters

The most primitive people of the deserts, if not of the world, are the Bushmen, the nomadic hunters of the Kalahari.[3] It is believed that this disappearing race was once lord over most of South Africa, but was pressed into the most inhospitable parts of the desert by stronger, more advanced groups. The Bushmen are dwarf people, seldom exceeding five feet in height. They now number less than 10,000, scattered in clans of a few families each, and are totally dependent upon the desert environment for their livelihood. Mere existence requires considerable ability, much hardship, and privation.

Game is their principal food. Clever hunters, the Bushmen have keen knowledge of habits of the wild animals that they kill with bow and poison-tipped reed arrows or throwing sticks. Their only other important item of equipment is the digging stick made of a sharpened spike of hardwood inserted in the hole of a round, flat stone. This implement is used by the women to secure succulent roots of desert plants. Lizards, snakes, frogs, worms, and ant eggs also are sources of foods, consumed especially when game is short. The Bushmen make no provisions for the future, thus there are times of feastings and times when these people are near starvation.

Within fixed tribal limits they change location frequently to follow the game supply; therefore the Bushmen cannot accumulate many possessions nor build substantial shelters. Dwellings are of the rudest construction, and are abandoned at a moment's notice when lack of game or water compels a move. Caves, shallow holes, or a few branches stuck in the ground and covered with skin or grass are usual types. Household utensils are limited to ostrich egg shells and a few crude earthen pots. Food is eaten raw or partially-cooked over an open fire started with fire sticks. Clothing is of the simplest form, composed of animal skins. Men wear breech clouts, triangular pieces which pass between the legs and are secured around the waist with a string. Women wear a piece of skin hung from the waist and reaching the knees. At night a cape, consisting of several skins sewn together, is worn to give protection from the cooler temperatures.

[3] For an excellent discussion of the peoples of the Kalahari Desert, see Chapter III of Huntington, Ellsworth, *The Human Habitat.* New York: D. Van Nostrand Company, Inc., 1927.

The Bushmen have changed little as the result of contact with other cultures and have sought to preserve their own way of life. Up to the present the opportunities offered by their environment have been too limited to tempt pre-emption by other people. At the same time their habitat and way of life rigidly restricts their numbers.

The Australian aborigines discussed in the Monsoon Tropics are comparable nomadic hunters who also utilize the desert. Their principal home, however, is in the monsoon parts of Australia.

Pastoral nomadism

In the Old World Deserts of Africa and Asia, pastoral nomadism exists as a picturesque and unique adjustment to an arid environment. The pastoral nomad is a wanderer whose life revolves around the care of animals and the search for grass. Most are not true desert dwellers, but confine their activities to the wetter margins more favorable for forage. However, some are found wherever life is possible, even in the "Empty Quarter" of Arabia. Nomads are not solitary wanderers, but group together in tribes or families with a patriarchal form of government. There is no aimless shifting of flocks and herds from pasture to pasture; movements usually follow time-tested routes. The tent serves as a home, and furnishings and equipment are geared for mobility. Except for his weapons and utensils, which he obtains from outside sources, the nomad is nearly self-subsisting. Sheep, goats, camels, and horses provide him with milk, cheese, meat, wool, and hides. Surpluses are traded to oasis dwellers for dates and grain. Spinning and weaving produce clothes, blankets, tents, and rugs. In our modern world where man in general is sedentary, the restless, independent pastoral nomad is distinctive, living by a strict code imposed on him through centuries of desert contact.

FIGURE 5-11. *Bedouin encampment at a water source. Here a well has been drilled by the Arabian American Oil Company. A number of such wells have been drilled along the oil pipeline across the desert. While a stable supply has been thus provided, a problem of over-concentration of Bedouins and their animals has occurred.* (Arabian American Oil Company.)

Oasis agriculture

Old World Deserts. Since the dawn of human history oasis agriculture has been the basic element in the life and economy of the Old World Deserts. Today it continues as the solid base which supports the majority of the people who live in this part of Asia and Africa.

Egypt, quite appropriately, has been called the Valley of the Nile. Its life—human, plant, and animal—depends almost entirely upon the water of that river and the fertile soil deposited on its flood plain and delta through the centuries. The total cultivated land of some six million acres is less than 2.5 per cent of the country's total area. An average of one and one-half crops per year is produced, extending the effective cultivated area to an equivalent of nine million acres. With 80 per cent of the Egyptians dependent directly upon the soil, farms are necessarily small, averaging about 2.5 acres. A further problem is the fact that 37 per cent of agricultural land is in the hands of absentee owners, whose tenants must pay rent.

Agricultural practices are a peculiar combination of ancient and modern methods. The sickle, flail, and wooden plow, ancient pole and bucket irrigation, and the water wheel drawn by animals exist side by side with great irrigation engineering works and the disc plow, tractor, and combine. Ignorance of agricultural science on the part of the peasants stands in striking contrast to a number of modern government projects. Taking into consideration all aspects of agriculture, Egyptian production still depends largely upon the *fellah,* or small farmer with the hoe. Abundant and cheap labor and the predominance of small farm units restrict the use of farm machinery. Yet the yields per acre are high; the major problem is that the production per individual is very low.

Cotton is the dominant enterprise in agriculture as well as in the total economy of Egypt. It is not only the most important cash crop but the major item among Egyptian ex-

FIGURE 5-12. *Agricultural scenes in Saudi Arabia: a view of Ain um Sabu, a natural water source at Hofuf.* (Arabian American Oil Company.)

ports, and normally occupies about 20 per cent of total cropland. Corn and wheat are the ranking bread grains, the former being the staple diet of the farmer and the latter produced for the city dweller. Rice, too, is a major crop; acreage is being expanded in response to high yields and ready world markets. Barley and grain sorghums are also important, and together all the grains occupy 50 per cent of the total cropland. Legumes, horse beans, lentils, and chick peas are supplementary food crops. Vegetables are grown abundantly in all seasons, and the production of sugar cane is well established.

Livestock are limited in number. Pasture space is lacking and competition for food crops is too great for feed production. The water buffalo cow is most important; this hardy draft animal is immune to most pests and diseases and is a good milk producer.

The oasis of the exotic Nile Valley completely overshadows others of the Sahara. Nonetheless small dots of irrigation agriculture exist wherever there is a water supply. The major distribution is found along the wadis descending from the Atlas Mountains and radiating from the Ahaggar and Tibesti Highlands.[4] In all, intensive agriculture prevails with large amounts of energy and time expended to produce the greatest yields possible. The abundant sunshine, controlled applications of water, rich soils, and general freedom from weeds and insect pests result in abundant harvests. A wide variety of fruits, grains, and vegetables is common. Throughout most of the Old World Deserts date palms

[4] For details on the oases of the Suf and the Mzab, see Chapter VI of Brunhes, Jean, *Human Geography*. Chicago: Rand McNally and Company, 1920

FIGURE 5-13. *Agricultural scenes in Saudi Arabia: a new well being put into operation at Qatif in eastern Saudi Arabia.* (Arabian American Oil Company.)

are a characteristic feature of the oasis landscape. The fruit of this high-yielding tropical desert tree is both subsistence crop and money crop. It provides food for the oasis dweller and his animals as well as an item for exchange. Frequently a two- or three-story agriculture is practiced to achieve the utmost from the land: an annual grain or vegetable crop forms the ground level, an intermediate height fruit the second, and the skyward-reaching date palm the third level. Some of the more accessible and larger oases produce commercial crops of cotton and sugar. The farmers normally live in villages with flat-roofed houses constructed of either sun-baked mud or stone. Thick walls and roof provide protection against the intense heat of the day and the cool of the night.

The oases of southwest Asia have similar characteristics. Those of Saudi Arabia are, for the most part, small. Of the wadis, Dawasir, with its extensive branches in the southwest part of the plateau, is outstanding; long stretches along this system have adequate subsurface water supplies for agriculture—some of the finest dates in the country are produced there. In the central part of the plateau there are a number of water pits, huge natural wells which range in diameter from 150 to 1500 feet, and from 420 feet upwards in depth.[5] Al Kharj and Aflaj are two of the most significant. Crops of dates, alfalfa, and sorghum are presently grown on several thousand acres, and the possibilities for increasing the arable area are excellent. The eastern part of the country offers the greatest potentials for irrigation. The likelihood for artesian wells exists in an area paralleling the Arabian Sea and extending westward for 100 miles. The

[5] For an excellent discussion of the development of natural resources in one area of southwest Asia, see Twitchell, K. S., *Saudi Arabia*. Princeton, N. J.: Princeton University Press, 1946.

Arabian American Oil Company has drilled a number of wells in this area, and several large springs exist. The Hofuf Oasis, the largest in Saudi Arabia, has some 25,000 acres under irrigation on which two million date palms are growing.

The most notable oasis of southwest Asia is found along the Shatt al Arab and the Tigris-Euphrates Rivers of Iraq. This ancient land produces about 75 per cent of the dates of commerce with thirty million date palms, one-third of all in existence, situated along the banks of these streams. The most productive area is along the Shatt al Arab where the palm groves follow the courses of hundreds of canals leading out into the desert, sometimes only a few hundred yards, but in other cases for distances of five miles. These canals receive water with the normal tidal rise of the Shatt al Arab. Iraqi farmers also cultivate wheat, barley, rice, corn, sorghum, and sesame. In recent years cotton has become established as an important crop. Agriculture has always been the basis of the general economy. There is little doubt that up to the thirteenth century A.D. a much larger area was under irrigation than at the present; the ruins of an obsolete irrigation system can easily be traced. Several modern developments have recently added to the cultivatable area and there remains a potential larger than the present total.

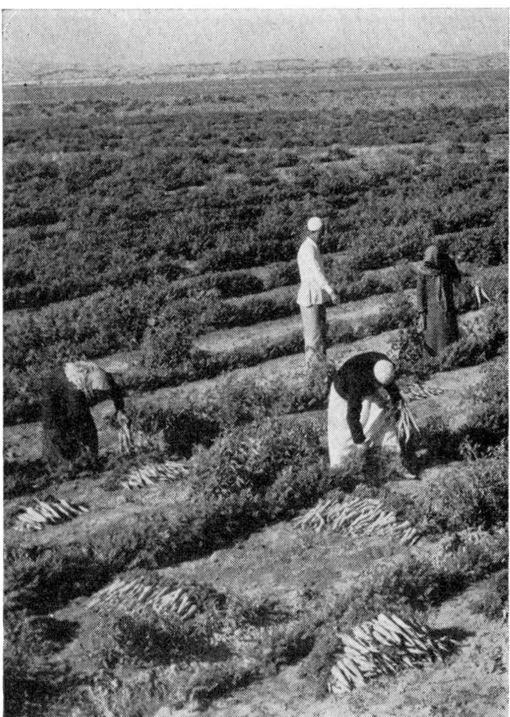

FIGURE 5-14. *Agricultural scenes in Saudi Arabia: harvesting carrots on a farm in Al Kharj Oasis.* (Arabian American Oil Company.)

Oasis agriculture in the Thar Desert is wholly in the exotic valley of the Indus River. The irrigated land has been greatly expanded during the past 25 years. The Sukkar Barrage completed on the lower Indus under British direction in 1932 provides water for over five million acres. This irrigated area has become a notable producer of such crops as cotton, rice, and wheat.

American Deserts. The Incas had established irrigation agriculture in the Peruvian desert before the coming of the Spaniards, but their carefully constructed and maintained water distribution systems fell into disrepair following Spanish conquests. Agriculture continued solely for local subsistence until near the end of the nineteenth century, when white and mestizo landlords began production of commercial crops, particularly sugar. Since the mid-twenties cotton has supplanted sugar as the leading crop. Rice has also become significant and numerous other crops such as corn, wheat, fruits, and vegetables are produced for local consumption. Today over a million acres are devoted to irrigation agriculture in the valleys of the coastal streams.

The waters of the Colorado and Gila Rivers which flow through the Sonoran Desert were long ago used to some extent by the Indians. When white man arrived, this usage was evidenced only by the ruins of canals and settlements. Modern irrigation began about the turn of this century. The most famous center is the Imperial Valley which is actually the north slope of the Colorado Delta, which through the ages pushed across the rift depression of the Gulf of California, completely cutting off the northern end. Water is carried from the Imperial Dam on the Colorado to a half-million acres by the All American

FIGURE 5-15. *Weighing alfalfa with ancient scales in Al Kharj, Saudi Arabia, for transportation in a modern truck.* (Standard Oil Company of New Jersey.)

FIGURE 5-16. *On the right a citrus grove in the Salt River Project—on the left the raw desert.* (United States Bureau of Reclamation.)

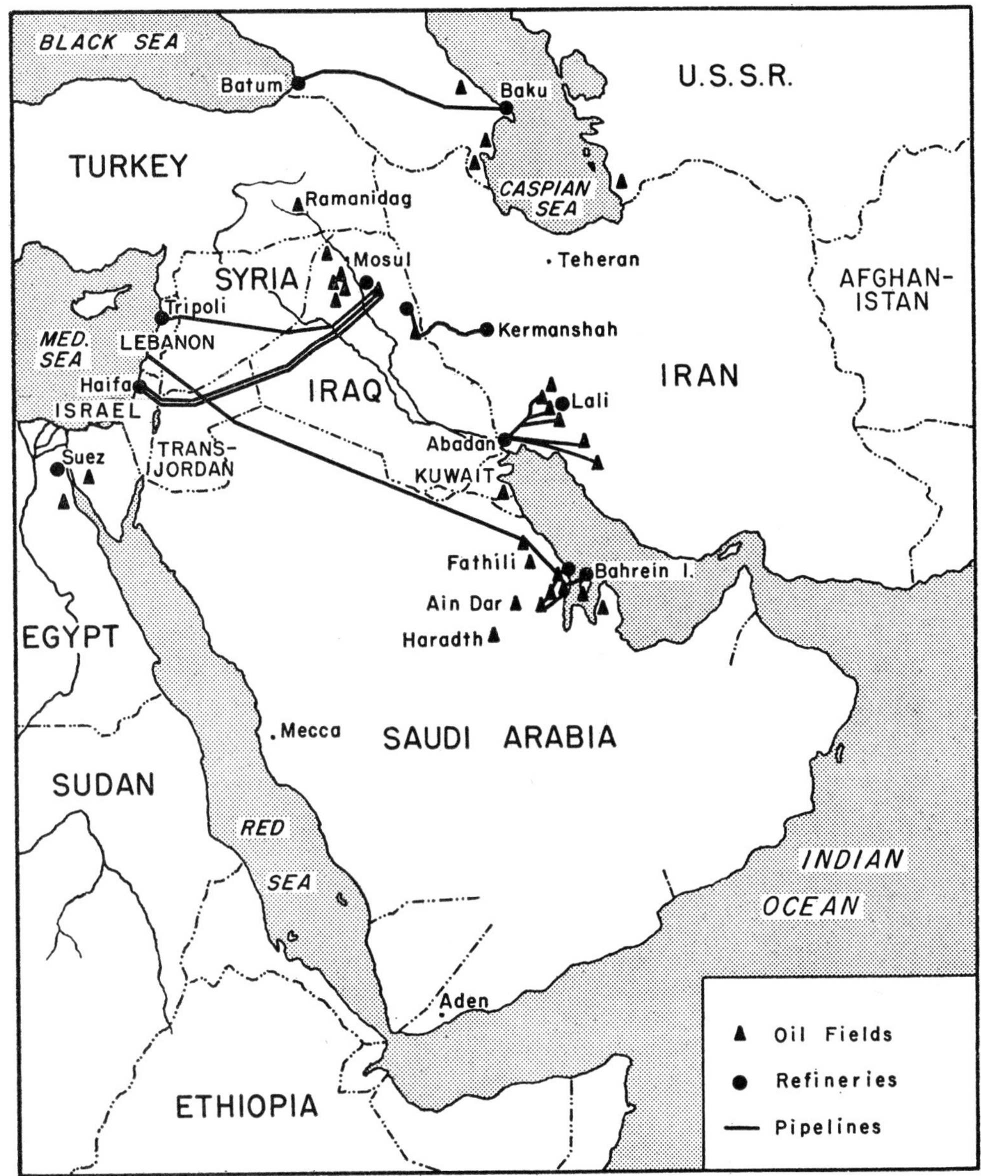

FIGURE 5-17. *Oil fields, refineries, and pipelines in southwest Asia.*

Canal. The Salton Sea, occupying the lowest part of the depression, 246 feet below sea level, serves as the drainage reservoir for the irrigation system. Continuous heat and sunshine make possible year-around production and a wide range of crops including melons, lettuce, cotton, citrus, alfalfa, and many varieties of vegetables. Crops are grown almost entirely for sale, and the advantages of high yields, quality produce, and off-season markets permit profitable shipment great distances to all parts of the nation. The Coachella Valley, north of the Salton Sea, is the major United States source of dates, and fruit from this district dominates the American quality market.

FIGURE 5-18. *Arabian oil development: an oil well in a sea of sand.* (Arabian American Oil Company.)

Mining

Minerals contribute to the significance of the deserts, and are the only reason for man's presence in certain portions. Their profitable extraction has caused some settlements to develop in barren areas. Water has had to be piped many miles or actually hauled in tank cars, and all necessities have to be imported to supply workers in these settlements.

Oil. The outstanding mineral resource from a tropical desert today is oil. One area, the Middle East, possesses about one-half of the world's proven reserves. Development has been largely by foreign interests, particularly by American and British companies. The major producing areas lie close to the Persian Gulf in Saudi Arabia, Qatar, Kuwait, Iraq, and Iran. Bahrein, a small Arab sheikdom consisting of a group of islands twenty miles off the Saudi Arabian shore, is also significant. The output of all these regions is steadily increasing; the major portion moves out to serve the industrial countries.

Nitrate. The importance of the Chilean section of the Atacama has largely revolved around its abundant deposits of nitrates. In the basins between the low coastal range and the Andes, the evaporation of former lakes left rich deposits of mineral salts. These beds, containing the nitrate-bearing material called *caliche,* vary from a few inches to several feet in depth and extend in an irregular belt 450 miles north-south. Many natural deterrents had to be overcome for exploitation. All workers, materials, equipment, and food had to be imported, and water had to be piped 100 miles from the Andes. Until World War I mining was crude, employing much hand labor. Production costs were high but so were profits. Chile held a virtual monopoly on the world supply of this valuable mineral fertilizer and industrial chemical, and for many years the export tax provided about half of the total revenue. Following the war, the high-cost Chilean product met serious competition from synthesized nitrates. The industry has recently modernized to cut costs; the nitrate companies have merged and new treating processes in a few large plants have been established.

Guano. Guano is a unique fertilizer product of South America. On the islands and headlands along the coast of Peru, this excrement of numerous bird colonies accumulates in large quantities. The cool Peruvian or Humboldt Current, which passes immediately offshore, abounds in microscopic organisms which support a tremendous fish life which, in its turn, supplies food for countless birds. No less than a score of species frequent the islands, but cormorants, pelicans, and boobies deposit most of the guano which accumulates rapidly in this arid climate. The guano was formerly exported in large quantities, but today the industry is a government monopoly and the total production is used to fertilize the oases fields of the Peruvian coastal lowland. The chain of relationship is interesting; the cool current not only accounts for the arid climate, but supports the pyramid of life that accounts for the guano, itself a factor in maintaining the high productivity of the oases.

FIGURE 5-19. *Arabian oil development: the American community at Dhahran.*

FIGURE 5-20. *Ras Tanura, the marine terminal, is situated on a strip of sand that extends into the Persian Gulf. The pier is located far enough offshore to allow the largest oil tankers to dock. From this pier, much of Arabian oil is shipped.* (Standard Oil Company of New Jersey.)

Urban centers

Cities are functional developments established at locations where they can perform useful services. Their size and rate of growth depend directly upon the needs of their surroundings. The deserts with scanty population, poor transportation, and limited needs to be served naturally support few cities. However, just as the margins of the oceans have their ports, so do the deserts. Ancient cities such as Damascus, Syria, Bagdad, Iraq, and Timbuktu, in French West Africa, developed as the result of favorable situations with respect to caravan routes and have long functioned as assembly and distribution points for items moving from and to their surrounding areas.

Many of the largest of the desert cities actually are ports. Included in this class would be Karachi, in Pakistan, Alexandria, Port Said and Suez, in Egypt, Dakar, in French West Africa, Lima, in Peru, served by the port of Callao, and San Diego, in California. Basra, date port of Iraq, is about 100 miles up the Shatt al Arab, but is reached by ocean-going vessels drawing up to 30 feet. Cairo, largest city of the realm, is the chief commercial and administrative center of Egypt. It serves all the Nile Valley as well as much of the eastern Sahara from its favorable river position at the head of the delta, where caravan routes funnel in from the east and west. Abadan, in Iran, owes its growth to oil refining and shipment.

A few cities have developed as the result of religious significance. Mecca, in Saudi Arabia, is an outstanding example. This city, birthplace of the Prophet Mohammed and seat of the Islamic religion, is the cherished destination of every person of Islamic faith at least once during a lifetime. During the pilgrimage season its permanent population of 80,000 is at least doubled.

OUTLOOK

Water has been, is, and will continue to be the limiting factor for development in the deserts. This is not to say, however, that existing water supplies are utilized to their fullest potentials, nor that other resources such as minerals will not be conducive to local progress. Oil, especially, will have a great influence.

The Middle East is the desert area of greatest change today. The tapping of its rich oil reserves is bringing capital for modern development. The impact upon the local peoples has been noteworthy. Stable income has attracted many former oasis dwellers and nomads to work in the oil fields and refineries. A number of new centers of settlement have become established. New markets for food have extended the outlets for oases produce. Royalties received by the governments from the oil are being used to establish schools, to install hospitals and modern sanitation, and to develop irrigation projects, as well as to improve transportation and the general economy. In general, the effects upon the inhabitants have been favorable.

With these developments the Old World Lands are assuming new importance in international affairs. Long significant as the early center of civilization and the sites where the great monotheistic religions were born, the region now has added importances. It is a strategic bridge head between three large land masses; it contains the Suez Canal and is a vital stepping stone in the trans-world airline systems; it is a major producer of petroleum. Although many racial groups are represented, there is an underlying cultural unity with the Islamic faith binding the peoples together. The Arab nations are beginning to act collectively for the benefit of the whole and are becoming a potent force in world affairs.

FIGURE 5-21. *Cities of the deserts.* Above: *Lima, Peru. The plaza shown here is typical of many Latin American cities.* (Pan American-Grace Airways.) Below: *Riyadh, capital of Saudi Arabia, looking down on the marketplace, which is filled with Bedouins, farmers, and villagers.* (Arabian American Oil Company.)

FIGURE 5-22. *Impact of oil on Arabia. Within two decades, the people of Saudi Arabia have become as familiar with the sight of high-speed streamlined trains as they once were with the slow plodding camel caravans dating from Biblical times. By camel the trip from Dammam, a Persian Gulf port, to the inland capital city of Riyadh, takes about 90 hours. In a self-propelled Budd car capable of speeds up to 90 miles an hour, the normal time of the 358-mile trip is 9 hours.* (Arabian American Oil Company.)

SELECTED REFERENCES

Bowman, Isaiah, *Desert Trails of the Atacama.* New York: American Geographical Society, 1924.

Crary, Douglas D., "Recent Agricultural Developments in Saudi Arabia," *Geographical Review,* XLI, No. 3, 1951, 366-383.

Cressey, George B., "The Land of Five Seas," *Journal of Geography,* L, No. 7, 1951, 265-276.

Gautier, Emile F., *Sahara, The Great Desert.* New York: Columbia University Press, 1935.

Hill, Ernestine, *Australian Frontier.* New York: Doubleday, Doran and Company, Inc., 1942, 237-315.

Hurst, H. E., *The Nile: A Graphic Account of the River and the Utilization of Its Waters.* New York, The Macmillan Company, 1952.

Madigan, C. T., *Central Australia.* London: Oxford University Press, 1944.

Musil, Alors, *In the Arabian Desert.* New York: Horace Liveright, 1930.

Pratt, Wallace E., and Dorothy Good, *World Geography of Petroleum.* New York: American Geographical Society, 1950, 159-229.

Raswan, Carl R., *Black Tents of Arabia.* Boston: Little, Brown and Company, 1934.

Sanger, Richard, *The Arabian Peninsula.* Ithaca, N. Y.: Cornell University Press, 1954.

CHAPTER 6.

Tropical Highlands

THE TROPICAL HIGHLANDS, DESPITE a ruggedness of terrain, are the favorite sites for settlement in the broad zone of the tropics. In contrast to the hot and humid lowlands, the higher altitude climates are invigorating—lower and more stimulating temperature and more healthful living conditions are the major attractions. Generalizations for a regional treatment of the Tropical Highlands are difficult because homogeneity as a regional characteristic is lacking.

Vertical zonation is the key to highland geography. Tropical Highlands display a vertical layering of climatic conditions, natural vegetation, and land utilization. Temperatures range from tropical to arctic, climates from perpetual summer to eternal spring to year-around sunny

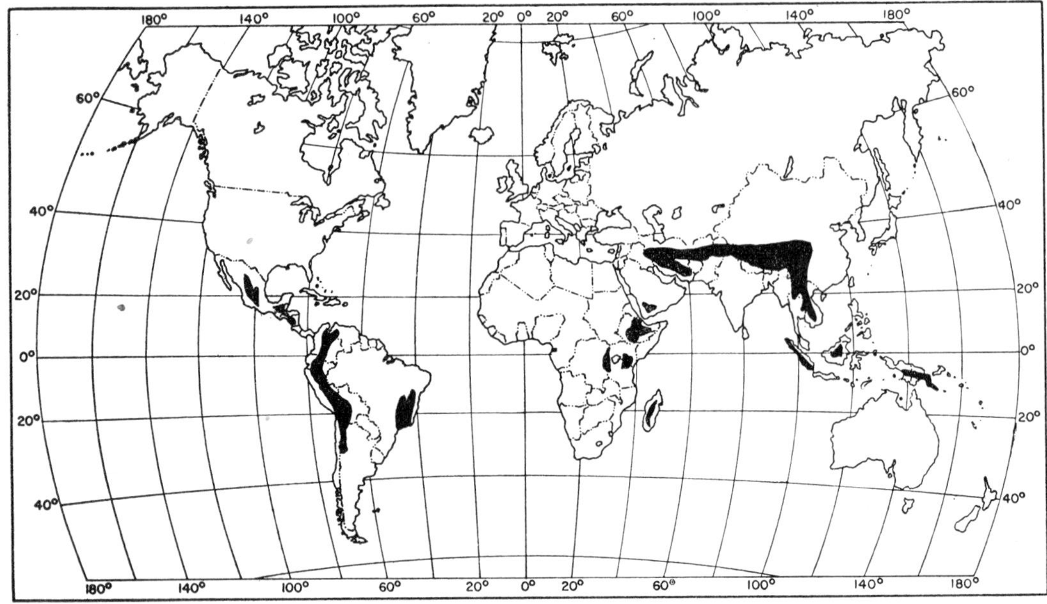

FIGURE 6-1. *The Tropical Highlands.*

winter. It is possible in a few hours climb to experience as many temperatures and landscapes as would otherwise require thousands of miles of latitudinal travel. Natural vegetation proceeds from that of selva and jungle to flora reminiscent of the cold tundra. Cultivated crops ascend the highlands in a ladder-like pattern, with tropical products at the bottom and the potato on the top rung.

Location

Highlands are widely scattered in the tropical zone; unlike the climate regions, they follow no definite pattern. Mountains and plateaus occupy a major share of Middle America and the lofty Andes form the backbone of western South America. Highlands are also present in the West Indies and in eastern Brazil.

Large sections of east-central Africa are filled with high tablelands which include portions of Ethiopia, Uganda, Tanganyika, Kenya, Nyasaland, and the Rhodesias. Mountains also form the backbone of Southeast Asia, and are scattered throughout Indonesia, the Philippines, and the islands of the central Pacific Ocean.

PHYSICAL ENVIRONMENT

Climate

There is no Tropical Highland climate as compared to that of the Rainy Tropics, Wet-Dry Tropics, or the Tropical Deserts. Uniform patterns of amount and distribution of rain and temperature are distinctive features of these other tropical regions. The many differences in exposure and elevation in the Highlands make it impossible to state averages in these climatic elements. One characteristic, however, that all Tropical Highlands have in common is the low annual ranges of temperature. Regardless of elevation of a given station, each month has an average temperature that is a near facsimile of its predecessor. Only daily varieties of weather break the yearly monotony.

The lower pressure of the higher altitudes has a physiological effect on man. Breathing becomes more difficult and lung trouble is often prevalent. Travelers are subject to mountain sickness, the *soroche,* which causes faintness, nose bleeds, insomnia, and loss of appetite. The rarefied air is rich in violet and ultraviolet rays and one either soon acquires a coat of tan or must constantly guard against

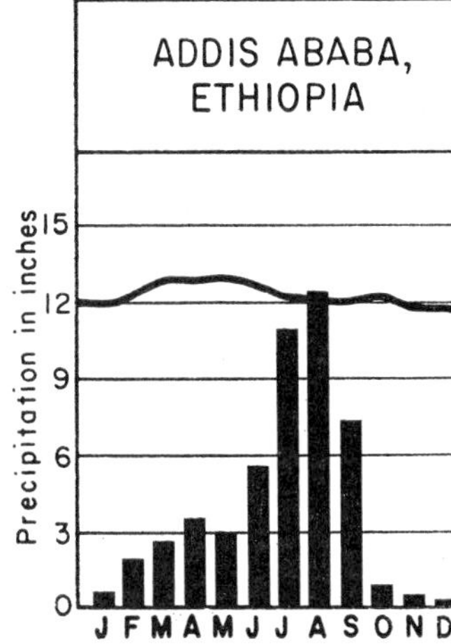

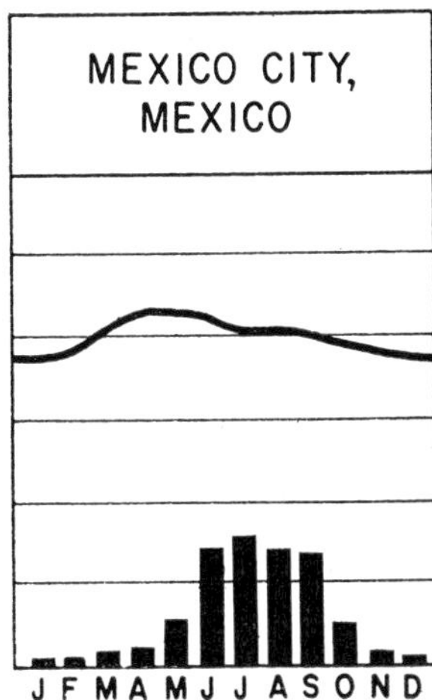

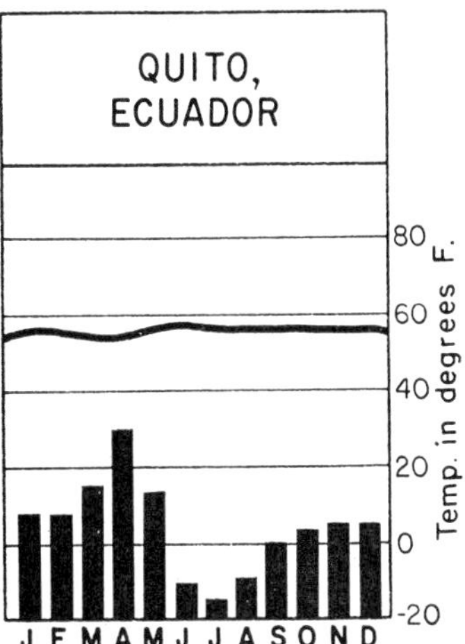

FIGURE 6-2. *Climatic graphs of Tropical Highland stations.*

serious sunburn. Cooking habits must be revised because the boiling point of water is lowered and food takes longer to cook.

Temperatures. Tropical Highland temperatures are controlled chiefly by altitude. Temperatures decrease about 3.3 degrees with each 1000 feet of elevation. Annual temperature ranges for stations remain about the same between high and low elevations; only actual temperatures differ. For example, Quito, Ecuador, at 9350 feet, has only a .7° range between the average temperatures of the warmest and coolest months, although Guayaquil, on the western coast of Ecuador, with an elevation of 39.4 feet, has a range of .5°.

Sunshine is intense in the dry, thin air and exposed surfaces heat rapidly. Noon temperatures are high except in the shaded areas. The Tropical Highlands are sometimes called the "Land of Hot Sun and Cool Shade." The same factors that allow rapid daytime heating operate when the sun sets, and night and early morning are uncomfortably cool. The rising sun is a welcome sight after the chill of the night.

Precipitation. Highlands in general receive more precipitation than the associated lowlands. Seasonal distribution varies with latitude. Areas subject to the constant influence of the equatorial low receive rainfall every month, whereas in Monsoon and Wet-Dry locations there are wide fluctuations. Addis Ababa, the capital of Ethiopia, located at 9.2° N and with an elevation of 8000 feet, receives about 70 per cent of its precipitation in the summer months. Quito, on the equator, has precipitation every month. Thundershowers typify the rain; snow falls only in the high elevations.

Slopes exposed to incoming moisture-laden air receive copious amounts of rain in contrast to the dry shadows on leeward sides. Windward sides of mountains with sufficient elevation receive precipitation even in desert areas such as the highlands of Arabia; this makes agriculture possible on slopes and provides a source of water for irrigation below.

Zonation. The Tropical Highlands are divided into four broad altitudinal belts based on temperatures, vegetation, and agriculture. The first belt is the *tierra caliente,* or hot lands, rising from sea level to altitudes of 2000 to 3000 feet; the environment is that of the associated lowlands. The second zone, the *tierra templada,* or temperate lands, extends to 6000 or 6500 feet and is often called the "Coffee Zone." Although coffee thrives at this elevation, sugar, cotton, and other crops are grown. The *tierra fria,* or cool lands, follows and reaches to 10,000 or 11,000 feet. This is a belt where wheat, barley, and root crops can be produced—crops suggestive of agriculture in the middle latitudes. The *puna* or *paramos,* the cold lands, is the zone reach-

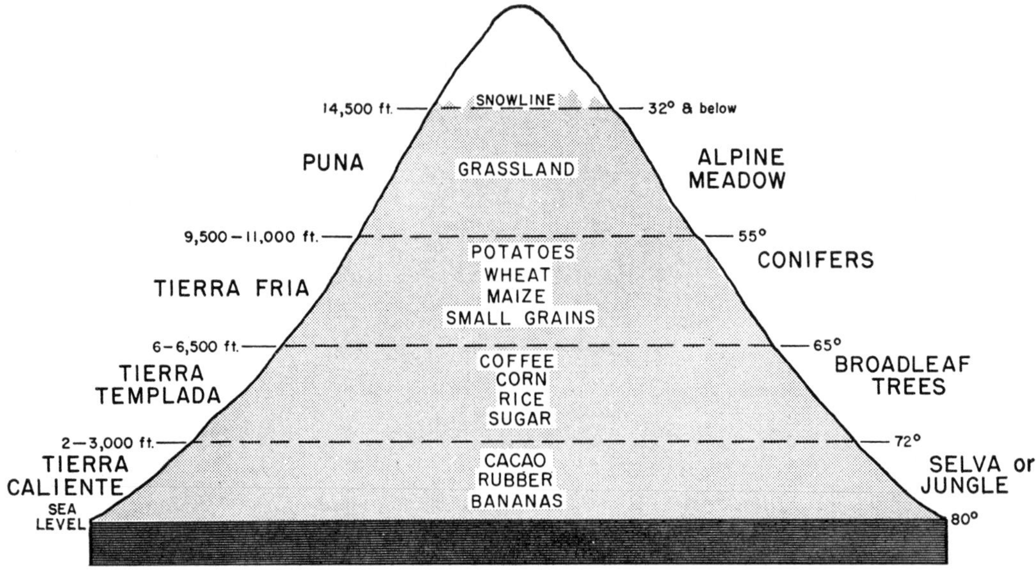

FIGURE 6-3. *Altitudinal zonation.*

ing as high as 15,000 feet. The puna is the limit of settlement; crops are unimportant, but some grazing exists on the lower margins. Permanent snow occurs at about 15,000 feet.

The four zones do not have a stable elevation, becoming increasingly lower with distances from the equator. Furthermore, the division lines are seldom parallel; wide variations exist due to factors influencing temperatures, such as exposure to winds and orientation to the sun.

Surface features

Highlands are the most spectacular of the earth's surface features, because of their bulk, height, and steepness of slope. They differ greatly, depending upon their earth materials, manner of formation, and age. Two primary divisions are recognized: mountains and plateaus.

Mountains may be defined as conspicuous elevations having small summits and the preponderance of their areas in steep slopes. Isolated mountains are common in all portions of the earth, but most are parts of larger groups which display considerable differences in size, shape, elevation, relief, origin, and age. There are small mountain groups like the Olympics of Washington, and in contrast there are great mountain systems covering large areas, like the Andes and the Rockies. In all cases local relief is over 2000 feet; on the basis of local relief, mountains with elevation differences of 2000 to 3000 feet are classed as low, from 3000 to 4500 as rough, 4500 to 6000 as rugged, and above 6000 sierran.

On the basis of their size and arrangement, it is common to divide the larger mountainous complexes into ranges, systems, chains, and cordilleras. A mountain *range* consists of a long, narrow ridge, or closely-spaced ridges which are similar in age and origin. The Cascade Mountains of Oregon and Washington and the Eastern (Oriental), Central, and Western (Occidental) ranges of the Northern Andes are examples. A mountain *system* includes a group of ranges somewhat related as to origin, structure, alignment, form, and age. Examples are the Rocky Mountains and the Northern Andes. A mountain *chain* is a long, narrow mountainous belt including ranges and systems which may be more or less independent in origin and age and without similarity of structure or form. The mountains of Central America and of southern Europe are often called chains. *Cordillera* is an inclusive

FIGURE 6-4. *The Buenaventura highway. Rugged terrain and heavy vegetation make road-building extremely difficult. This highway is winding down the slopes of the Western Cordillera into the Cauca Valley of Colombia.* (Standard Oil Company of New Jersey.)

term which is used to refer to a group of ranges, systems, and chains which are fairly compact and cover a vast area. It is applied to the mountains of western North America and to the Andes of South America.

Plateaus, not so easily distinguished as mountains, may be defined as tabular uplands having local relief of more than 500 feet. They usually stand well above bordering areas on at least one side. According to position on the continents and relationship to other landforms, they are of three major classes: *piedmont* plateaus, which lie between mountains and neighboring seas or plains, such as the plateau of Patagonia in Argentina; *continental* plateaus, which rise rather abruptly on all margins from bordering lowlands or seas, like that occupying a large part of Africa; and *intermontane* plateaus, which are more or less surrounded by mountains, as is the plateau of Mexico.

Latin America. The most continuous and largest area of highlands in the tropics fills much of Middle America and extends southward in the Andes of South America. The highlands of Middle America are diverse and difficult to characterize. They are neither simple in geology nor in surface configuration, ranging from broad plateaus to towering active volcanoes. The highlands of the Mexican portion have essentially two elements, a central plateau which is by no means uniform, and dissected mountainous borders. The mountains, higher on the west, converge in the south and continue through the isthmus countries, broken occasionally by intermontane basins. The Andes are the highest continuous mountains in the world, running the

FIGURE 6-5. *Paricutin volcano.* (Kodak Mexicana, Ltd.)

length of the continent of South America. This great barrier, rising virtually out of the Pacific Ocean, is 100 to 400 miles wide and has a crest that is seldom under 12,000 feet high. Many peaks reach above 18,000 feet and Mt. Aconcagua in Argentina (22,835 feet) is the highest peak in the Western Hemisphere. This massive system is made up of several ranges, often complexly knotted; from Ecuador southward into Argentina between the two principal ranges there is a string of high intermontane plateaus, collectively known as the *Altiplano.*

The ancient Brazilian Highlands, in contrast to the youthful Andes, have been subjected to weathering and erosion through countless ages. Most of the area stands at elevations between 2000 and 4000 feet and is generally hilly or plateau-like in character, although some peaks do reach 8000 feet and more, particularly in the southeast. The steep and severely dissected eastern escarpment appears like a range of mountains from the sea.

Africa. The continental plateau of Africa reaches its greatest elevation in the east-central portion of the continent. Starting from the knot of the Abyssinian Mountains, the highlands run southward through the lake region. They have a relatively uniform surface and are of volcanic origin, built up by layer upon layer of lava poured out upon the plateau. The region is traversed lengthwise by a series of rift valleys, part of the great system that extends for 4000 miles from Lebanon at the east end of the Mediterranean Sea southward through the Red Sea and into central Africa. Linear lakes occupy the two main branches in Africa with Lakes Albert, Edward, and Tanganyika along the western line, and Lakes Rudolf and Nyasa along the eastern line; Lake Victoria lies on the tableland between the two rift valleys.

This great rift system was produced by down faulting; as the result of tremendous compressional and tensional stresses, parallel faults occurred and portions of the earth literally slipped downward. The resulting trench-like structure is termed a *graben* or rift valley (see Figure 6-6). Such features are present in other parts of the world, but nowhere are they so spectacular.

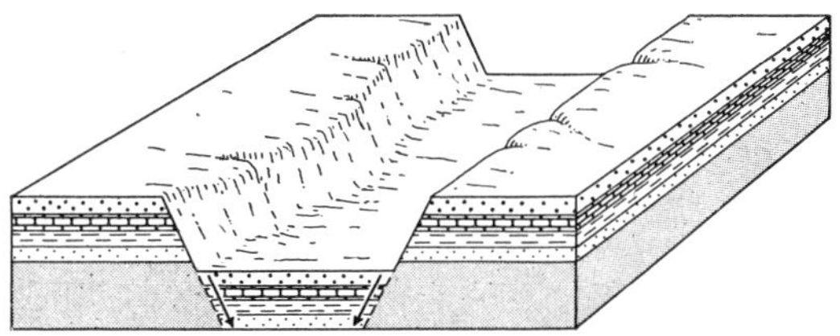

FIGURE 6-6. *Diagrammatic sketch of a rift valley.*

Southeast Asia and adjoining islands. The principal characteristics of Southeast Asia and the adjoining islands have been discussed in the chapters dealing with the Rainy Tropics and the Monsoon Tropics. It will be recalled that mountains are the most widespread landforms of Southeast Asia, with many ranges spreading southward from eastern Tibet in a fan-like pattern through Burma, Thailand, and Indochina; one range continues farther southward to form the backbone of the Malay Peninsula. Elevations tend to be highest in the north where deep gorges and steep slopes often dominate; however, the Annam Mountains of Indochina rise to over 10,000 feet as do the mountains along the India-Burma border.

The geology of the islands adjoining Southeast Asia is extremely complicated. The western islands of Indonesia, including Sumatra, Java, and Borneo, stand on the comparatively shallow continental shelf of Asia, whereas the easternmost islands, including New Guinea, are on the shallow continental shelf of Australia. Celebes and the Moluccas are essentially mountaintops which rise from the deeper seas between. The Philippines are similar to the central islands of Indonesia—mountains in the process of rising from the sea. Actually, two mountainous areas form the main outlines of the archipelagoes; one, the Sunda Arc, reaches from Sumatra eastward through the Lesser Sunda group (Bali eastward through Timor); the other, the Sulu Arc, reaches southward through the Philippines into the Moluccas. Both contain many extinct and active volcanoes; Indonesia is one of the most active volcanic areas on earth today.

Natural vegetation

Vertical zonation characterizes Tropical Highland natural vegetation; broad zones ascend the slopes, roughly paralleling types found in a horizontal range from the equator to the poles. The forest sequence includes tropical rain forest and jungle in the low levels, followed by zones of broadleaf evergreens, deciduous broadleafs, and ending with a belt of conifers. The forest zones are often disrupted by patches of grass and bare areas; occasionally there is a mixture of types. Spotty distribution is a result of local conditions such as exposure to sunshine, dry shadow locations, or bare rock surfaces. Alpine meadows begin at about 13,000 feet and stretch to the snow line. On the wet windward side of mountain slopes the forest zone will attain higher elevations resulting in a smaller amount of alpine meadow. The reverse is true on the dry leeward side, where the alpine meadows reach their greatest extent. Rainfall also influences types of vegetation on lower slopes. Where definite wet and dry seasons are experienced, savanna and scrub forest may displace the selva as the dominant lower cover.

Native animal life

Native animal life follows a pattern similar to other elements of the physical environment in that zonation features distribution. Lack of food and reduced temperatures, however, limit many species to the middle and lower elevations. Fauna in the tierra templada are quite similar to types living in the adjacent lower levels.

Two wild members of the camel family, the vicuna and guanaco, are distinctive in the high Andes. Both are smaller in stature than a camel and do not possess a hump. Vicuna-hunting during the Inca regime was restricted to the rulers and today law protects the animals from extinction. The alpaca, raised for fine fleece, and the sure-footed pack animal, the llama, are the domesticated animals of the Andes.

MAN IN THE TROPICAL HIGHLANDS

Study of the distribution of the world's population reveals that man generally prefers the lowlands as a dwelling place; at least 90 per cent live at elevations below 2000 feet. Difficulties of cultivation, transportation, and isolation usually make highland environments unattractive to large scale settlement; nevertheless, few of the larger areas are without people. In the tropics an irregularity in the "general rule" exists—the Tropical Highlands are often inviting. The most pleasant and healthful climate is found in the tierra templada zone, which has attracted concentrations of population. The more invigorating highland climates have stimulated the development of the highest orders of civilization within the tropics. This is certainly true in Latin America, where the Inca and Aztec civilizations flourished and where the Spanish and Portuguese colonizers soon recognized the more favorable qualities produced by elevations.

The center of Brazilian life and economy is on the plateau in the east and southeast portions of the country, where the preponderance of that nation's fifty million people lives. Similarly the peoples of Middle American and Andean countries have chosen the favorable basins, valleys, and plateaus of the highlands rather than the hot and humid lowlands. The greatest concentrations of cities and developments are located at moderate elevations. In the Andes there is frequently a zonation of peoples as well as climate, vegetation, and crop possibilities. The occupants of the tierra caliente zone are largely native migratory agriculturists and Negro descendants of former slaves. A few areas have been developed for plantations. The accessible basins and neighboring gentle slopes of the tierra templada are occupied by native and mixed breeds as well as people of European background who are engaged in commercial agriculture. The tierra fria and the puna are sparsely populated by native Indians pushed into these higher elevations by European settlement; their livelihood is based upon the production of hardy crops and the pasturing of animals. The population is by no means evenly spread, but is patchy in response to the distribution of land suitable for agriculture and to transportation and accessibility.

In contrast to the long-settled Latin American Highlands, concerted effort to develop the African regions other than by native peoples has been recent. Delay was due to such factors as the recent penetration of the continent by Europeans, a lack of the lure of stored native riches, the problem of accessibility, and the fact that colonizing powers had richer lands to develop elsewhere. These highlands, usually 3000 to 6000 feet above sea level, have a moderate pleasant climate, and many sections are favored with wet and dry seasons and youthful volcanic soils. Development possibilities have been recognized by the British and increasing attention is being directed toward commercial agriculture. Kenya in particular plays a significant role today as a supplier of agricultural raw materials to industrial Great Britain.

The highland corners of the southern fringes of the Arabian peninsula comprise Yemen and Oman which have long been fruitful "islands" in a sterile desert region. These portions are sufficiently elevated to intercept regular precipitation from the Monsoons. Yemen on the west receives summer rain in large enough quantities to support four million people and their agriculture. Flowing streams for centuries have been diverted to irrigate carefully-terraced slopes that produce cereals, fruits, and the famous mocha coffee in marked contrast to the arid wastes of the lower deserts. Oman, somewhat further north on the eastern corner, receives less rainfall and that during the winter season, hence it supports fewer people.

Little attention has been given to the highlands of the Monsoon Tropics of the Asian mainland. There, the mountainous areas are sparsely populated by primitive tribes who make little imprint upon the land except as their fire-cleared fields cause alterations in the nature of the vegetation. In some areas hill stations have been established for the use and comfort of Europeans during the hot season.

FIGURE 6-7. *Peruvian Indian farmer and his pack llamas.* (Martha Carbonne.)

The highlands on the islands bordering Southeast Asia, especially Java in Indonesia and Luzon in the Philippines, support notable populations. The all-important activity is the production of rice for food. For example, the rice terraces of the semi-primitive Igorot people in the Central Mountains of northern Luzon are famous. These giant terraces, covering 250 square miles, cling to the steep sides of the valleys with retaining walls 20 to 30 feet in height. It is believed that more than 2000 years were required to build them. They are an admirable engineering feat even in modern engineering terms.

Settlement in the Tropical Highlands is based primarily upon agriculture and mining. In the more progressive countries of Latin America processing of raw materials is establishing manufacturing as an important part of their economies.

Agriculture in Latin America

Three distinctive forms of agriculture are recognized in the Latin American Highlands. The first and least complicated is that practiced by the Indians of the tierra fria in the Andes, where climate rigidly restricts cropping possibilities. Here people live in crude mud or stone huts and cultivate small fields in the valley bottoms or on the slopes, which are sometimes terraced. Unresponsive to government attempts to introduce efficient methods, the people practice agriculture in a traditional and simple manner. Crops are adjusted to altitude; in the highest limits of agriculture, the potato is the principal crop, grown at approximately 14,000 feet in Peru; grains are produced between 10,000 and 13,000 feet. Most groups also keep animals, with the native llama and alpaca signifi-

FIGURE 6-8. *Coffee plantation. Notice that the coffee trees are confined to the higher slopes to avoid frost danger of the valley bottoms.* (Brazilian Government Trade Bureau.)

cant in Bolivia and Peru, while mules, sheep, and goats are more important further north. A few Indian people living above the cropline are dependent entirely upon a pastoral economy; sheep are their principal animals.

The second and slightly more advanced form of agriculture, is practiced in the tierra templada by the Indians and by mixed breeds —the mestizos, white and Indian; mulatto, white and Negro; zambo, Negro and Indian; and a mixture of all three. These groups comprise the major segment of the Latin American populations. Corn is their principal food, supplemented with beans, often grown in the same field. Other crops include chile, peas, and small grains. Some produce a limited amount of commercial products. Holdings are small, usually occupying poor sites, equipment is simple, and living standards are very low. The old civilizations exist beside the new, little altered by 400 years of contact.

In direct contrast is the third form—commercial agriculture under the administration of people with European background. Holdings are large and equipment and methods are modern. Coffee is the most prominent and distinctive crop. Brazil is the great world producer, with centers chiefly in the states of Sao Paulo and Minas Geraes where the hot, moist growing season and the cooler, dry harvest season, together with large expanses of gently-sloping land with porous dark-red loam soils, provide an ideal environment. Although there is some production on small farms, the characteristic unit is the *fazenda* or coffee plantation, resembling the English manor of the fourteenth century—each tends to be a more or less completely integrated economic unit. Some operators are producing other crops or grazing cattle in valleys where there is danger of coffee-damaging frost.

Coffee is also a major commercial crop in the highlands of the Northern Andean countries, especially in Colombia, as well as in

Middle America and the West Indies. Often the greater part is grown on small farms. Several other export crops are produced, including cotton, sugar, and tobacco.

Agriculture in Africa

Parallel forms of agriculture are found in the African Highlands. In the high, dry grasslands natives live by pastoral activities; lower, in areas where climate, slope, and soil are suitable, permanent agriculture has become established. The nature of native farming varies from one sector to another; some groups, such as those found at 3500 to 5000 feet on the Uganda Plateau, have developed a relatively advanced culture, living in villages of neat, round, grass huts surrounded by fields of yams, peanuts, manioc, grains, vegetables, and fruits. Others plant crops and then follow herds about the grasslands, returning to their fields only for the harvest. During this century the impact of white settlement has in part encouraged some commercial production.

White settlement has been almost wholly for the purpose of commercial agriculture. The completion of a railroad from the coast across Kenya to Uganda at the turn of the century initiated the development, making possible the export of crops. The largest white colony is found in the tierra templada zone of Kenya. The administration here has allowed European people to gain control of an area the size of the state of Maryland. Since the beginning, coffee has been the chief crop; it is grown on plantations using native labor. Other crops include sisal, tea, cotton, sugar cane, and wheat. In recent years large-scale plantings of peanuts have been attempted, but with little success.

Mining

Minerals were the first attraction of the Latin American Tropics; exploitation has continued and in the modern era the metallic minerals of the richly-endowed highlands contribute significantly to the economies of a number of countries. Mining is the entire basis for settlement in some localities. The most noteworthy minerals of the Andes are copper and tin. Copper was mined by the Indians before the coming of the white people, but this century has witnessed the major development. Several countries mine copper, but Chile, with one-quarter of the world's reserves, is outstanding. The working of the largest deposit at Chuquicamata, 10,000 feet above sea level, supports a community of 25,000 people, largely Indians. The tin deposits are in Bolivia, with the principal mining districts in the mountains at elevations of 14,000 to 18,000 feet. This country has also been famous for silver production in the past.

Mexico has been a leading mineral-producing land since the arrival of the Spaniards. Today important quantities of silver, lead, gold, zinc, and copper are mined. Brazil possesses one of the largest high quality iron reserves in the world in central Minas Geraes, but exploitation is restricted by lack of quality coal and the distance of the reserves from the sea. However, a small iron and steel center has been established at Volta Redonda, despite the difficulties. Manganese is also present in the same area and is being mined largely for the United States market.

The extensive stretches of volcanic rock which bury the possibly mineral-bearing crystalline rock over much of the African Highlands have hindered exploration, except where eroding streams have exposed the underlying formations. Where the volcanic cover is lacking, as elsewhere in the humid tropics, the solid rocks are obscured by a deep mantle of decomposed rocks and soils which also hinder mineral discovery. Despite these conditions some spectacular mineral developments have occurred in recent decades, and doubtless there will be others. The mineral development of Tanganyika has been especially noteworthy; diamonds are the leading product, gold is significant, and tin, lead, and mica are also being mined.

Manufacturing

The Tropical Highland regions of Latin America have developed industry as an important segment of their economic activities. Industrial plants here, using local

FIGURE 6-9. *Steel mill at Volta Redonda illustrates the spread of modern industrialization to tropical countries.* (Brazilian Government Trade Bureau.)

raw materials, are manufacturing goods chiefly for home consumption in an attempt not only to bolster their own economies but also to lessen their dependence upon other areas. The industrial center of Latin America is the district around Sao Paulo, Brazil, where thousands of factories ranging from small workshops to large modern plants produce textiles and clothing, machinery, cement, and a variety of other products. A recently established plant at Volta Redonda, between Sao Paulo and Rio de Janeiro, has elevated Brazil to the iron and steel leadership of Latin America. While this development is vital to Brazil, it is small, less than one one-hundredth of the steel production of the United States and only about one-sixth that of Belgium. Medellin, a cotton textile city in the Andean highlands, dominates industry in Colombia. Mexico also contributes materially to Latin America's industry. The diverse products of Mexico's factories include iron and steel, textiles, pottery, food products, and a host of others. Major industrial concentrations are centered near Mexico City.

Urban centers

The highlands of the Latin American Tropics support most of the largest cities of the realm. Sao Paulo, at an elevation of nearly 2700 feet, is the second city of Brazil and one of the fastest growing urban centers in the world; it is rapidly approaching a population of 2.5 million. Mexico City, of similar

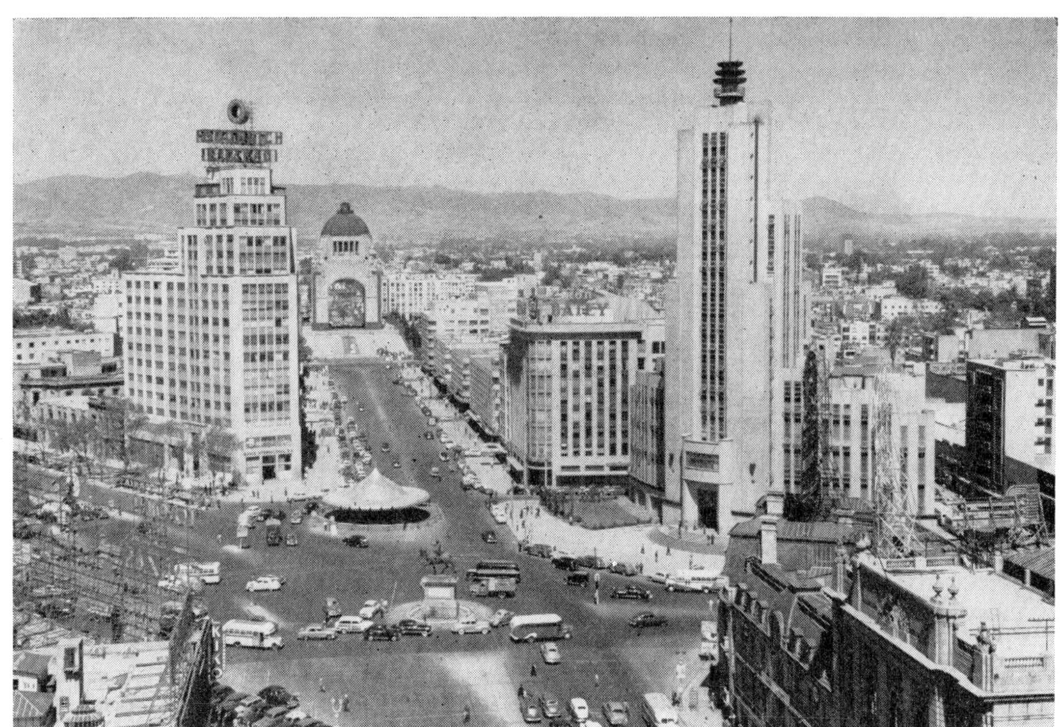

FIGURE 6-10. *Cities of the Tropical Highlands.* Above, *the business section of Mexico City.* (Pan American World Airways.) Below, *a panorama of Sao Paulo.* (Brazilian Government Trade Bureau.)

size, is situated in the basin of Mexico 7200 feet above sea level and is the center of government, commerce, industry, and culture. Caracas, in a productive valley at 3000 feet, is the outstanding city of Venezuela, with a population of 500,000. La Paz, Bolivia, with about 300,000 people at an elevation of 12,000 feet in the Andes, is the highest major city in the world. Quito, Ecuador, with a population in excess of 200,000, is 9350 feet above sea level; Bogota, cultural center and capital of Colombia, with over a half-million population, is situated at an elevation of 8700 feet. At least a dozen additional cities exceed 100,000, and there are many in the 25,000 and 100,000 class.

The African Highlands have as yet few large cities. Only Addis Ababa, capital and commercial center of Ethiopia, exceeds 100,000.

OUTLOOK

The Tropical Highlands appear to have the most promising immediate future of all the lands in the low latitudes. More moderate climate and a core of people with western technique are the great advantages. The Brazilian Plateau and the highlands of British East Africa have especially good possibilities for continued development; both have large areas adaptable to modern agriculture, plus room for more people. Agricultural raw materials as well as minerals and forests should encourage expansion in industry. The state of Sao Paulo, Brazil, especially exemplifies the trend toward industrial awakening. A promising area also exists in the central Andean range of Colombia, where Medellin and Manizales, with cheap hydroelectric power, a progressive citizenry, and low air freight rates, are establishing notable industries today.

Careful mineral surveys have not yet covered large areas of the Tropical Highlands and there are possibilities of further discoveries. Although minerals are essential for modern development, in the long run mining constitutes a weak foundation for continuous support of communities, since a mineral is an exhaustible resource.

SELECTED REFERENCES

"Big Time in Sao Paulo," *Fortune,* XLII, July 1950, 65-71.

Monges, Carlos, *Acclimatization in the Andes.* Baltimore: Johns Hopkins University Press, 1948.

Platt, Robert S., *Latin America.* New York: McGraw-Hill Book Company, Inc., 1942.

Rudolph, William E., "Chuquicamata Twenty Years Later," *Geographical Review,* XLI, No. 1, 1951, 88-113.

Tilman, H. W., *Snow on the Equator.* New York: The Macmillan Company, 1938.

White, C. Langdon, "Altitude: Its Role in the Life of Man in the High Peruvian Sierra," *Journal of Geography,* LII, No. 9, 1953, 361-373.

White, C. Langdon, "Huancayo and Its Famous Indian Market in the Peruvian Andes," *Journal of Geography,* L, No. 1, 1951, 1-10.

Wikkramatileke, Rudolph, "Ella Village, An Example of Rural Settlement and Agricultural Trends in Highland Ceylon," *Economic Geography,* XXVIII, No. 4, 1953, 255-363.

CHAPTER 7

Dry Summer Subtropics

THE DRY SUMMER SUBTROPICS ARE almost universally known as the mediterranean regions, a name derived from the lands bordering the Mediterranean Sea, where the unique climatic pattern of mild, rainy winters and hot, dry summers is most extensively developed.[1] Similarity is a distinctive feature of mediterranean lands. Mountain slopes or plateau escarpments form picturesque backgrounds for every region, and all face the sea. Low shrubs and brush mantle hillsides, interspersed with scrubby gray-green or bluish broadleaf evergreens. Cultures are complex and varied, but farming is the dominant activity in all regions. Types of agriculture are similar, and

[1] Dry Summer Subtropics and the term mediterranean are used interchangeably. When Mediterranean is capitalized, it refers to the sea or basin.

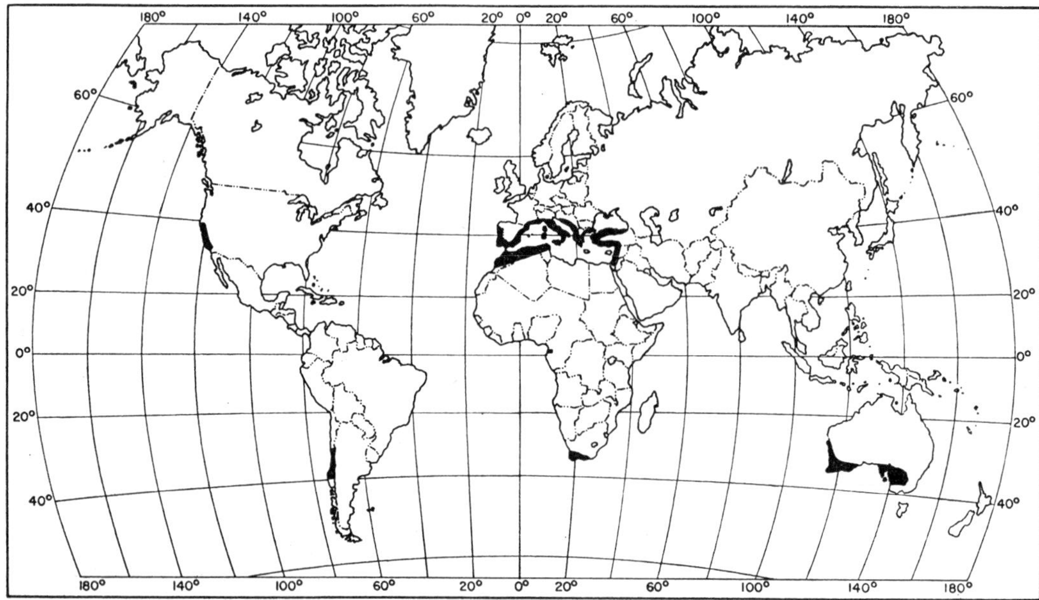

FIGURE 7-1. *The Dry Summer Subtropics.*

crops are almost identical; a definite mediterranean clue is the olive-citrus-vine trio. Sunshine, sea, and scenery are the bases for a flourishing resort activity in all regions of the Dry Summer Subtropics.

The imprint of new cultural patterns is still fresh in the mediterranean lands of the Americas, South Africa, and Australia whereas the actual borderlands of the Mediterranean Sea have a rich, colorful past and have made countless significant contributions to western civilizations. Many of the classics in art, literature, and science stemmed from the early Greeks. The Romans made many contributions to the basic principles of justice, law, and order. Roman roads were epic in land transport and the Mediterranean Sea was a nursery school for navigators. Three of the great monotheistic religions were nurtured here. The impact of the Mediterranean Basin lands on the entire world is clearly stated by Ellen Churchill Semple: "All the world is heir of the Mediterranean. All the world is her debtor. Much that is finest in modern civilization traces back to seeds of culture in the circles of the Mediterranean lands and transported thence to other countries." [2] Certainly, these total a great heritage.

Location

The Dry Summer Subtropics border the tropical zone on the western margins of the continents, usually between latitudes 30° and 40°, with extensions inland varying with continental outline and surface. All continents are represented.

The greatest areal development is in the lands fringing the Mediterranean Sea. All the European countries touching the Mediterranean Sea have areas included within the type; so do Portugal on the Atlantic west coast, Turkey, Syria, Lebanon, and Israel on the east shore of the basin, and the Barbary Coast states of Africa on the south shore. The region extends through the Bosporus Straits, along the Black Sea coast of Turkey, and includes southern Crimea of the U.S.S.R.

[2] Semple, Ellen Churchill, *The Geography of the Mediterranean Regions.* New York: Henry Holt and Company, 1931, 3.

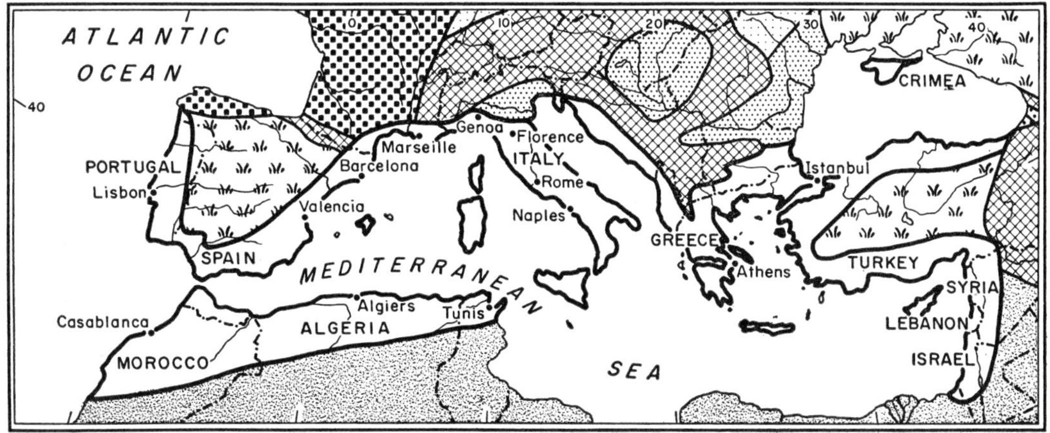

FIGURE 7-2. *The Mediterranean Basin.*

The North American region is restricted wholly to California west of the Sierra Nevada Mountains, but excludes the desert to the southeast and the cool, moist north coast. The middle one-third of Chile, from about Coquimbo (30° S) to the Rio Bio Bio, comprises the South American region. On the southwest tip of Africa there is a small region known as the Capetown District. Two areas occur in Australia, one on the southwest fringe including the city of Perth, the other bordering the Great Australian Bight on the east and extending through the southern margin of the Murray Basin.

PHYSICAL ENVIRONMENT

Climate

The Dry Summer Subtropics are transitional areas between arid and humid climates; the equator margins of the regions are fringed by deserts, and the humid lands are normally poleward. Winter is the season of rain; aridity rules during the summer. Seasonal changes are the result of alternating controls. During the dry-summer season the mediterranean regions are dominated by the dry, settling air of the subtropical high and the trade winds. In winter the high pressure belt and the trades shift equatorward and the regions come under the influence of the rain-bringing cyclonic westerlies.

A high percentage of sunshine is a mediterranean trait. Summer skies are clear and blue and even in the rainy winter there is still a high percentage of sunny weather. Sea breezes are common during the summer, moderating high daytime temperatures. Summer sea breezes in the Mediterranean, however, are

FIGURE 7-3. *California.*

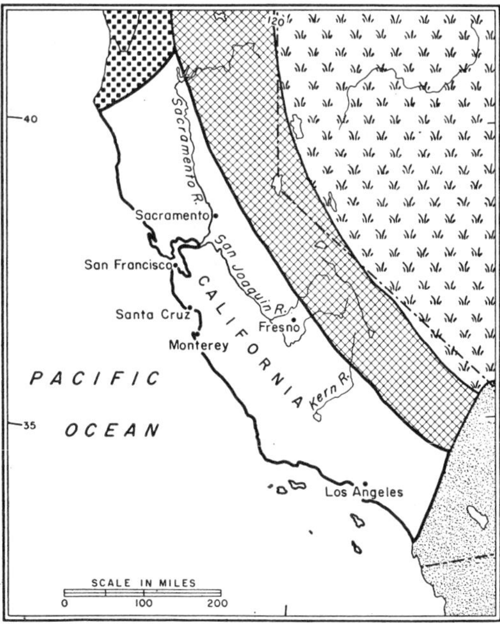

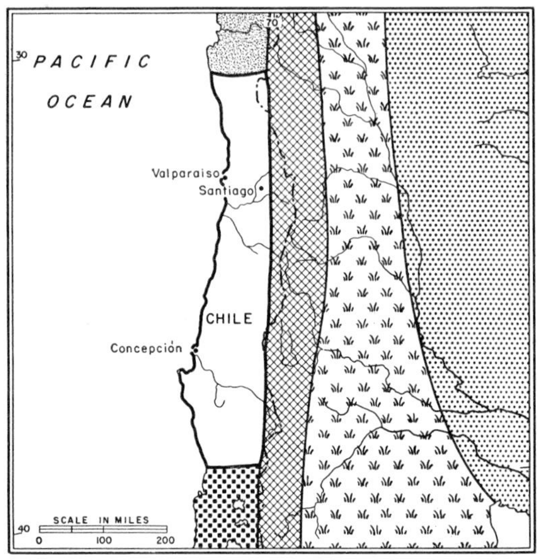

FIGURE 7-4. *Central Chile.*

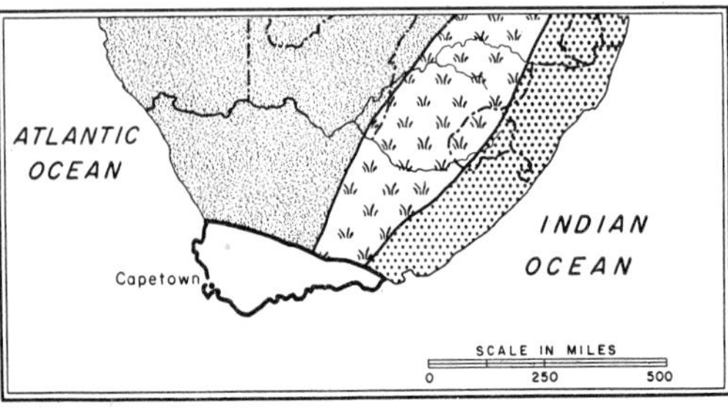

FIGURE 7-5. *The Capetown district.*

rarely cool due to the warmth of the sea. Furthermore, the sirocco, a hot, dust-laden, parching wind occasionally sweeps in from the Sahara. A similar desert wind, known as the Santa Anna, occurs in southern California. There are several local winter winds in the Mediterranean Basin, such as the mistral and bora, which cause considerable discomfort to the inhabitants. The cold, dry mistral ranges from Barcelona to Genoa but is especially pronounced in the lower Rhone Valley where farmers plant screens of cypress trees to protect crops from the cold blasts. The bora, a similar winter wind, occurs along the Adriatic coast of Yugoslavia.

Temperatures. Winters are mild with average temperatures between 40° and 50°. Frost-free periods range from nine to twelve months. Frost is most likely to occur when nights are cool, clear, and calm, when the earth heat is rapidly radiated into the atmosphere. When the cool layer of air near the surface reaches a temperature of 32° or lower, the water vapor usually condenses into white frost, or tiny ice crystals. Frost is especially hazardous to citrus fruits and out-of-season vegetables. Citrus growers utilize the slopes, which are safer from frost since dense cold air flows down the hill sides and settles in the valley bottoms. The most common weapons for combating frost are small heaters scattered throughout the

FIGURE 7-6. *Australian Dry Summer Subtropics.*

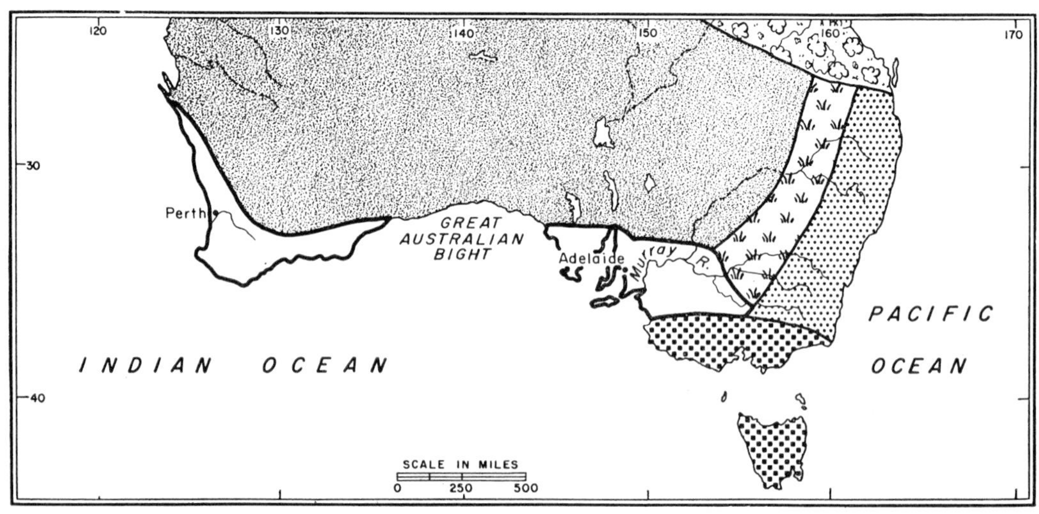

orchard. Another method, but more expensive, is the use of wind machines that attempt to mix the cold surface air with warmer air aloft.[3]

Summer average monthly temperatures range from 70° to over 80° and compare with desert recordings. Like the deserts, too, relative humidity is low and heat is dry. The clear skies are ideal for rapid heating and noon temperatures frequently soar above 100°. Temperatures drop sharply in the evening and summer diurnal ranges are high.

Precipitation. Dry Summer Subtropic precipitation is moderate, with yearly totals averaging from 10 to 30 inches. The distribution is uneven, with the greater part of the precipitation falling during the cool season. Rain is usually a summer rarity. Light showers followed by sunshine are typical, but occasionally there are periods of cloudiness with rain occurring as a persistent drizzle. Snow is rare on the lowlands, but during winter usually falls in the mountains, where a deep snow cover is especially significant since it provides irrigation water for the summer dry season. Thunderstorms, except in the higher elevations, are uncommon. Fogs occur on those coasts which have paralleling cold ocean currents; parts of the California coast are some of the foggiest areas in North America.

[3] Winstrom, William Holmes, *Weather and the Ocean of Air.* Boston: Houghton Mifflin Company, 1942.

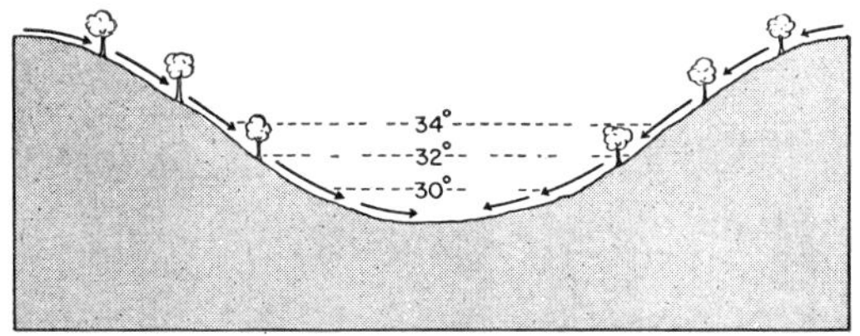

FIGURE 7-7. *Air drainage. Cold air, like water, tends to flow down slopes and settle in low places. Thus there is less danger of frosts on slopes than in valley bottoms.*

Mediterranean precipitation is unreliable; annual amounts and time of arrival both fluctuate. Low amount, poor distribution, and unreliability of precipitation place distinct limitations on possible land uses and make irrigation necessary for the growth of many crops. It is fortunate that rain coincides with the cool season; a summer maximum would lose much of its effectiveness due to the high evaporation rate.

Location and local differences. Location in respect to latitude, water bodies, deserts, and mountains causes many local differences in mediterranean temperatures and precipitation. Coast locations not only have cooler summers but milder winters than interior stations. Several California stations illustrate these conditions—the average January and July tempera-

FIGURE 7-8. *Climatic graphs of Dry Summer Subtropic stations.*

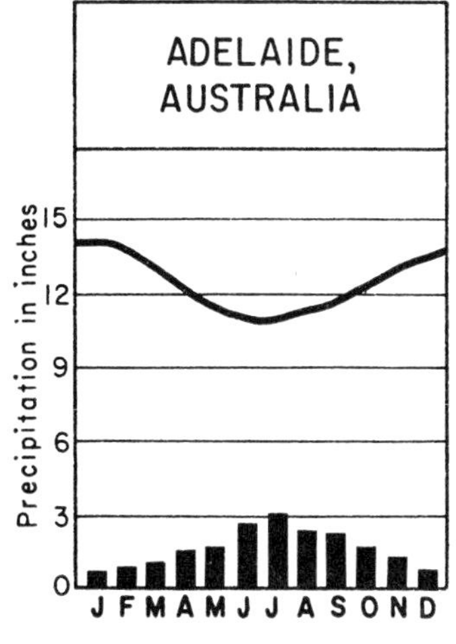

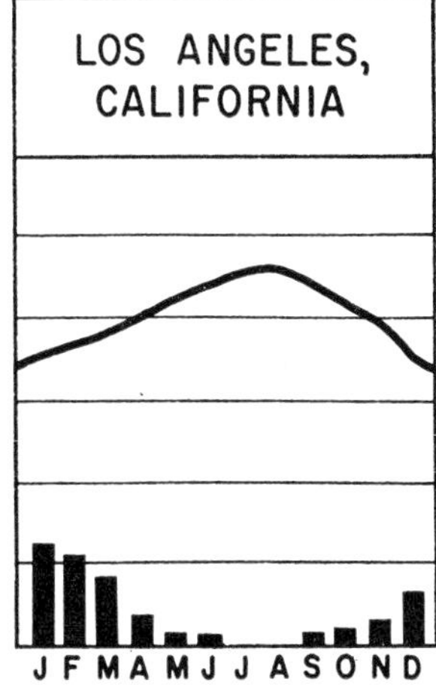

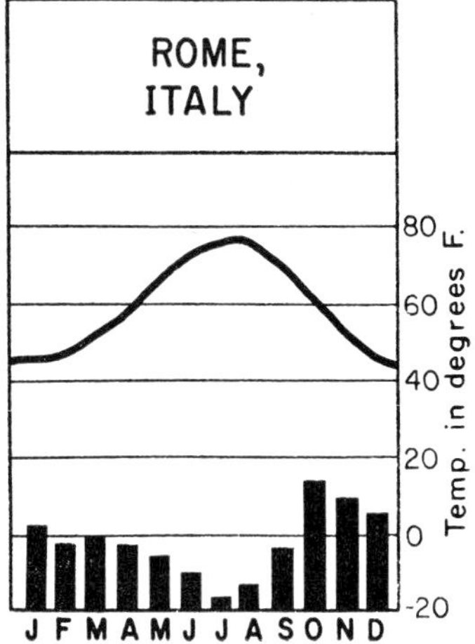

tures of Santa Cruz on the coast are 50° and 63° as compared to 45° and 79° at Merced in the interior. Desert margins are drier and have shorter seasons of rain in contrast to poleward locations. Chico receives 24 inches whereas Fresno, over 185 miles to the south, has an average of 10 inches. Exposed slopes receive amounts considerably higher than the neighboring lowlands. Mountains in many areas also form effective barriers as protection against invasion by cold continental air.

Surface features

Plains occupy a relatively small portion of the Dry Summer Subtropic regions. Rugged topography frequently dominates the landscapes, restricting the amounts of land suited to cultivation.

The greatest complexity of landforms is found in the Mediterranean Basin, most of which is surrounded by mountains. The three southward-jutting peninsulas, Iberian, Italian, and Balkan, along with the Turkish Peninsula, consist of complex groups of highlands bordered by small and disconnected plains. Most of the plains are depositional, having been built by mountain-fed streams dropping their sediment loads in quiet, protected bays. Within the region there has been a widespread development of karst topography, particularly in southern France, southeast Italy, the Dalmatian Coast of Yugoslavia, and in Israel.

The coast line of the Mediterranean Sea is of interest for its influences on man's activities. The shores of the Aegean Sea, formed by subsidence of mountains and valleys at right angles to the sea, are rugged with numerous islands, inlets, and protected harbors. Difficulties of land travel in these regions led to the early development of water transport and navigation. Elsewhere mountains parallel the sea, often rising steeply from the shore, forming few protected harbors and leaving little room for man. Some such coasts, however, such as the Rivieras of France and Italy, do have beautiful settings amid blue water and sunny slopes and have become resort areas of world acclaim.

Man has severely altered the surface features of the Mediterranean Basin. Through the centuries, population crowding on the plains has forced wider use of the hilly and mountainous areas than is common in most other climatic regions. In places the slopes have been terraced to make agriculture possible. Removal of the natural vegetation, ex-

FIGURE 7-9. *Physiographic diagram of the Mediterranean Basin.*

FIGURE 7-10. *A view of Amalfi, Italy. Because of the dearth of level land settlement has been forced up the slopes.* (Italian State Tourist Office.)

posing the slopes to rainfall, has caused many serious erosion problems. The results have been denudation of soils from slope land and an increase in flood and silt problems on many river plains. This has reduced the habitability of some lowlands by producing swampy and malarial conditions.

In the regions of North and South America the landforms have a north-south orientation and in both, three parallel units are found—high bordering mountains, central valleys, and low coastal uplands. The Central Valley of California, lying between the Sierra Nevada and the coast range, is the largest and most important lowland area of the entire realm. Its alluvial surface was built principally by streams of the Sierra Nevada. Drainage is provided by the Sacramento River system in the north, the San Joaquin in the central portion, and the Kern and King Rivers, which flow into the Tulare Basin, in the south. The Central Valley of Chile, between the towering Andes and the low coast range, also forms a long corridor, but differs from its counterpart in California by being divided into separate basins by spurs of the Andes. The drainage pattern differs in that the major streams are transverse, descending from the Andes and directly crossing the basins and coast range to the ocean.

The Capetown District of the Union of South Africa is separated from the continental plateau by the rise of the land in a series of steps that form the Little and Great Karoos. The coastal zone is not a plain, but an area of broken topography characterized by rugged hills and small fertile valleys.

Only in the Australian regions are mountains absent from most scenes. In the southwest, hills are even lacking, but an escarp-

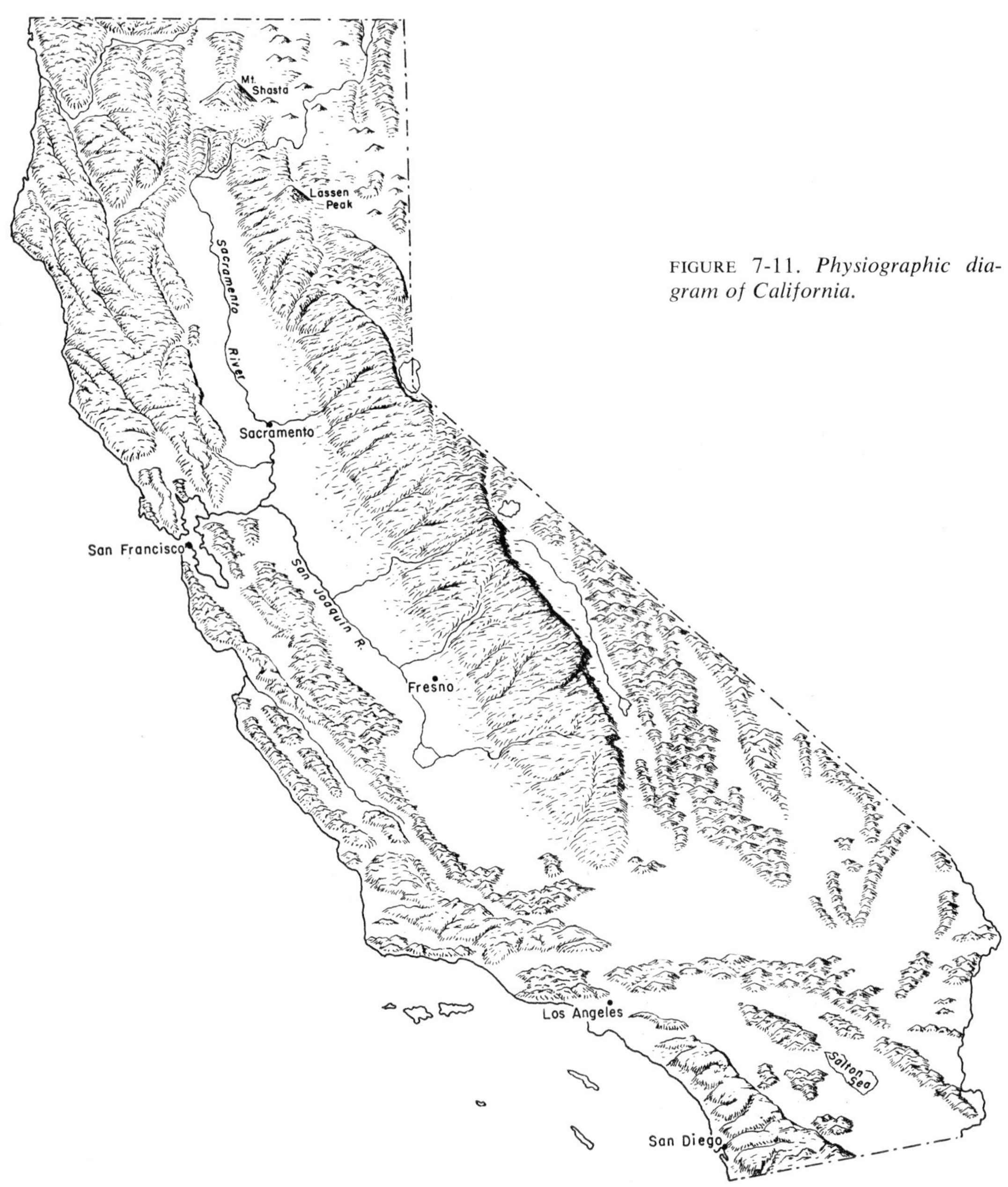

FIGURE 7-11. *Physiographic diagram of California.*

ment separates the coastal plain from the western plateau. The lowland character of the Murray Basin is broken in the east by the Flinders Range, which extends northward from Adelaide and the Gulf of St. Vincent, and by the Mount Lofty group of hills immediately east of Adelaide.

Natural vegetation

Vegetation is similar throughout all the mediterranean regions, although species differ from continent to continent. Most of the species have xerophytic characteristics such as thick bark, small, stiff,

FIGURE 7-12. *Capetown.* (Union of South Africa Government Information Office.)

shiny leaves, thorns, waxy surfaces and other devices to protect against excessive transpiration. The most common type consists of low evergreen shrubs and brush thickets known as *chaparral* in California and *maquis* in the Mediterranean Basin. Forests are composed mainly of broadleaf evergreens; conifers grow on the higher and wetter mountain slopes. The broadleaf trees are widely spaced, with large trunks and gnarled branches, typified by the olive, myrtle, holly, and cork oak. Tall trees are rare, except for the stately stands of eucalypti in southwestern Australia.

The natural vegetation of the Mediterranean Basin has been altered by overgrazing and by centuries of timber cutting without provision for reforestation. Many slopes are almost bare.

Grasses are most common in California where they were probably introduced by the early Spanish. The seasonality of precipitation is clearly marked where grass is found; in winter the landscape is green, but in summer the parched blades are dry and brown.

Soils

There are decided differences in the soils from locality to locality in the mediterranean regions, resulting from diversity of landforms and parent material, as well as from variations in rainfall. On slopes, which are especially common in the Mediterranean Basin, the soils are frequently shallow and poorly developed. In the more rainy sections, leaching is advanced and the abundant moisture and warmth cause the residual soils to be a reddish color. In the leeward and lower rainfall areas, leaching is less pronounced and fertility tends to be high. Many of the best agricultural lands are found in localities with alluvial soils that are particularly productive under irrigation.

MAN IN THE DRY SUMMER SUBTROPICS

The highland-dominated Dry Summer Subtropic regions comprise about one per cent of the world's land mass and are the homeland of four per cent of the world's population. The complex nature of the topography results in an uneven distribution of population; concentrations are generally centered on the plains but even some mountain sections are crowded. The old lands of the Mediterranean Basin, occupied for thousands of years, have densities comparable to the settled lowlands of India and China. The native peoples of the other Dry Summer Subtropic regions made relatively little imprint upon the land, and their numbers were small and cultures simple when white settlers arrived. Effective settlement in these new mediterranean lands dates back only about a century but, despite their later development, these areas are rapidly filling. The state of California has made remarkable strides in population growth and today ranks second among the states of our nation. Approximately ninety per cent of the population of Chile is located in the Dry Summer Subtropic portion, which forms the heart of the country.

Almost all mediterranean lands lack the raw materials and energy resources for major industrial development. Resources for the extractive industries—mining, forestry, and fishing—are also limited. Climate, soil, and water are the attractions and agriculture is the core element in all the economies. In no other regions of the world is farming so diverse and yet so specialized. Agriculture was, is, and will probably continue to be the dominating activity of man in the mediterranean regions.

Agriculture in the old mediterranean lands

From the earliest settlements, man in the Mediterranean Basin has depended upon agriculture for his livelihood; he has shown remarkable ingenuity in developing crops which completely utilize the "niggardly given gifts of nature"—the light and poorly distributed rainfall for general agriculture and the high proportion of land in steep and uncultivatable slopes. As Miss Newbigin points out, Mediterranean man has, "whenever possible, replaced the natural vegetation by a series of crops which make use of every drop of water, every square foot of soil, and yield him a complete dietary." [4] The suitability and success of the crops that he has been growing since ancient times is indicated by the fact that these same crops form the base of agriculture wherever man has settled in regions of Dry Summer Subtropic climate.

Conditions for farming are not altogether unfavorable. The long growing season, long hours of sunshine, high temperatures of summers, and mild, moist winters, together with the naturally fertile soils of many of the farming areas, are desirable for certain crops. Indeed, when irrigation is possible, mediterranean areas with smooth topography have agricultural possibilities rivalled by no other climatic region. The advantages of irrigation for extending the range of crops and increasing the supporting capacity were recognized by the ancients who built reservoirs and aqueducts, some of which are still in use. Unfortunately only a small portion of the region can be irrigated; much is too steep, and in many cases sufficient water is not available.

The most dense agricultural populations in the world, outside the rice lands of Asia, are found in the Mediterranean Basin. Italy, for example, has an average density of about 385 persons per square mile. However, population is far from being evenly distributed. The greatest numbers are found in the most habitable lowlands, where more than 400 persons per square mile are common. The lowest densities are in the mountains and drier sections, but even there 100 to 150 persons per square mile is not unusual. Population pressure has caused use of the poor lands wherever possible. Everywhere settlement is near the limit of capacity. Nearly one-half of the Italians are farmers, and an even higher portion of the

[4] Newbigin, Marion I., *The Mediterranean Lands.* New York: Alfred A. Knopf, Inc., 1924, 63.

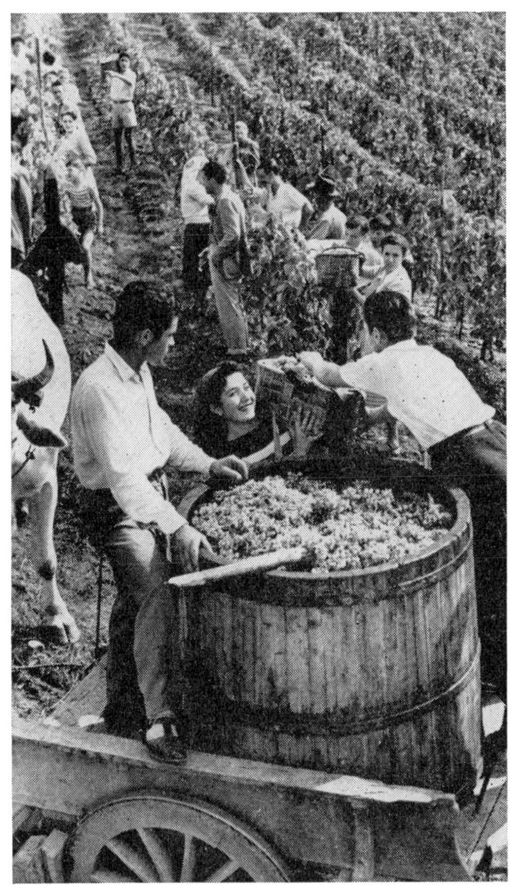

FIGURE 7-13. *Grape harvest in Italy. This activity is a family enterprise and also attracts many visitors to the vineyards.* (Italian State Tourist Office.)

population of other countries of the basin is engaged in tilling the land. Farms, frequently rented, are necessarily small; most are under twenty acres, and at least one-third are no more than five acres. Fragmentation of holdings is common; tillers live mainly in small villages. Farming must be intensive to support the large families that are typical throughout the Basin.

Through the ages, three general classes of crops have been developed to secure maximum use of water and land. These include (*1*) crops utilizing winter rainfall, such as wheat, barley, and beans—these are planted in the fall, to take advantage of cool-season moisture to mature before the encroachment of the long, hot, dry season; (*2*) drought-resisting crops whose large root systems and other special adaptations permit growth even during the dry-summer season—these include grapes and tree crops such as olives, nuts, and various fruits; and (*3*) crops grown under irrigation, including a great variety of vegetables and many fruits.

Crops are also adjusted to slope. Annuals occupy the lowlands, and tree crops and vineyards are usually planted on alluvial fans and on hill slopes, which are sometimes terraced. These locations provide good air drainage and minimize the danger of frost for fruits; furthermore, erosion dangers are lessened as tree crops require a minimum of cultivation and have large root systems which aid in holding the soil in place. Citrus fruits are restricted

FIGURE 7-14. *World-famous Turkish tobacco being dried. Tobaccos of the Mediterranean Basin are in world demand for blending purposes.* (Turkish Information Office.)

to the warmer portions; vineyards are often given the choice south-facing slopes that produce superior quality grapes. Olive and fig orchards occupy the less favorable sites, both being hardy, drought-resisting trees. Chestnuts are sometimes the breadstuff in the poorer mountain agricultural areas.

A two- or three-story agriculture, common in some localities, secures the maximum use of land and water. Annual crops are planted between rows of grapes, and the vines frequently climb fruit or olive trees. Agriculture tends to be on a subsistence basis; however, a portion of the citrus, nuts, olives, grapes, and tobacco flow out into world commerce.

The pressure upon the cropland restricts the keeping of animals. Generally there are few dairy or beef cattle, but large numbers of sheep and goats, used for meat, milk, and fiber, are found in the non-arable areas throughout the hills and mountains. These animals, able to live on the scant vegetation, have contributed directly to the serious erosion problem by overgrazing until slopes become bare to the winter rains.

Agriculture in the new mediterranean lands

In contrast to the subsistence agriculture accent of the Mediterranean Basin, the other Dry Summer Subtropic regions are engaged in commercial agriculture. This difference is explained in terms of their development during the Industrial Age and their lack of encumbering populations and

FIGURE 7-15. *Shasta Dam. This structure is a key element in the Central Valley Project. The Sacramento River flood-waters are held for release during the dry summer season for irrigation benefits downstream and in the San Joaquin Valley. Electricity is also generated, recreation facilities are provided on the artificial lake, and navigation is improved in the lower reaches of the river.* (United States Bureau of Reclamation.)

ancient cultures. The crops are usually similar, but the farms are larger, more modern, mechanized, and the products are grown principally for markets outside the region.

California. California offers the prime example of agriculture in the new mediterranean lands. This state has advantages over other regions in possessing the largest continuous lowland suited for agriculture, in having a sufficient water supply for big-scale irrigation, and in having access to extensive domestic markets and the latest developments of technology. Specialty agriculture, consisting primarily of horticultural crops, is characteristic.

The general patterns of mediterranean crops were set by the Spanish missions in California toward the close of the eighteenth century. During the short period of Spanish reign, the bulk of the land was used for wheat and cattle, with fruits and vegetables commonly grown in small plots near the missions. In the modern era, extensive grazing and grain production have decreased and specialty crops with higher unit value have increased, thereby allowing California, despite unfavorable distance, to compete for eastern and mid-western markets. The agriculture of this state has been aptly described by the phrase "variety in abundance." Most crops produced in the intermediate zone can be found in the Central Valley. In recent years no less than fifty commodities have each returned five million dollars or more annually to farmers. Altogether the agricultural enterprises return more than two billion dollars to California farmers, placing the state first in the nation in total farm income.

Crops are usually localized in well-defined areas where the details of climate, soil, slope, and water supply are most suitable. For example, citrus groves are found on the alluvial fans of the Los Angeles Lowland and along the slopes fringing the southeast portion of the Central Valley where air drainage is good and frost danger is low. Acres of peaches are planted in the San Joaquin Valley; grapes are grown in many localities—Fresno is the raisin center; olives are largely produced in the drier sections; a variety of vegetables is found on the delta lands of the Sacramento and San Joaquin Rivers; cotton has become a big crop in the southern end of the valley. Alfalfa, producing five or six cuttings a year, has encouraged the fattening of beef cattle and large urban markets have favored dairying. Truly agriculture is big business in California!

Southern Hemisphere regions. Middle Chile, the Capetown District of Africa, and the regions of Australia are significant agricultural areas in their respective continents. Development, as in the case of California, is historically recent, but again mediterranean crops form the basis of the economy.

In the Central Valley of Chile physical conditions for agriculture are excellent, with fertile alluvial soils, favorable relief, long growing season, and ample water for irrigation. Summers are slightly cooler than the average for California or the Mediterranean Basin regions. Development has lagged behind other similar lands for several reasons: (*1*) Large estates, known as *haciendas,* still contain well over half the cultivated land of central Chile; the owners have preferred stock-rearing to plow-agriculture and thus much potential crop land is only extensively used. (*2*) Modern methods have been slowly introduced to Chile and in many cases primitive systems still prevail. (*3*) The isolation of the region, even from South American markets, has restricted sales for commercial production. Wheat is the principal crop. Corn, not a true mediterranean crop, is grown extensively by tenant farmers and is their most important food grain. A variety of fruits and vegetables is found, but acreages are limited because of small markets; only grapes are produced in sufficient quantities for export and these leave the country as wine.

South Africa was one of the first areas of the Dark Continent to be colonized by Europeans. Colonization from the beginning was for the purpose of permanent settlement. There are many parallels in early history between this area and the United States.[5] The colonization of both began in the seventeenth century; early difficulties with the natives of Africa may be likened to those with the In-

---

[5] See Stamp, L. Dudley, *Africa, a Study in Tropical Development.* New York: John Wiley and Sons, Inc., 1953, Chapter 19.

FIGURE 7-16. *Rural landscape in the Paarl Valley of South Africa. Orchards and vineyards dominate land utilization. The white strip in the far background is a newly-constructed highway.* (Union of South Africa Government Information Office.)

dians in America; the revolt of the Dutch settlers against the British may be compared to the American revolution, and the need for labor supplies in both led to importations of slaves which became the basis for similar race problems.

The Capetown District bears more similarity to European and American agriculture and settlement than any other part of Africa. Wheat is the principal crop and is grown on large farms which average two and one-half sections (a section equals one square mile, 640 acres). Owing to limited rainfall, about half of the wheat land lies fallow each year. This district is also one of the chief fruit-growing areas of Africa. The Dutch began producing grapes at an early date in the area around Capetown and during the first half of the nineteenth century they shipped large quantities of wines to England. Plant diseases and insect pests have retarded this phase of the industry, and although grapes for wine are

FIGURE 7-17. *Australian wheat harvest. This demonstrates how one man with modern machinery can operate a farm with a large acreage.* (Australian News and Information Bureau.)

still important, the Capetown District as an exporter is overshadowed by other areas. Production for fresh markets is also worthy of mention—grapes and other fruits ripen here in March and April when Northern Hemisphere countries are still without fresh supplies. There is some export of fine table grapes to Great Britain in the "off season," along with peaches, plums, and citrus fruits. Orange production is a young, but growing, activity. Improved transportation to western Europe, irrigation development, and the advantage of "off season" markets have been the main factors in its establishment.

Wheat and sheep are the important enterprises of the Australian regions. Both provide commodities well suited for long-distance export. Farming is still extensive with units ranging from one to two sections or more in size. In the Murray Basin where large-scale irrigation works have been developed, there is more intensive agriculture, characterized by tree fruits, grapes, and dairying. Markets and labor supply are the main limitations for full development of agriculture at the present time. The total population of Australia is only nine million, thus the home consuming capacity is relatively small.

Fishing

Fishing is of local significance in almost all the mediterranean economies, and has developed as an important commercial activity in many. A string of fishing villages with small fleets occupy inlets and bays along the Mediterranean Sea coasts, where fishermen have combed the waters for thousands of years. Sardines constitute the chief commercial catch, but Greece and Mediterranean North Africa have long-established sponge fisheries. Large catches of sardines and tuna have made California the American leader in the value of fish products. Much of

FIGURE 7-18. *California fishing fleet. Port of Los Angeles boasts the greatest fishing industry in the world. Nearly 2000 fishermen are employed on the fleet of large vessels that catch fish for the fresh fish trade.* (City of Los Angeles.)

FIGURE 7-19. *Cork oak grove in Spain. Notice that the trunks and large limbs have been stripped of bark, which is used for the cork of commerce.* (Crown Cork and Seal Company.)

FIGURE 7-20. *Open pit mining scene at Zonguldak on the Black Sea coast of Turkey. This is the nation's leading coal producing area.* (Turkish Information Office.)

this catch is made beyond mediterranean waters by California fishing fleets ranging the open Pacific; "clippers," boats of special design, sail as far south as the equator in search of tuna.

Forest industries

The sparseness of the forest cover has limited lumbering industries. There is some milling, but the timber comes from the wetter mountain slopes that border the region. One exception is noted in southwest Australia, where valuable stands of jarrah and karri, eucalyptus species, are exploited. The cork oak furnishes the most valuable forest product in the Mediterranean Basin, with concentrations in the western portion. Commercial cork comes from the outer bark of the tree, which is stripped about every ten years for a total of seven to eight peelings during its lifetime.

Mining

Mining is a noteworthy activity in several areas of the Dry Summer Subtropics. Quantities and varieties conducive to great industrial developments are lacking in the Mediterranean Basin, but a number of

FIGURE 7-21. *Signal Hill. This is the world's greatest concentrated oil field; its voluminous output can be gauged by the dense, man-made forest of derricks.* (Los Angeles Chamber of Commerce.)

minerals are significant. Bauxite is mined in the southern Rhone Valley of France and near the coast at several points in Yugoslavia. Italy is a leader in mercury production. Rich iron deposits are worked in Algeria, and the ore is shipped to western Europe; phosphates in quantity are also mined and exported. Turkey is one of the leading producers of chromium and also mines coal, molybdenum, lead, and zinc. Spain has considerable mineral wealth but, except for copper in the south, most deposits are on the plateau and in the mountains outside the mediterranean fringe. The quarrying of building-stone is of some importance throughout the Mediterranean Basin. Shortages in timber have caused stone to be used extensively. In addition the statuary marbles of Carrara, Italy, are world famous.

California is outstanding for petroleum, ranking as a leading producing state, with major fields in the Los Angeles area and the southern part of the Central Valley. Petroleum has been the answer to California's lack of coal for industrial development.

The major mineral wealth of Chile, the nitrates of the desert and the copper of the Chuquicamata area in the highlands have already been discussed. It is chiefly for these two minerals that the country is noted, although some coal and iron is also mined. The Tofo mines near Coquimbo, which are controlled by the Bethlehem Steel Corporation, are the principal producers of iron; the ore, handled entirely by machinery from mine to ship, is hauled to Sparrows Point, Maryland, for smelting. A small steel plant has been established near Concepción and limited amounts of the ore from the Tofo area are now locally utilized. Chile, the leading coal-mining country of South America, mines just over two million tons annually. This fact indicates that the entire continent is short in domestic supply of the greatest source of industrial energy. The coal mined in Chile, primarily near Concepción, is of low grade, but its domestic use is forced by high tariffs on foreign imports.

The two most notable metallic-mineral areas of Australia are closely associated with the eastern Dry Summer Subtropic region. Broken Hill, in west central New South Wales, has one of the great lead-zinc ore bodies of the world. Production has been continuous since 1883, and the end is not yet in sight. The continent's largest iron deposits are west of the head of Spencer Gulf with the bulk of the production coming from Iron Monarch. The ore is hauled by rail to the port of Whyalla, 34 miles away, for shipment by boat to steel mills at Newcastle and Port Kembla on the east coast.

Industry

Factory towns characterized by belching smoke stacks, clusters of industrial plants, and raw material stockpiles typical of the manufacturing belts of western Europe and eastern United States are not common in the Dry Summer Subtropics. Heavy industry is curtailed by a scarcity of

FIGURE 7-22. *Grasse, France—the perfume center. A long tradition in this industry has made Grasse synonymous with perfume. Raw materials such as musk, moss ambergris, oils, and flowers are drawn from all parts of the world.* (French Embassy Press and Information Division.)

coal and iron; shortages in fibers limit textile production. Much of the regions' industry is associated with the products of the orchards, vineyards, and fields. The Mediterranean Basin countries and California are especially important in the processing of agricultural commodities. Varieties of fruit are dried or canned, and fresh or frozen fruit juices are canned and bottled. Olives are pressed for oil, bottled or tinned. Tons of grapes are crushed by vintners who have gained world-wide reputations for the quantity and quality of their wines. Many varieties of vegetables are canned or frozen for market. In the Grasse area of southern France, acres of flowers are processed for essential oils used in the perfume industry that is centered there.

The sea also contributes to the food-processing industry. Sardine canneries are important in the Mediterranean Basin; Monterey, California, is known as the world's sardine capital. California tuna canneries concentrated in Los Angeles and San Diego [6] prepare much of the United States' pack.

California stands out as the major industrial area of the mediterranean lands. Petroleum for energy, local and nation-wide markets with substantial buying power, and the sunny climate have stimulated the largest and most diversified industrial development on the Pacific Coast. The motion picture industry has concentrated in Hollywood to take advantage of the sunny climate and the variety of California scenery. Favorable flying weather and outdoor working conditions were important factors in the establishment of four leading aircraft companies. The Hollywood label places the stamp of approval on sports clothes and southern California competes with New

[6] San Diego falls into the Tropical Desert classification in this book.

FIGURE 7-23. *Menton—resort center on the French Riviera.* (French Embassy Press and Information Service.)

York and Paris as a style-setting center. Tons of petroleum are refined and thousands of automobiles are assembled. Iron and steel, rubber, pottery, ships, and furniture are also included in the industrial diversification. Industries are concentrated chiefly in the populous Los Angeles Basin and the San Francisco Bay area.

Tourism

People of the mediterranean regions "sell" their sunshine, winter climate, scenery, and beaches. The rugged shoreline, narrow beaches, and sun-facing slopes of the Rivieras of France and Italy, the Dalmatian Coast of Yugoslavia, and the Crimea of the U.S.S.R. are the winter playgrounds of Europe. Scattered along the Mediterranean coast are clusters of small settlements, as well as larger centers such as Nice and Cannes, all directing their energies to the tourist and resort trade. Much of the economy of the little principality of Monaco revolves around its famous gambling casino. California and "America's Playground" are synonymous to many people in the Western Hemisphere. This state has been especially active in promoting its recreation opportunities; it attracts thousands of visitors as well as many retired persons who establish permanent residences there. As yet tourism is a minor activity in the Southern Hemisphere regions.

FIGURE 7-24. *Athens, Greece—beauty in stone. More than 400 years before the dawn of the Christian era, Greece enjoyed its "Golden Age." Under the direction of Pericles, some of Athens' finest monuments were reared on the Acropolis, a hill near the city. One of the principal works of architecture built at that time was the Parthenon, shown at the center.* (Trans World Airlines.)

Urban centers

Since the days of ancient Greece, a large percentage of the people of the Mediterranean Basin has lived in towns and cities. The early development was a response in part to commercial activity and in part to the need of massing for protection. The centers that grew during the ancient period and flourished through the Middle Ages contributed much to the plan and function of later urban centers throughout the world; here cities first developed the specific functions that are now peculiar to them—service as centers of commerce, manufacturing, culture, education, and political activity.

Istanbul, Athens, Naples, Rome, Florence, Genoa, Marseille, Barcelona, Valencia, Casablanca, Algiers, Tunis, and Beirut are but a few of the ancient cities which today are busy metropolises. In Italy alone there are a dozen cities over 100,000 population. In contrast to the long established centers that dominate the urban activity of most of the nations that fringe the sea, most of the city needs of Israel are served by two new centers, Tel Aviv and Haifa. Both have grown during this century to become major ports and commercial centers. There is little dispersed settlement through the Basin and even the farming populations are concentrated in villages scattered through the countryside. Many cling to the slopes, using land not suited to agriculture; in the earlier periods these sites offered some protection.

In the more recently developed regions, city development is naturally less advanced. Each region tends to have one or two dominating centers. Santiago is the great city of Chile and Valparaiso is its port. Capetown is both port and urban center of the Cape Province of Africa. Adelaide is the main city serving the Murray Basin, and Perth serves southwest Australia. In California there are three major

FIGURE 7-25. *Los Angeles, the expanding city of the West Coast, is a major center of commerce, industry, agriculture, and entertainment.* (Los Angeles Chamber of Commerce.)

FIGURE 7-26. *Bird's eye view of San Francisco—the city by the Golden Gate. A great harbor and easy access to the Central Valley are responsible for the development of San Francisco.* (San Francisco Chamber of Commerce.)

cities, Los Angeles and San Francisco on the coast, and Sacramento in the Central Valley; the first is the fastest growing urban center of the entire Dry Summer Subtropic realm.

OUTLOOK

Agriculture will remain the bulwark of the economies of the Dry Summer Subtropic countries. The possibilities for development, however, are distinctly limited. Mediterranean Basin lands are presently farmed to near capacity—little can be added to their arable acreage. Any material change will have to result from multifarious approaches such as erosion control, reclamation of marshlands, intensification of farming, reforestation, increased fishing activity, extension of industries utilizing hydroelectricity, local raw materials, and ancient skills, and greater capitalization upon the "glorious past" as well as climate and scenery to attract tourists in increased numbers. Probably the greatest potentials lie in the improvement of farming techniques, and although programs are underway to raise the standard of living of the peasants, progress is extremely slow where rural populations are dense, traditions are long established, and education and capital are low.

California, the "Giant of the West," is the rapidly developing mediterranean region. Present trends indicate no diminishing of pace. Problems undoubtedly will arise, especially in shortages of water supply. Technology, unified effort, and available capital are major assets for combating this limitation as evidenced by transport of water from the Colorado River to the Los Angeles Basin. Additional future supplies may be obtained from the sea or from outside the region, particularly by reservoir storage in the Sierra Nevada Mountains.

Isolation has been the major deterrent of the Southern Hemisphere regions. The worldwide trend toward greater national self-sufficiency has been the impetus for recent attempts to reduce dependence upon outside areas. Because of present under-development Chile probably has the greatest relative potentials for future growth.

SELECTED REFERENCES

Burck, Gilbert, "The New Australia," *Fortune,* XLII, September 1950, 85-91 and 147-161.

Hubbard, George B., *The Geography of Europe.* New York: Appleton-Century-Crofts, Inc., 1952.

Lewis, Norman N., "Lebanon—The Mountain and Its Terraces," *Geographical Review,* XLIII, No. 1, 1953, 1-14.

Pearcy, G. Etzel, Russell H. Fifield, et al., *World Political Geography.* New York: Thomas Y. Crowell Company, 1948.

Pounds, Norman J. G., *Europe and the Mediterranean.* New York: McGraw-Hill Book Company, 1953.

Sedgwick, Ruth, "Chile's Economic Problems," *The World Today,* V, No. 1, 1949, 39-46.

Simpich, Frederick, "California, Horn of Plenty," *National Geographic,* XC, No. 5, 1949, 553.

Taylor, Griffith, *Australia.* New York: E. P. Dutton and Co., Inc., 1943.

"The World's Cheapest Steel," *Fortune,* XLII, November, 1950, 83-86 and 186-192.

Van Valkenburg, Samuel, and Colbert C. Held, *Europe.* New York: John Wiley and Sons, Inc., 1952.

Vouras, Paul, "Greece's Means of Livelihood," *Journal of Geography,* LII, No. 1, 1953, 1-13.

CHAPTER 8

Humid Subtropics

THE HUMID SUBTROPICS ARE THE final outposts of the tropics. They represent transitional zones between the continuously warm climates and those where winter cold becomes a definite characteristic. In Africa and Australia, however, they fail to serve this role because of the limited poleward extent of these continents.

A mild rainy climate favors the cultivation of a wide variety of crops, hence agriculture dominates land utilization; however, sharp contrasts occur from region to region in farming types and crop accents. Commercial farming, with an emphasis on cotton, is traditional in the Humid Subtropics of North America, commonly called the American Cotton Belt. Commercial farming also predominates in the Southern Hemisphere regions. Food crops for

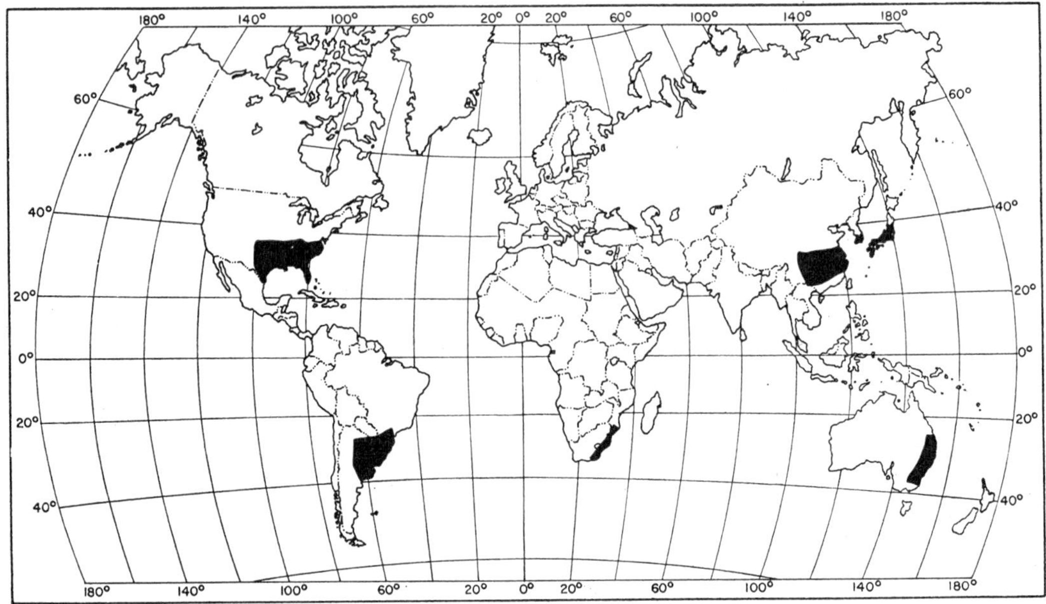

FIGURE 8-1. *The Humid Subtropics.*

FIGURE 8-2. *The Humid Subtropics of the Orient.*

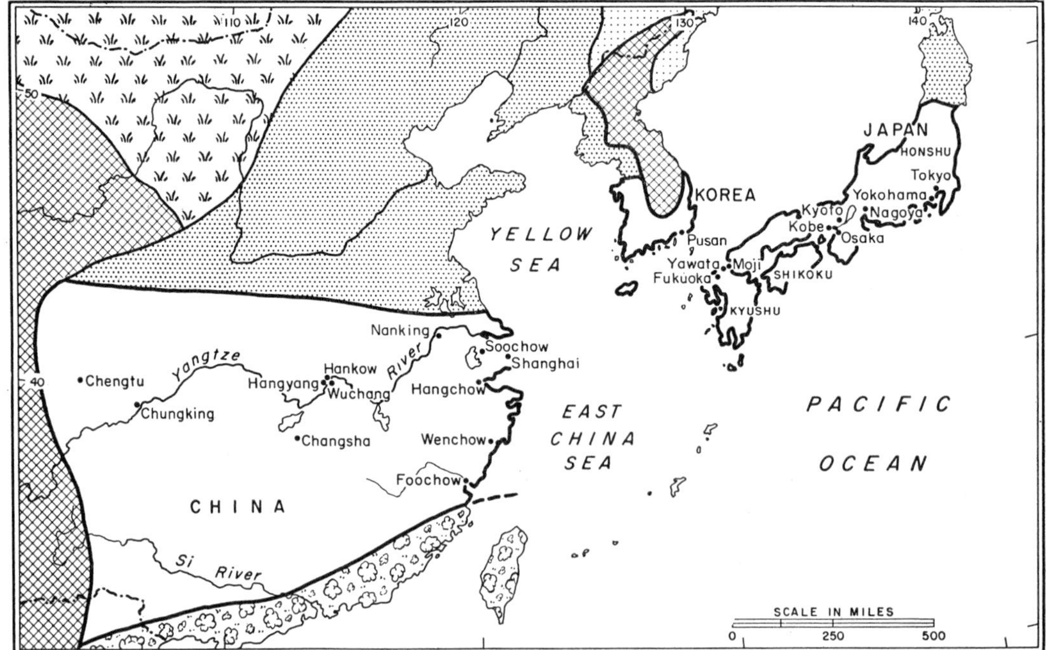

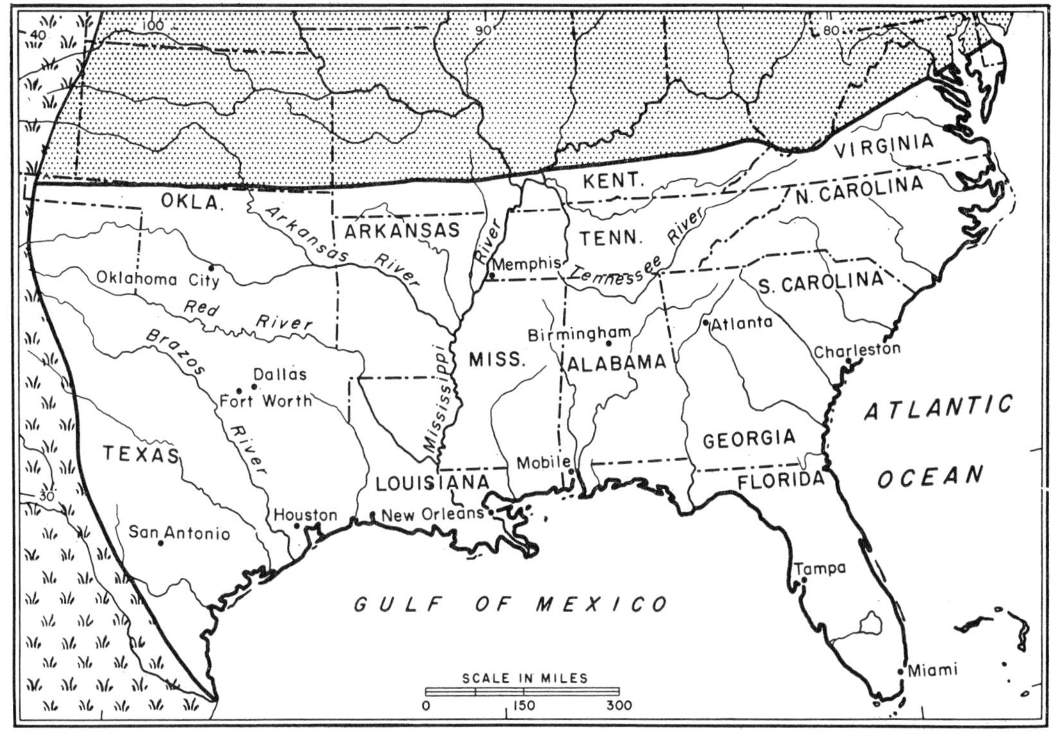

FIGURE 8-3. *The United States South.*

hungry millions take precedence in the Orient, where farmers have tilled the soil for thousands of years. Where land is arable, man is everywhere; his roots are deep in the earth and landscapes are completely altered by his works.

Though agriculture dominates, the exploitation of forests, minerals, and sea provides considerable diversification. Two of the regions have had significant industrial awakenings in the past seventy years. In the twentieth century, Japan rose from a feudal state to become the industrial giant of the Orient. The United States Humid Subtropics is now developing its storehouse of raw materials and has entered an era of industrialization.

Location

The Humid Subtropic regions lie on east sides of continents, generally between latitudes 25° and 38°. The interior borders are usually marked by increasing aridity and are set at the 20-inch rainfall lines. All continents are represented in these regions.

The largest region is found in Asia, where the Humid Subtropics occupy virtually all of China between the Tropic of Cancer on the south and the Central Mountains north of the Yangtze Valley. Also included are southern Korea, the Japanese Islands of Kyushu and Shikoku, and the portion of Honshu south of latitude 38°.

In North America the region includes the southeastern quarter of the United States southward from the line denoting the annual frost free season of 200 days and eastward from the 20-inch annual rainfall line that bisects the panhandles of Oklahoma and Texas and bows slightly westward to terminate near the mouth of the Rio Grande. Hereafter this area will be called the United States South. The Humid Subtropics of South America center upon the middle and lower parts of the Parana

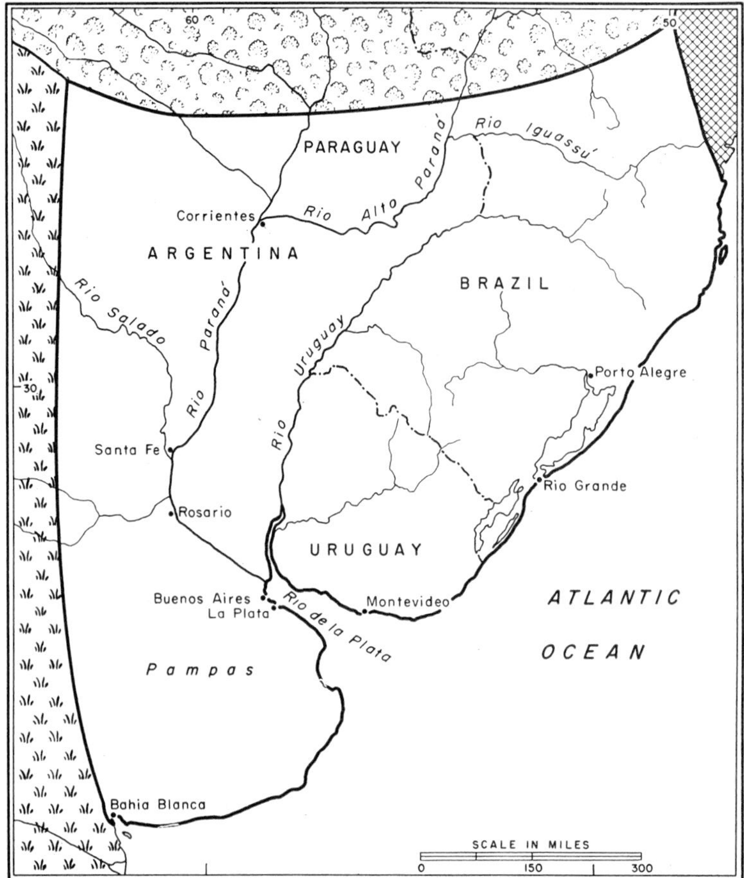

FIGURE 8-4. *The Humid Subtropics of South America.*

Basin and the Rio de la Plata. The region contains the pampas of northeastern Argentina, all of Uruguay, most of the southern projection of Brazil, and the southern portion of Paraguay.

The African region is restricted by the Drakensberg Mountains to a relatively narrow belt comprising the Natal Coast along the eastern border of the Union of South Africa. In Australia the Eastern Highlands restrict the Humid Subtropics to a coastal location from about Brisbane, Queensland, southward along the margin of New South Wales to Cape Howe.

A small area not conforming in continental position is found at the eastern end of the Black Sea in the U.S.S.R. With its base on the sea, it is pinched into a wedge shape by the converging mountains.

PHYSICAL ENVIRONMENT

Climate

The Humid Subtropics have hot, moist summers, and generally mild winters. All regions, except the small area in the U.S.S.R., occupy east coast positions in similar latitudes, but the character of their continental backgrounds accounts for climatic differences. The regions in the Northern Hemisphere are contiguous to sources of cold continental air in winter, whereas those in the Southern Hemisphere fringe tropical land masses and cold air from the Antarctic is modified by movement over oceans. The great differences in the heating and cooling of the Northern Hemisphere continents and their surrounding seas create monsoon tendencies

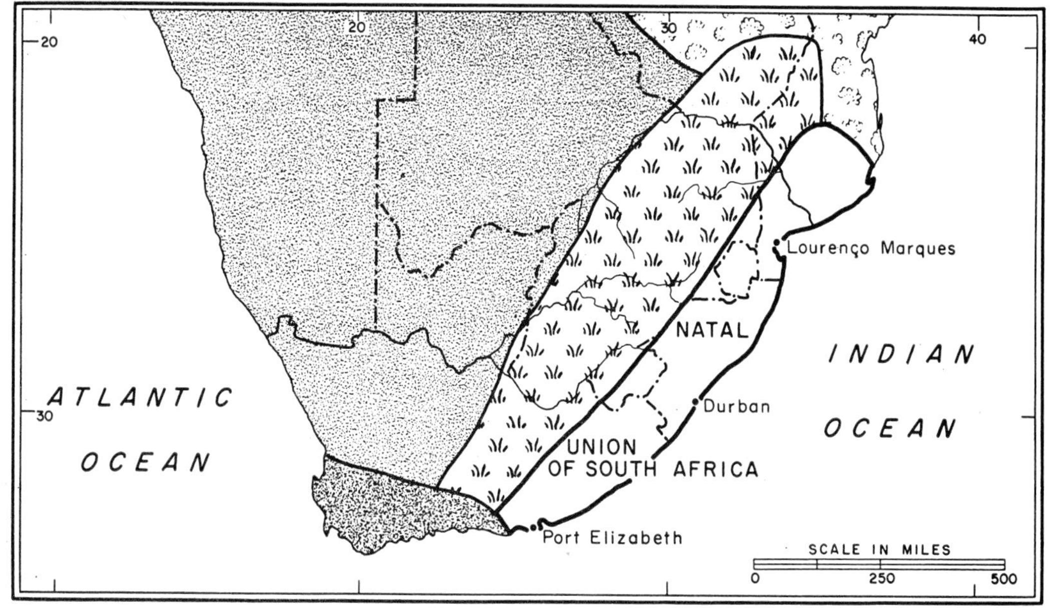

FIGURE 8-5. *The Humid Subtropics of Africa.*

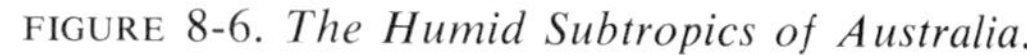

FIGURE 8-6. *The Humid Subtropics of Australia.*

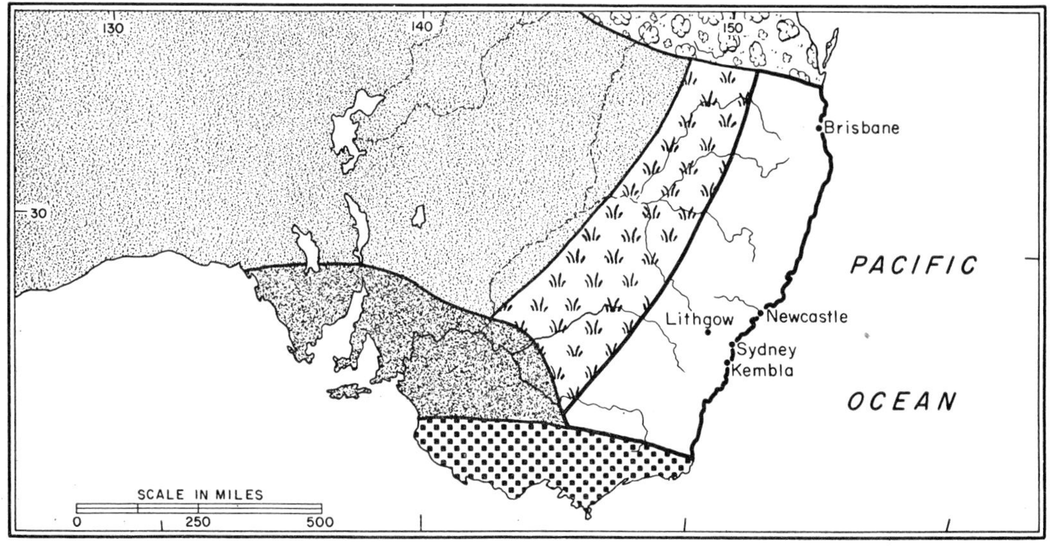

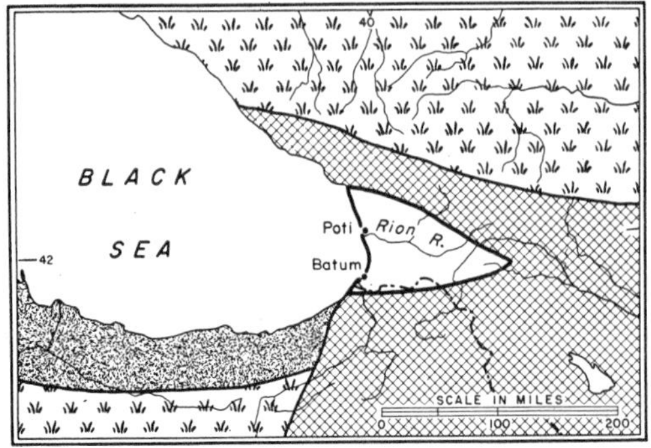

FIGURE 8-7. *The Humid Subtropics of the Soviet Union.*

in the Asian and North American regions, especially pronounced in the former.

Temperatures. Summer temperatures are high with averages of 75° to 80°; daytime readings are often above 90° and occasionally exceed 100°. Humidities are also high and, with the oppressive heat, make summer weather particularly uncomfortable. Nights remain warm and sultry, offering little relief from the heat. Summers parallel the climate of the Rainy Tropics. Winters are mild with average temperatures between 40° and 55°. In Asia and North America, cold continental air is a close neighbor, manifested by wintry blasts. No barriers block the southward movements of cold air into the American South and it streams into the region via the Mississippi Valley. These cold waves, sometimes called "Northers," occasionally bring below-freezing weather even to Florida. China has a series of mountain ranges which create blocks to polar air from the cold interior of Asia; however, the Lower Yangtze Plain is exposed and experiences lower winter temperatures than are common for the Humid Subtropics as a whole. Lacking cold continental backgrounds, all three of the Southern Hemisphere regions have higher average winter temperatures. Growing seasons are long, ranging from 200 to 260 frost-free days in the United States and Asiatic regions to a continuous growing season on the Natal Coast; the equatorward margins of all regions occasionally have entire frost-free years.

Precipitation. Rainfall is abundant and occurs throughout the year, with most regions having a summer maximum. Averages range from 20 inches, on the sub-humid borders, to about 60 inches. Summer precipitation is chiefly a result of convectional storms; the American Humid Subtropics average between 40 and 60 thunderstorms a year. Weak cyclonic storms account for a part of the summer precipitation. Heavy rains in late summer and early fall are a result of tropical cyclones—known as hurricanes in the Atlantic and typhoons in the Pacific. Despite a prevalence of summer rain, there is a high percent of

FIGURE 8-8. *Typical climatic graphs of Humid Subtropic stations.*

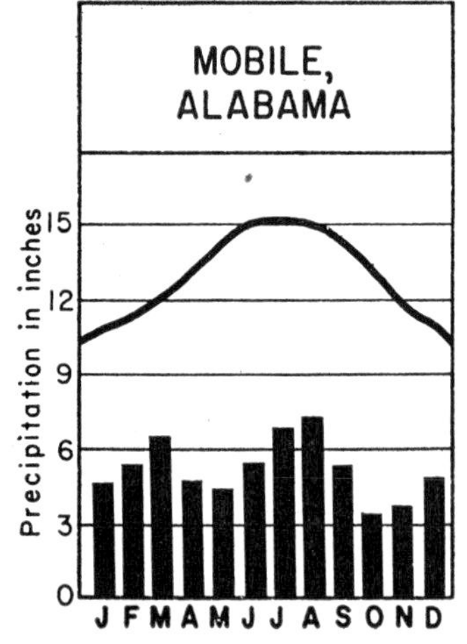

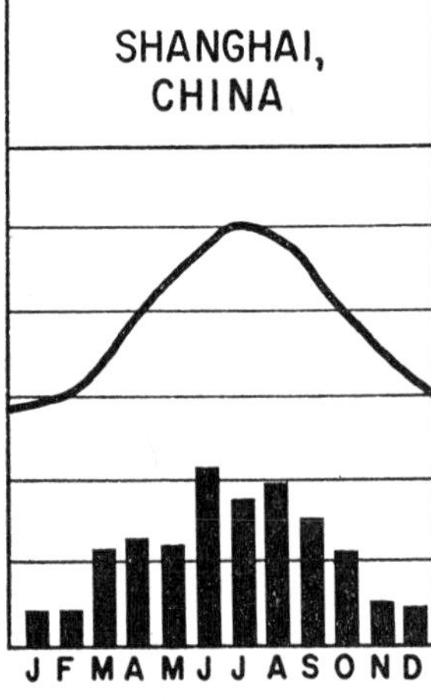

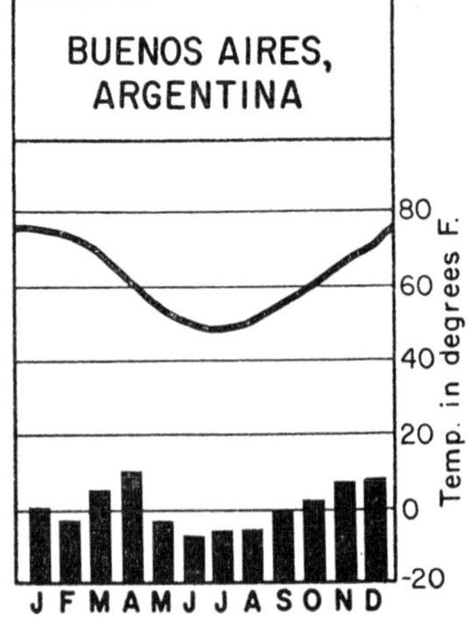

FIGURE 8-9. *Hurricane damage on the Atlantic coast. The entire backs of houses were blown off by the terrific winds.* (United States Weather Bureau.)

sunshine. Winter precipitation is mainly cyclonic. Instead of the sunshine-shower weather of summer, winter rain more often falls as a persistent drizzle from dull gray skies. Less rain falls in winter but there are generally more completely overcast days. Snow is a rarity in the Southern Hemisphere regions, but is not uncommon in the American South and the Orient, especially near the northern boundaries.

Local phenomena. Several local phenomena are important in the climatic picture of the Humid Subtropics. Coastal areas of the Northern Hemisphere regions are subject to violent tropical cyclones in the late summer and early fall; hurricanes blow out of the West Indies through the American coastal states; typhoons create destruction on the south China coast and sweep into southern Japan. Cold winds occur occasionally in the Southern Hemisphere regions; the *pampero,* a violent wind of short duration, strikes the Pampas of Argentina in summer, and the "Southerly Bursters" cool the Australian coast. Hot northwest winds from the interior of Africa descend upon the Natal Coast during spring and summer. Tornadoes, small violent storms, occur in the spring and summer, chiefly in the North American region. They hang from large cumulonimbus clouds like a funnel and spin with tremendous speeds. The portion that touches the surface may be from 300 to 1500 feet in diameter. When a tornado strikes, property destruction is almost complete.

Surface features

The Orient. There is little similarity in surface features from one Humid Subtropic region to another. Mountains fill the bulk of the Oriental regions, although the plain of the Yangtze River is one of the great lowlands of the world. This powerful stream, with its numerous tributaries, has laid an alluvial

FIGURE 8-10. *Terraces in south China. The press of a huge population has made necessary the careful terracing of many of the slopes to make more land available for food production.* (Theodore Herman.)

surface which reaches 600 miles inland and varies from 20 to 200 miles in width. According to George B. Cressey, the delta is building seaward at the rate of one mile in 70 years.[1] Water features are an outstanding characteristic of this plain; canals, rivers, and lakes are everywhere.

South China is a land of broken topography—the major portion is in slope. Streams draining into the Yangtze, the ocean, and the Si River have carved it into a maze of hills and valleys. Level land does not exceed ten per cent of the area.

The most important section in western China is the Red Basin of Szechwan Province, the gathering area for the principal headwater tributaries of the Yangtze River. This basin, named for its brick-red sandstones, is rimmed by mountains but is by no means of uniform surface; sharp, dissected anticlines and gentle synclines trending northeast to southwest are numerous. The only major level area is the Chengtu Plain, formed by the alluvial fan of the Min River.

South Korea is thoroughly hilly. Mountains paralleling the east coast drop sheer to the Sea of Japan but descend gently westward and send out low spurs which separate a number of significant basins with lowlands in the west and south.

Japan is a mountainous island country; everywhere highlands form the background. The largest lowland is the Kwanto or Tokyo Plain of eastern Honshu, with an area of about 5000 square miles. Most of the plains are peripheral, formed by rivers depositing their sediments in quiet bays. Altogether these plains comprise no more than 15 per cent of the country.

[1] Cressey, George B., *China's Geographic Foundations.* New York: McGraw-Hill Book Company, 1934, 284.

FIGURE 8-11. *The Florida Everglades. This is the "Sea of Grass" on the rim of Florida's vast and sprawling Everglades. View shows cabbage or sable palm islands. In other sections, the Everglades are forests of cypress and provide refuge to huge flights of colorful native birds and rare wild flowers, and a home for Florida's Seminole Indians.* (Florida State News Bureau.)

United States South. The United States South lies dominantly within the physiographic province known as the Atlantic-Gulf Coastal Plain. The outer margin is remarkably featureless; broad flat-bottomed valleys with bordering bluffs rising 20 to 50 feet in height provide the only relief features. Along the coast, which merges imperceptibly with the sea, there are vast stretches of swamps. Inland, drainage is better and the surface, longer exposed to the forces of degradation, displays a greater variety of relief owing to the difference in resistances of the sedimentary materials. The harder members form low hilly ridges parallel to the coast in Alabama, Mississippi, and Texas, and the weaker strata have been lowered to form broad vales.

The Mississippi River bisects the region and its broad flood-plain, 50 to 75 miles wide, is one of the most productive areas of the nation. On the west the region makes contact with the Great Plains and on the north merges with the Interior Lowlands and the Appalachian Highlands. The low Ouachita and Ozark Highlands break the smooth transition to the interior.

South America. The South American region has relatively uniform relief. The only significant hilly area is in southern Brazil. Uruguay is generally a rolling plain; the plain of the Parana River comprises southern Paraguay; and a lowland known as the Argentine Mesopotamia continues southward through the area lying between the Parana and Uruguay Rivers.

FIGURE 8-12. *A view of the Piedmont, taken on the Blue Ridge Trail between the Virginia and North Carolina state line. This marginal land, formerly cultivated, is now being used for pasture.* (Standard Oil Company of New Jersey.)

FIGURE 8-13. *A view across the Mississippi River near Natchez. The flat floodplain of this great river varies from 25 to 75 miles in width. Notice the convectional storm in the background. The tugs, old and new, are both towing oil barges.* (Standard Oil Company of New Jersey.)

This merges with the flat and featureless pampa of northeastern Argentina, the most important segment of the region.

Africa and Australia. The regions of Africa and Australia are similar. Both are compressed between highlands and the sea, and in each the slopes rise steeply from narrow and discontinuous coastal lowlands. Special mention should be made of the broad and fertile Hunter Valley in the Australian region (see Figure 8-16). The Hunter River separates the New England Plateau from the Blue Mountain Plateau, forming an important passage inland from Newcastle to the interior.

U.S.S.R. The region of the U.S.S.R. is the triangular-shaped lowland of the Rion River and the lower slopes of the bordering Caucasus Mountains on the north and the Armenian Highlands on the south. The area along the coast consists mainly of marshes and lagoons, although a large-scale reclamation project has been underway to make this portion suitable for agriculture.

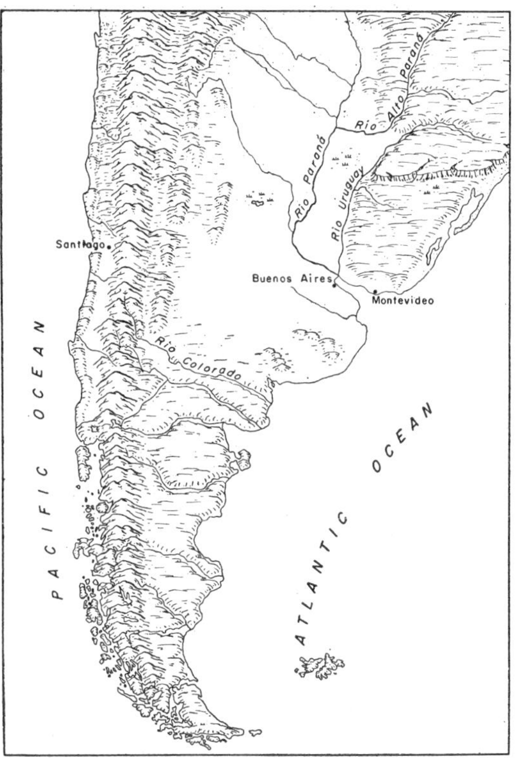

FIGURE 8-14. *A physiographic diagram of southern South America.*

Natural vegetation

Forests that constitute much of the natural cover are favored in the Humid Subtropics by an abundance of moisture and a nearly year-round period of growth. In the long-occupied land of the Orient, forests have been cut over many times and virgin forests remain only in the inaccessible areas. Broadleaf evergreens prevail on the equator margins, with occasional understories of bamboo thickets; northward there is a replacement by mixed forests.

In the United States South conifers occupy the sandy, less-fertile coastal plains as well as margins of the Piedmont, with longleaf, shortleaf, loblolly, and slash pine predominating. The pine forests grow in open stands with a low undercover of coarse grass and shrubs. Dense forests of hardwoods, including cypress, red gum, and tupelo, thrive in the poorly-drained river bottoms. More open hardwood stands occupy the better-drained bottom land sites. Hickory, chestnut, oak, and poplar form a cover in the rougher Appalachian Uplands. Toward the drier western margins the forests are gradually replaced by grasses, with trees restricted to the river banks.

The Parana Basin of South America has a mixture of pine and deciduous species, including the yerba maté tree. Coarse marsh grasses abound in the poorly-drained areas. Starting in southern Uruguay and stretching to the Rio Colorado is a broad expanse of grassland, the Argentine Pampa. This level to undulating plain appears like a sea of grass broken only by solitary umbrella-shaped ombu trees. The grass cover of the pampa is unusual in a climate type normally associated with forests. Many scientists have offered explanations; some believe that repeated fires by Indians favored the grasses and prevented the establishment of a tree cover. The pampa has a spectacular seasonal color pattern; black in the spring from the burning of old growth, then green, turning to brown, and culminating in silver when the grass spikes flower.

FIGURE 8-15. *A landscape in Natal. Note the rolling nature of the countryside.* (Union of South Africa Government Information Office.)

FIGURE 8-16. *The Hunter Valley of Australia. Aberdeen Angus cattle fatten on improved pastures flanking the Hunter River, which winds through the foothills of the New England Plateau.* (Australian News and Information Bureau.)

FIGURE 8-17. *A live-oak forest. The forests on the southern border of the United States South are evergreen. The Spanish moss hanging from the branches is gathered for use in packing and cheap upholstery.* (Standard Oil Company of New Jersey.)

Subtropical forests are the characteristic cover on many of the wet coastal slopes in Humid Subtropical Africa. Some of the better forests of Australia are found along the east slopes of the coastal ranges. The forests north of Sydney contain red cedar and several varieties of pine; south of Sydney pure stands of eucalypti are dominant.

Native animal life

Animal life is often a picturesque part of the physical environment especially where man's numbers are few, but in the Humid Subtropics man is nearly everywhere. Consequently the native animals of these regions are found chiefly in areas generally avoided by the farmer—the mountainous lands, the forests, and the swamps. Native animals are scarce in the closely-settled lands of the Orient. The United States South, with its many square miles of forest and swamp, still has a variety of native animals. Game birds, as well as others, deer, fox, squirrels, opossums, and raccoons are found in the forest. Mink, otter, and especially the muskrat inhabit the great marshes along the Gulf Coast. Muskrat trapping in the Louisiana swamps is a major winter activity for thousands of trappers.[2] The greatest concentration of wild life is found in the Everglades of Florida. This 5000 square miles of swampland

[2] For an interesting account of this activity see "Muskrat Trapping," *Fortune,* XL, November 1950, 117-22.

FIGURE 8-18. *A cypress grove. Unusually dry weather has exposed the peculiar swollen butts of the cypress, which are usually covered by water.* (United States Forest Service.)

FIGURE 8-19. *A virgin stand of longleaf pine. Notice the open nature of the stand and the flatness of the terrain.* (United States Forest Service.)

FIGURE 8-20. *Raccoon. This is a characteristic animal of the United States South.* (United States Fish and Wildlife Service.)

FIGURE 8-21. *Opossum. The marsupial of the United States South.* (United States Fish and Wildlife Service.)

has a rich variety of water birds including herons, cranes, ibises, egrets, and others. Crocodiles, alligators, manatees or sea cows, turtles, and snakes are abundant. Living on the drier islands in the area are typical forest animals. The Everglades are one of the most colorful animal refuges in the United States.

A few small animals live in the forests on the northern rim of the Humid Subtropics in South America; birds are plentiful on the pampas. The South African region contains many animals that are typical of the drier grasslands to the west, such as species of antelope and the scavenging hyenas. Snakes are common, and crocodiles and hippopotami are found in streams near the coast. Marsupials are associated with the Australian region; the major representatives are the kangaroo, wallaby, and flying opposum. Here, too, are found many unusual birds such as the lyre bird and emu.

Soils

Red and yellow soils, named for the characteristic color of their subsoils, are typical of the Humid Subtropics, but exceptions are common. The red soils are dominant on sloping land and the yellow soils prevail on the more level, flat or imperfectly-

FIGURE 8-22. *Even the rivers of China are crowded. This scene on Soochow Creek in Shanghai shows the permanent homes of many Chinese. Boats are means of livelihood as well as homes.*

drained sites. The prominent factors in their development are the warm and humid climate and the associated forest vegetation. The climate promotes intense chemical breakdown, strong oxidation, and leaching reminiscent of the humid tropical soils. The forest returns relatively little organic material. The soils tend to be acid, and low in organic matter and plant nutrients. Though low in inherent fertility, they are easily tilled, respond well to fertilization, and are potentially fruitful. Good management practices, however, are essential to continued cultivation.

Many of the better agricultural soils, particularly in the Orient and the Mississippi Bottoms, are of recent alluvial origin. In the areas of lower rainfall, such as the western edge of the United States region and the South American plains, the soils have developed under a grass cover, have been subjected only to slight leaching, and are rich in organic and mineral matter; consequently they are highly productive. Excellent soils also have developed on limestone in several places in the United States South; those of central Florida, the Black Belt of Alabama, and the Black Waxies of east Texas are especially important. Not all the exceptions are on the favorable side. Along seaward fringes, youthful soils on marine sands are frequent; these are inherently infertile, but are often easily cultivated and responsive to fertilization. Poorly-drained organic soils are found in areas of coastal swamps. The soils of the Argentine pampa are unusually fertile, having developed under grass vegetation and moderate precipitation. The smooth topography of the region enhances its utility for agriculture.

MAN IN THE HUMID SUBTROPICS

The Humid Subtropics are the most populous of all the regions. The long-settled rice lands of eastern Asia abound with people. Japan, with an area of 147,000 square miles, supports upward of eighty-seven millions, the greatest concentration being in the narrow belt extending from the Kwanto Plain westward along the borders of the Inland Sea to north Kyushu. The Chinese are crowded into the agricultural lands of the Yangtze Plain, and the narrow shoestring valleys among the hills; the Red Basin stands out in the west as an island of black on a population map. Population density in the China region usually amounts to 1000 persons per square mile of agricultural land and 2000 or more is common.

The United States South has the greatest rural densities of any major region of the United States, containing nearly half of the total agricultural population. Similarly, the Humid Subtropical regions are some of the most highly populated sections of South America, Africa, and Australia.

Agriculture

The Humid Subtropics are rivalled only by the Monsoon Tropics in the numbers of farmers they support. The abundant moisture supply, warmth, and long growing season combine to produce excellent conditions for plant growth. A great variety of crops is possible, including subtropical fruits, tea, fibers, vegetables, and grains. The combinations and emphases vary from one region to another depending upon man's needs, numbers, techniques, and markets. In the Orient farming is for subsistence, but in the other

FIGURE 8-23. *Agricultural scene in the Orient: collecting human excrement from cesspools to be used for fertilizer.* (Theodore Herman.)

FIGURE 8-24. *Preparing the paddies for rice in a south China valley. The men on the treadmill are lifting irrigation water from the canal to the fields in the traditional manner.* (Theodore Herman.)

regions commercial agriculture tends to prevail.

The Orient. Agriculture in the Orient is farming in its most intensive form. In few other portions of the world does man live so close to the earth and depend so wholly upon the products of the soil. The small holdings, two or three acres in size and commonly fragmented into half a dozen plots, must be made to yield the complete support of the farm family. Thus the people toil from dawn until dark giving infinite care to the crops which are grown predominantly for food.

Rice, the most desired crop because of high yields and food value, dominates the landscape during the warm rainy season, growing on every field which has suitable impervious subsoil and water supply for irrigation. The paddies, seldom larger than a fraction of an acre, are level and surrounded by dikes, for rice must grow most of its life standing in water. Other summer crops include corn, sweet potatoes, soy beans, sugar cane, sesame, and vegetables; cotton is grown in portions of the Yangtze Plain where the autumn is relatively dry. Following the harvest in late summer or early fall, the fields are planted to winter crops of wheat, barley, beans, or other hardy vegetables. This double cropping is practiced wherever physical conditions permit. When vegetables are grown, their shorter maturing period allows the production of several crops during the yearly cycle. Little land is unused; even the dikes surrounding the paddies are usually planted. Such intensity of production is possible only with heavy fertilization; all waste vegetative matter, animal and human excrement, ashes, and sediments from the canals are used to keep the growing capacity of the land high.

Little land can be spared for pasture or feed crops, and except for swine and chickens, which can live on household refuse, animals are scarce; even draft animals are limited to larger farms. For the same reason, commercial crops are limited—silk and tea are the only noteworthy commercial products of oriental agriculture. Sericulture, important for many centuries, is an admirable adaptation; the

FIGURE 8-25. *Transplanting rice in the Orient. The rice is germinated in seed beds to allow winter crops to mature and fields to be prepared as well as to give an early start to the new crop.* (Theodore Herman.)

FIGURE 8-26. *Rice harvest in the Orient. With a small hand sickle every stem of the rice is carefully cut and gathered into bundles for drying and threshing.* (G. Martin.)

FIGURE 8-27. *A Japanese farm village. House roofs are of thatch and tile. The thatch roofs are steep to shed the heavy rain. Drying racks for rice are in the right foreground. Deciduous trees are in the background.* (G. Martin.)

FIGURE 8-28. *Mending errors of man's careless use of the land. Reforestation is not only arresting erosion but is providing a crop for the future.* (Magnolia State Publishing Company.)

mulberry trees frequently occupy slope lands and the feeding of the leaf to the silkworms requires great amounts of careful, patient labor. Tea, similarly, is a slope-land crop utilizing areas that would otherwise be in natural vegetation.

United States South. One crop, cotton, has dominated agriculture in the United States South since Eli Whitney developed the cotton gin. The impact of a century and a half of "King Cotton" has reached into every phase of economic, political, and social life, and in general has tended to suppress other latent possibilities of the region. The cultivator's life has been one of poverty; although not as grinding as in the Orient, it has been in striking contrast to other agricultural regions of the nation where the farmers have enjoyed the highest standard of living of any agrarian people in the world. Farming practices of the past have tended to impoverish the land and, consequently, the people. Continuous production of cotton on slope lands has resulted in severe erosion and in diminishing fertility.

The benefits of agricultural research and education are being felt and something of a revolution is bringing great changes in Southern farming. A small army of county agricultural extension agents and soil conservation service workers are bringing the latest information to the farmers and are aiding them in organization and execution of proper farm management plans. The new patterns emerging are characterized by: reduction in cotton acreage, increases in acreage of other specialty crops, better seed, plant, and animal selection, mechanization, increases in pasture, forage, and feed crops, reduction in work stock and increases in commercial livestock, higher yields, greater attention to conservation farming, and some decrease in tenancy.[3]

Cotton is no longer "King" in the sense of 25 years ago. Acreage has been reduced nearly 50 per cent during this period and gross return amounts to but 25 per cent of the total farm income. This does not, however, present the accurate situation. Two factors must be noted: first, cotton acreage has decreased, but as the result of the use of improved strains, cultural practices, and fertilization, the total return from cotton is about as high as it was 25 years ago; second, and more important, land has been made available for production of other crops and livestock through this cotton acreage reduction and through the decrease in work stock numbers made possible by mechanization. The net result has been to continue a high level of cotton output and at the same time increase other farm enterprises, greatly expanding and diversifying the farming economy of the region.

Cotton has been concentrated into a number of well-defined areas where physical, economic, and cultural conditions are most favorable, but even in these areas cotton does not approach 50 per cent of the acreage. Other cash crops of significance include corn, peanuts, and soy beans. A number of localities favored by climate and soil have established vegetable and truck-crop production as specialties; the development of canning and quick-freezing industries has aided in expanding the marketing possibilities. Fruits are grown in some sections; the citrus of Florida and the peaches of the Carolinas and Georgia

[3] For an excellent discussion on this new agriculture see Prunty, Merle Jr., "Land Occupance in the Southeast, 'Landmarks and Forecast,' " *Geographical Review*, XLII, No. 3, 1952, 439-461.

FIGURE 8-29. *Mechanical cotton picker. Agriculture in the United States South is being mechanized and numerous "hands" are being released for more remunerative occupations.* (Mississippi Agricultural and Industrial Board.)

are notable. The major tobacco-producing districts of the United States lie along the northern margins of this region, with centers on the Piedmont and inner coastal plain of the Carolinas and Virginia and in the Nashville Basin of Tennessee. Tobacco is also produced in the states of Florida, Georgia, and Louisiana.

The livestock enterprises represent the most important additions to Southern agriculture. A number of factors have combined to promote the development, including (*1*) cotton acreage reduction, (*2*) incentive payments given farmers for conservation farming, such as legume production and the planting of permanent pasture on lands subject to erosion, (*3*) a greater use of hay-forage-cash crop rotations, and (*4*) improvements in cattle, with stockmen up-breeding their herds—many are cross-breeding with Brahman cattle to produce stock well-suited to the warm, humid environment. Cattle rearing appears to be firmly fixed and the advantages of year-around grazing, minimum needs for shelter, low production costs, and adaptation to the evolving farming systems point toward future growth. Development of urban markets is encouraging increases in dairying and poultry-raising. Both activities are now established and the possibilities of further expansion are good.

Clearly the United States South has taken on new importance as an agricultural region and there is little doubt that this portion of the country will assume an increasingly significant role in the economy of the nation.

South America. The South American Humid Subtropics are the outstanding Southern Hemisphere agricultural region. Crop production centers in the Argentine pampa where fertile soils, plain topography, climate, and a small population favor commercial agriculture. The large-scale operations characterized by land holdings averaging several thousand acres in size, mechanization, and extensive crops, contrast sharply with the paddy-garden agriculture of the Orient. Wheat, corn, and sunflowers and flax for seed are the leading commercial crops of the pampa, and most of the production enters the channels of world trade. Millions of acres of alfalfa are grown

FIGURE 8-30. *Mechanical cane cutter. About one-quarter of a million acres of land are devoted to sugar cane in the Mississippi delta. The cane in this picture will be used for planting stock. When planted, the bamboo-like stalks sprout new roots from each joint.* (Standard Oil Company of New Jersey.)

to feed local cattle. Crops are adjusted to rainfall. The corn and flax are concentrated in the more humid northern sector; alfalfa is produced in the same district but extends somewhat farther westward and southward; and the wheat zone forms a crescent extending 600 miles from Santa Fe in the north to the city of Bahia Blanca on the coast in the south.

Crop production is overshadowed by livestock-grazing in other portions of the South American region. In Uruguay, for example, less than ten per cent of the land is devoted to crops. Led by Argentina, attention is being given to improving the quality of livestock, both through breeding and pasture improvement. Today at least half of the fresh beef in world trade is produced in this region. Cattle dominate in most areas, except in Uruguay where sheep for wool are of outstanding importance.

Africa and Australia. Commercial agriculture in southeast Africa revolves around the production of sugar cane, pineapples, and other tropical fruits, citrus on the coastal lowlands, and cattle in the rougher inland districts. This region, which includes Zululand, has a large African Negro population and a considerable portion of the cultivated land is given over to raising food crops, mainly corn and kaffir corn.

Southeast Australia, though restricted by mountains and sea to a narrow lowland fringe, is one of the most important districts of the continent. Dairying and beef cattle production are the chief phases of agriculture and much of the land is devoted to pasture and forage crops. Sugar cane is a major cash crop in the northern district. The Brisbane area is the principal source of commercial tropical fruits. Oranges are grown in the vicinities of Newcastle and Sydney. Much of the land is still in extensive use.

U.S.S.R. The small Rion Valley region is more significant to the agricultural economy of the U.S.S.R. than its size would indicate. With the exception of the small Lenkoran lowland of Azerbaidzhan, this is the only area of the country where tea and citrus fruits, or industrial crops such as tung trees, geranium, camphor, ramie, and the like can be grown. Tea and citrus fruits cover the greatest acreage, but recently grape vineyards have expanded, as have areas devoted to tobacco, almonds, and corn. Sericulture is practiced in eastern margins.

FIGURE 8-31. *A citrus grove in central Florida. Thousands of acres are devoted to citrus production in this section of the state, where fertile limestone soils, sunshine, rain, and minimum frost danger allow the production of finest quality fruit.* (Florida State News Bureau.)

FIGURE 8-32. *Beef cattle grazing on planted pasture in Louisiana. This represents a new element in southern agriculture.* (United States Department of Agriculture Soil Conservation Service.)

FIGURE 8-33. *Acres of sunflowers on the Argentine pampa. Argentina rates second only to the U.S.S.R. in the production of this significant oil crop. Note the level expanse of this great Argentine plain.* (Pan American-Grace Airways.)

Fishing

Fishing activities are present in the offshore waters of all Humid Subtropic regions although the importance of the economy as well as the type of catch varies. Fish are especially important in oriental countries, where they form a significant item in the diet. The numerous sheltered coves in the indented China coastline south of Shanghai are clustered with small fishing vessels which supply local markets. Japan has an outstanding fishing industry and prior to World War II was credited with one-fourth of the world's commercial catch. Fish products at that time constituted the seventh largest export commodity. Sardine, cod, salmon, mackerel, and tuna, as well as crab, figure high in the export trade. Other varieties, many considered inedible by non-oriental standards, are con-

FIGURE 8-34. *The Tarpon Springs sponge fleet. The sponge industry is the chief source of livelihood for the Greek inhabitants of this small town on Florida's west coast. The sponge docks offer a sight that can be duplicated in no other place in the nation. The boats are of the same design as the boats used on the Sea of Galilee 2000 years ago.* (Florida State News Bureau.)

sumed locally and often eaten raw. Even seaweed is gathered for food, fodder, and fertilizer. Japanese fishermen, although restricted from certain waters, are rapidly regaining their pre-war standing. One and one-half million Japanese are engaged in fishing—approximately one-half are part-time farmers. Every Japanese village fronting the sea has some type of fishing activity. Japan could not support her millions without the bounty of the sea.

Much of the fishing industry of the United States South is concentrated in the Gulf of Mexico, with red snapper, pompano, grouper, and sheepshead making up much of the food species caught for market. Large catches of menhaden, seldom used for food, are taken for use in the manufacture of fish oil and meal. Several types of shellfish are harvested with a special emphasis on shrimp and oysters. Numerous fleets are employed in shrimp fishing; the Texas shrimp industry yields about seventy million pounds annually, leading all other states. Chesapeake Bay, at the northeast margin of the region, is the site of the major oyster fishery. Tarpon Springs on the west coast of Florida is the headquarters of the United States sponge fleet. This fishery has recently suffered a decline due to a sponge disease.

The three Southern Hemisphere regions all have small fishing fleets that provide seafoods mainly for local consumption. South Africa, however, is gaining favorable reputation for the high-quality lobster it is sending into world trade. Lack of markets in the Southern Hemisphere is the principal limitation to present expansion in all three regions.

Forest industries

Forest industries are a minor activity in the Orient. Fast-growing bamboo is used extensively as an Oriental substitute for lumber. Charcoal for fuel is an important Japanese forest product; its value exceeds that of lumber. The dwarf-like character of many Oriental trees makes them unsuitable for lumber. The Japanese follow an orderly plan of forest conservation, realizing that trees can be a crop on land unsuited to agriculture, as well as significant in preventing soil erosion and floods.

The United States South has many natural advantages for forestry. The southern pines grow rapidly in the warm, moist climate and can be harvested for pulp in about 20 years, although at this age lumber yields are low. Logging operations can be carried on all year, facilitated by relatively level terrain and lack of dense underbrush. The region also benefits from proximity to the large eastern United States market. Today it is the outstanding pine-producing area in the nation and is taking over leadership in the pulp industry. It produces approximately one-half of the world's naval stores—turpentine and resin distilled from the gum of longleaf and slash pines. Paints, soaps, and medicines are other products that use pine gum. The hardwoods are forming the basis for increasingly important veneer and furniture industries.

The Parana pine, an important lumber species of southern Brazil and Paraguay, is exploited for marketing in the large tributary urban centers, such as Buenos Aires and Montevideo. Yerba maté leaves are gathered in Paraguay and southern Brazil for making the popular South American tea. There are small forest operations in the Humid Subtropics of Africa and Australia. The forests of southern Queensland furnish raw lumber and materials for plywood and veneer; the eucalypti are important for structural timbers.

FIGURE 8-35. *Felling eucalyptus in Australia. The men using spring boards are cutting the tree 15 feet off the ground to avoid the more difficult cut near the butt. This tree is 145 feet high and about 12 feet through at the butt. The Australians have developed a long-range policy of regenerating forests as they are cut over; a 75-year cycle of planned cutting should assure perpetual timber supplies for the future.* (Australian News and Information Bureau.)

Mining

The mineral possibilities of China have not yet been fully determined. Large coal deposits are known to exist in the Red Basin, but transportation difficulties have limited mine production to supplying local needs. This same area is the country's most important salt producer. A few small iron deposits are worked along the Yangtze River; tin is mined in Yunnan Province of southwest China; and antimony and tungsten are extracted from the hills of south China.

Japan has a dearth of minerals; only in coal, copper, gold, and sulphur does she approach self-sufficiency and reserves of these are small. Northwestern Kyushu contains the leading producing coal fields of the southern part of this island nation. Most Japanese coal is of

FIGURE 8-36. *Laying an oil pipeline. This is an important means of transporting petroleum products to market from most of the oil fields of the world.* (Shell Oil Company.)

mediocre quality, poorly suited for metallurgical purposes.

The United States South is the outstanding mining region of the Humid Subtropics. Fuels are particularly important; the largest oil and gas province of the nation is situated in the western half, coking coal is found in eastern Oklahoma, and the Appalachian coal fields reach into north central Alabama. In addition, lignite and sub-bituminous deposits are numerous in Mississippi, Louisiana, and Texas, but exploitation is as yet minor. Notable iron reserves are being worked in the Birmingham District of Alabama, and virtually all of the domestic bauxite comes from Arkansas. The major sulphur production of the world is centered on the Gulf Coast of Texas and Louisiana. Most of the nation's phosphate rock comes from deposits in Florida and Tennessee. Two-thirds of America's kaolin is produced in Georgia.

The South American region is without important mineral deposits. The only production worthy of mention is that of petroleum in Argentina, but even here quantities are not sufficient to meet the nation's needs. The

FIGURE 8-37. *The coal and oil fields of the United States.*

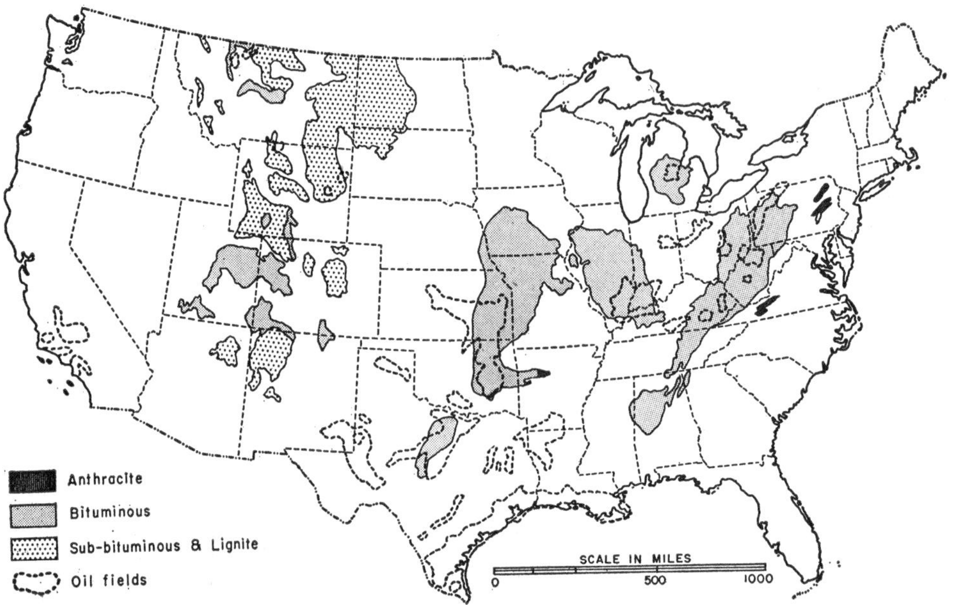

FIGURE 8-38. *Phosphate mining near Bartow. Eighty per cent of the nation's supply is mined within a few miles of this central Florida town.* (Florida State News Bureau.)

FIGURE 8-39. *Sulphur loading facilities at Port Sulphur, Louisiana.* (American Waterways Operators.)

African and Australian regions are both coal-producers. The African deposits extending from central Natal into Transvaal are the main source for that continent. The bulk of Australia's high-quality coal is produced in the Sidney-Newcastle area.

The Chiatura manganese deposits of Soviet Georgia are closely associated with the Rion Valley of the U.S.S.R. These deposits have been mined for 75 years and Chiatura is one of the major manganese-producing centers of the world. The mineral is shipped from the ports of Poti and Batumi on the Black Sea to other parts of the U.S.S.R. and the world.

Manufacturing

Japan, since the mid-nineteenth century, has become the industrial leader of the Orient, despite basic weaknesses. The "Island Empire" had limited resources but it had some coal, water for power, and a large docile labor supply, in addition to a strong will to succeed. Soon she branched into every type of industry. The country became a competitor for markets throughout the world and the "Made in Japan" label ran the gamut from expensive chinaware and efficient textile machinery to cheap ornaments and toys. Commerce was (and is) the life blood of the industrial economy—raw materials had to be imported and, due to the small buying power of the home market, finished goods had to be sold abroad. Thus Japan became a trader nation with Japanese ships moored in every major port of the world.

The disastrous effects of World War II crippled Japan's industry, alienated her foreign markets, and lost her territories furnishing raw materials. Furthermore, the growth of economic nationalism has restricted access to many of her former markets. The country is making a rapid recovery and the rich assets of experience and "know-how" should re-elevate Japan to a prominent position in the industrial world.

FIGURE 8-40. *All phases of the petroleum industry are found in the United States South. This large refinery is located on the Mississippi, where it is accessible to cheap water transportation.* (Corps of Engineers, U. S. Army.)

FIGURE 8-41. *Aluminum plant. Natural gas for generation of required electricity and ease of access to the Surinam bauxite deposits are the attractions for the industry here.* (American Waterways Operators.)

The Japanese industrial belt extends 800 miles from Tokyo to Nagasaki with major industrial nodes located in the Kwanto Plain, Nagoya, the Osaka-Kobe district, and on the coast of northern Kyushu. Industries include iron and steel, textiles, chemicals, tools, ceramics, rubber goods, petroleum products, and a host of articles for the variety store trade. All the manufacturing of Japan is not associated with large factories—actually small plants are the backbone of the nation's industry. Many commodities for local markets are produced in small workshops having usually less than four workers. Some export goods such as electrical equipment, bicycles, rubber footwear, and ceramics are also made in small plants.

Manufacturing in the Humid Subtropical region of China is concentrated in the Yangtze valley. Shanghai, on the Yangtze delta, is the silk and cotton textile center. A blast furnace is located near Hankow, the principal processing center of the upper plain. Cottage or workshop industries are typical for the manufacture of everyday needs and even some goods for the luxury trade, such as silks and lacquerware.

The traditional agrarian economy of the United States South has been disrupted and a combination of favorable ingredients has stimulated an industrial revolution. Mines, forests, fields, and the sea provide a diversity of raw materials. Coal, petroleum, natural gas, and water produce power. Labor and capital are available; markets are widespread, but easily reached by water and rail transport.

FIGURE 8-42. *A sidewalk shop in Tokyo. American tourists are attracted by the display of* geta, *the typical Japanese footwear.* (Pan American World Airways.)

Cheap land for factory sites, industrial water supplies, low taxes, low-cost plant heating, and other factors are added inducements.

The textile mills of the Piedmont lead the nation in the production of coarse and medium cotton goods. The Piedmont contains hosiery mills and furniture factories; tobacco manufacturing is concentrated on its northeast margin. The South is a leader in rayon; pulp and paper industries are significant; the region produces most of the kraft paper and has a start in newsprint production. Other industries include shipbuilding, petroleum refining, chemicals, cottonseed and food processing, and fertilizers. The iron and steel plants at Birmingham, Alabama, have the three basic requirements for smelting—iron ore, coking coal, and limestone—in juxtaposition. Industrial diversification is typified by the state of Texas, which has steel mills, light metal plants, aircraft manufacture, automobile assembly plants, and petrochemical industries, which use natural and refinery gases as raw materials to produce synthetic rubber and plastics.[4] The blast of the factory whistle has become a familiar sound in the South.

Manufacturing in the Humid Subtropics of the Southern Hemisphere is minor; these areas lack many of the industrial bases and are principally concerned with producing raw materials for processing in other countries. Industry in the South American area is chiefly associated with processing agricultural commodities such as wheat and meat for export, and textiles for local markets. The Natal Coast of Africa manufactures some consumer goods and also has a small iron and steel industry. The major manufacturing belt of Australia, as well as of the Southern Hemisphere Humid Subtropics, extends from Brisbane to Sydney with iron and steel plants at Newcastle, Port Kembla, and Lythgow. Food, shoes, textiles, and other goods are produced for home consumption.

Tourism

Tourism is an important activity of most Humid Subtropic regions. The Japanese resort beaches, wooded islands, mountains, especially Fuji, hot springs, and temples and shrines are frequented by thousands of visitors and vacationists. The coast areas in southeast United States draw hundreds of thousands of people each year, particularly from the heavily-populated regions of the Mid-West and East. Florida has become the recreation center of the South; its revenue from the tourist business exceeds one-half billion dollars yearly. In addition to genial winter climate, the region has many interesting cities, historical attractions, and features festivals, sports fishing, and athletic events to attract visitors. Leading tourist and recreational centers in the Southern Hemisphere include Durban in South Africa, the Uruguay

---

[4] See Arbingast, Stanley A., and Robert H. Ryan, "Diversified Resources Spark Economy," *Editor and Publisher*, LXXXVIII, Oct. 31, 1953, 157-164.

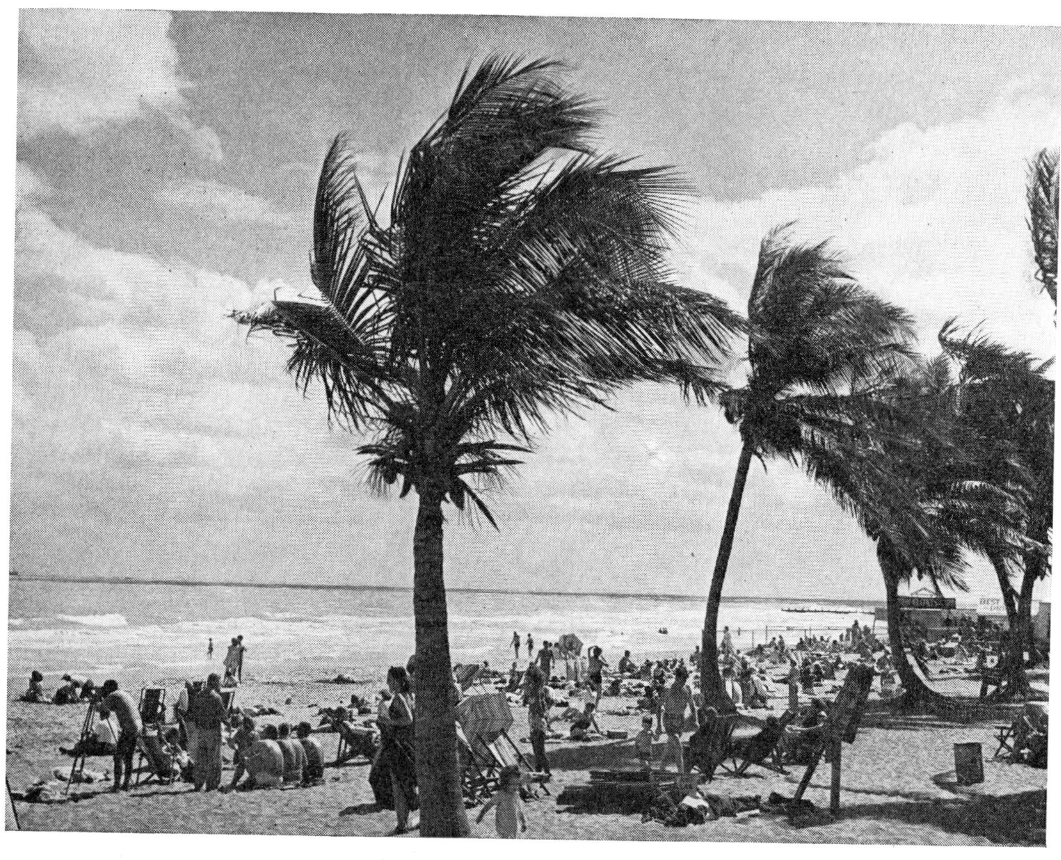

FIGURE 8-43. *Miami Beach, Florida's mecca for American sun-lovers.* (Florida State News Bureau.)

beaches near Montevideo, and the Australian coastal area from Brisbane to south of Sydney. Many popular health and seaside resorts of the U.S.S.R. are located along the Black Sea littoral.

Urban centers

Although primarily lands of rural populations, some of the largest cities of the world have also developed in the Humid Subtropic regions.

The Orient. The Yangtze Plain alone has a score of centers with over 100,000 population, at least a half-dozen of which exceed 500,000. The dominating city of the plain, and of China, is Shanghai, whose admirable situation on the delta of the Yangtze makes it the natural outlet for the richest region of the country; as a result it has become the leading commercial, industrial, and cultural center, with a population in excess of 5.4 million. Nanking, 200 miles to the northwest, has over one million population. The Wu-Han cities—Hankow, Wuchang, and Hangyang—630 miles from the sea, are in an excellent position to serve the upper portion of the plain. Their combined population is about 1.5 million. Others exceeding a half-million include Hangchow, Soochow, and Changsha. Chungking, about two million, and Chengtu, over 600,000, are the principal cities of the Red Basin. Each of the delta plains along the southeast coast tends to have one large, dominating city; the most important are Wenchow and Foochow.

The main concentration of cities in Japan is found in the thin belt extending from the Kwanto Plain to northern Kyushu. Here are

FIGURE 8-44. *Shanghai, the gateway to the Yangtze valley. Note the western influence in advertising displays. The "pedocab" is replacing the rickshaw in many of the Oriental cities.* (Pan American World Airways.)

centered the major activities of the nation, including agriculture, industry, and commerce. Within this belt there are four principal nodes of development; from east to west they are: Tokyo-Yokohama, Nagoya, Osaka-Kobe-Kyoto, and northern Kyushu. Tokyo is the largest city with about six million people. Yokohama, its ocean port, is approaching one million. Osaka, leading industrial center, has a population of nearly two million. Kyoto, a city of one million people, contrasts sharply with the modern industrial-commercial Osaka and Kobe. It was the imperial capital and is today the center of arts and crafts. Nagoya, of similar size, is a modern industrial city. There are no great metropolitan centers in the northern Kyushu industrial node comparable to those of the other areas. Fukuoka with over 300,000 is the largest, Yawata is the main steel center, and Moji and Nagasaki the main ports.

United States South. Recent industrialization and commercial development have had tremendous influence upon city growth in the United States South. As long as the region was dominantly agricultural with cotton the only major commercial crop, cities were small and few in number. During the past 15 years urban developments have been more rapid than in any other portions of the United States, and probably more rapid than in any other area in the world for a comparable period of time. Many cities have increased by 50 per cent and several have doubled in size; today 30 cities exceed 100,000. Houston, Texas, the largest city of the region, now surpasses 600,000, having grown from 292,000 in 1930. New Orleans, outlet of the Mississippi Valley and second city of the region, has a population of nearly 600,000. Dallas, Texas, about 450,000, has increased from 260,000 during the same interval. San Antonio, Texas, and Memphis, Tennessee, exceed 400,000, and five additional cities have populations over 250,000—these include, in order of size, Atlanta,

FIGURE 8-45. *New Orleans, the great river city of the United States South. This commercial center owes its importance to its situation near the mouth of the Mississippi, where it intercepts trade from the Mississippi Basin to the north and tropical products to the south.* (American Waterways Operators.)

Birmingham, Fort Worth, Miami, and Oklahoma City.

Southern Hemisphere. There are fewer urban centers in the Southern Hemisphere regions, but each has one or two large cities. Buenos Aires, on the Rio de la Plata estuary, has over three million people and is *the* great city of the Southern Hemisphere. A favorable situation, with a rich agricultural hinterland and land and water transportation, has stimulated it to become the major port, and the commercial, industrial, and governmental center of Argentina. Montevideo, with 850,000, dominates Uruguay even more completely, handling virtually all of the nation's commerce as well as serving as the federal capital. Rosario, Argentina, 200 miles upstream from Buenos Aires on the Parana River, is the third city of the region with over one-half million population.

Durban, about 475,000 population, is the only center of note in southeast Africa. Situated on a fine harbor and connected by rail to the interior, it is the principal port of the Union of South Africa. Sydney, with 1.6 million people, is the main city of Australia. It also has a splendid harbor, excellent rail facilities, and easy access to the great coal basin. Newcastle, emulating its English namesake, is the leading coal port and heavy industrial center of Australia.

OUTLOOK

Although similarities in the physical environments and the basic economies provide foundations for considering the Humid Subtropics together in this world study,

FIGURE 8-46. *The cities of Hampton Roads—Norfolk, Portsmouth, Newport News, and Hampton, Virginia. The sunken coast drowned the mouth of the James River, making Hampton Roads one of the finest harbors in the world.* (American Waterways Operators.)

it must be clearly understood that major differences exist between the individual regions in terms of human aspects of culture and standards of living.

The oriental way of life today is similar to that of centuries past. This, together with the press of an immense population, long a burden on the land, has hampered technological advances and kept the living standards near the bare margin of existence. The future of the Orient is restricted by these factors.

Everywhere man lives by using nature's resources; his material well-being is a function of population, technology, and the quantity and quality of resource endowments. This concept can be expressed in a formula in which resources, divided by population and modified by technology equals standard of living: $(R/P)^t = S.O.L.$

In the Orient, this balance is unfavorable. Moreover, recent wars and changes in political organizations in three oriental countries have placed both economic and social orders in a state of flux. The futures of these nations depend in part upon their abilities to emerge and move forward with concerted multiple approaches to their problems. Like the Monsoon Tropics, industrialization cannot solve all the problems in this region destined to be predominantly agrarian.

The United States South appears to have a bright future. Science and machines are being applied to a rich resource base and the region has emerged from a soil-robbing monoculture to a diversified economy. To be sure there are many problems—erosion, tenancy, race, and rural slums. The blight of the past will not be quickly erased from the landscape.

The South American region has achieved a high degree of development in commercial agriculture. Possibilities for diversification of the economy are limited by small mineral and resource endowments. The region could undoubtedly support closer settlement by intensification and diversification of agriculture, however, the absence of markets and large holdings presently discourage immediate consummation.

The relative potentials are good for further development in the Humid Subtropics of Africa and Australia. Although their areas are small, each has room for more people. Agriculture can be expanded and forests, fisheries, and minerals are present and future assets for more diversification.

SELECTED REFERENCES

Buchanan, Keith, and N. Hurwitz, "Land Use in Natal," *Economic Geography,* XXVII, No. 3, 1951, 222-237.

Cressey, George B., *Asia's Lands and Peoples.* New York: McGraw-Hill Book Company, 1951.

Fitzgerald, Walter, *Africa: A Social, Economic and Political Geography of its Major Regions,* New York: E. P. Dutton and Co., Inc., 1949.

Fitzgibbon, Russell H., "Uruguay's Agricultural Problems," *Economic Geography,* XXIX, No. 3, 1953, 251-266.

Jen, Mei-Ngo, "Agricultural Landscape of Southwestern China: A Study in Land Utilization," *Economic Geography,* XXIV, No. 3, 1948, 257-269.

Martin, Howard H., "Blueprint for the New Japan," *Education,* LXXII, No. 2, 1952, 394-404.

Parson, James J., "Recent Industrial Development in the Gulf South," *Geographical Review,* XL, No. 1, 1950, 67-83.

Prunty, Merle, Jr., "Recent Quantitative Changes in the Cotton Regions of the Southeastern States," *Economic Geography,* XXVII, No. 3, 1951, 189-208.

Shabad, Theodore, *Geography of the U.S.S.R., A Regional Survey.* New York: Columbia University Press, 1951.

Trewartha, Glenn T., *Japan: A Physical, Cultural, and Regional Geography.* Madison, Wis.: University of Wisconsin Press, 1947.

CHAPTER 9

Long Summer Humid Continentals

THE CONTINUOUS POLEWARD PROGress in these regional studies has finally eliminated the tropical modifier. Continentality, denoting land control with high temperature ranges and marked seasonal differences, now assumes a foreground position. Furthermore, the book of climate now contains more varied chapters—only the summer section has tropical reminiscences.

The Long Summer Humid Continental regions encompass extensive areas of choice agricultural land. Everywhere the farmer is a potent force in the economic life. Grains govern the crop patterns, but remarkable differences in methods and standards are present from region to region. The farmers of the agricultural interior of the United States have the highest living standards—com-

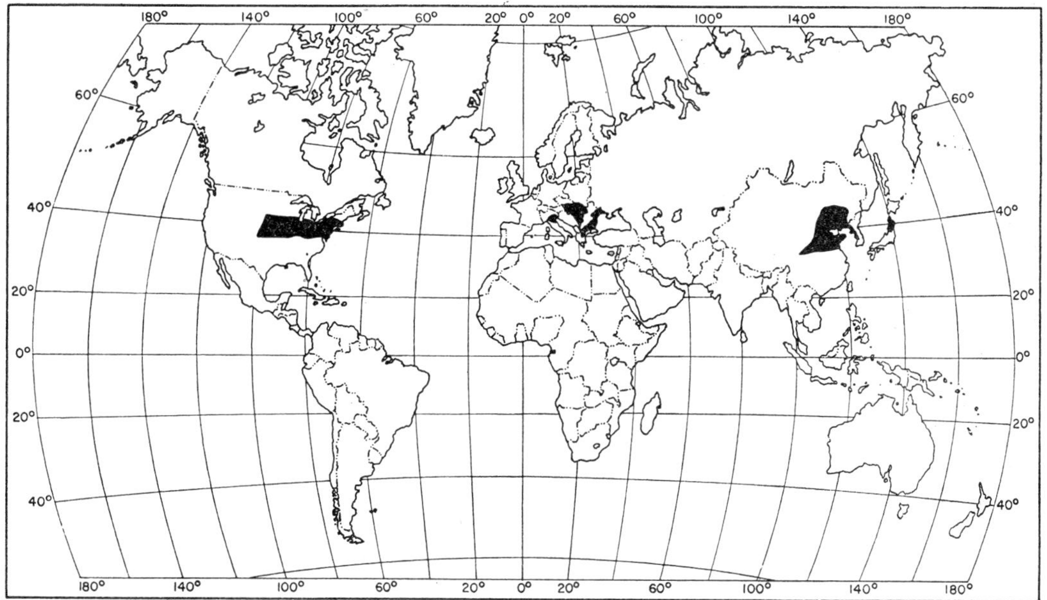

FIGURE 9-1. *The Long Summer Humid Continentals.*

mercial farming is the rule. The state controls the destinies of the peasant in the U.S.S.R., while the usual oriental practices and objectives persist in the Far East.

Agriculture is "big business" in the United States; however, an abundance of raw materials, energy resources, skilled labor, transportation, and markets have established a firm base for industry. The world's greatest industrial concentration, the American Manufacturing Belt, lies almost wholly within the region. Factories, employing workers by the thousands, produce nearly every conceivable manufactured article.

Location

Long Summer Humid Continental regions occupy interior and eastern margin locations in the Northern Hemisphere continents poleward of the subtropics and extending to about latitude 45° N. The

FIGURE 9-2. *The Long Summer Humid Continentals of the United States.*

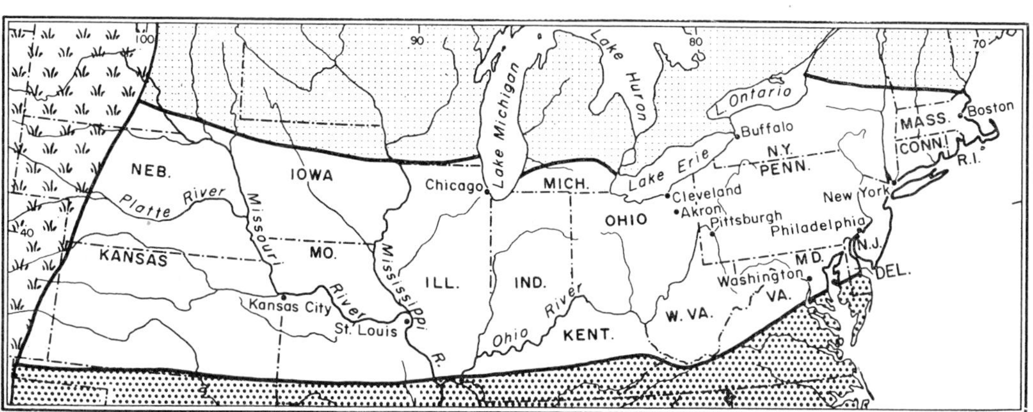

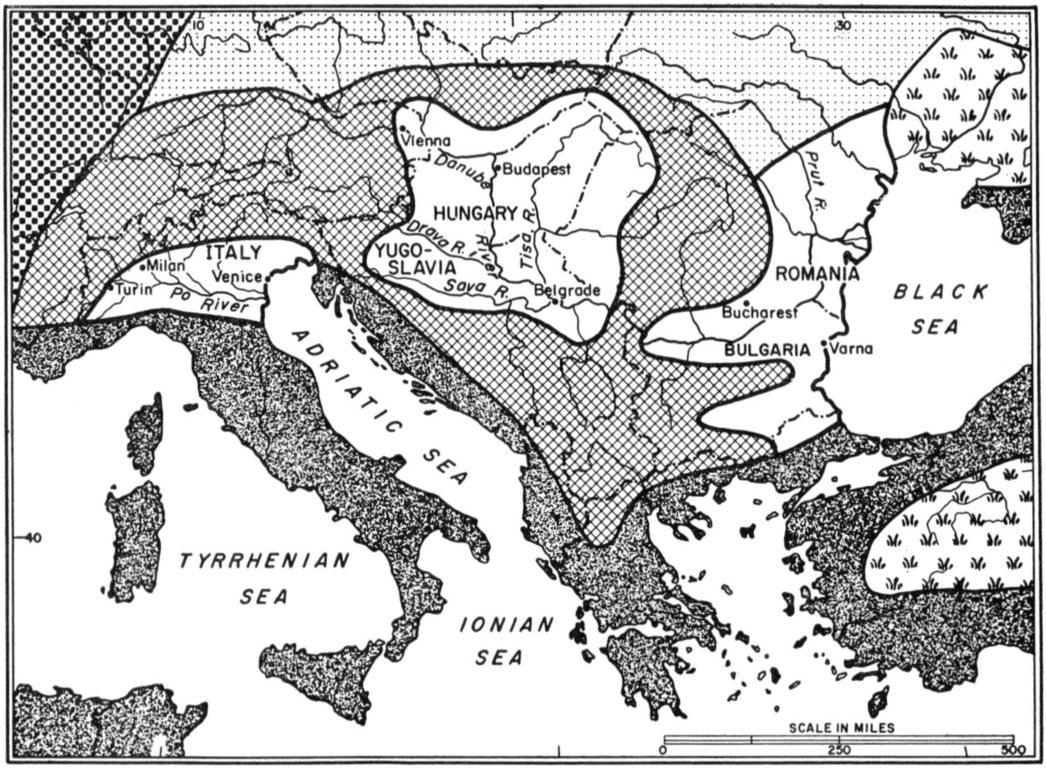

FIGURE 9-3. *The Long Summer Humid Continentals of Europe.*

FIGURE 9-4. *The Long Summer Humid Continentals of Asia.*

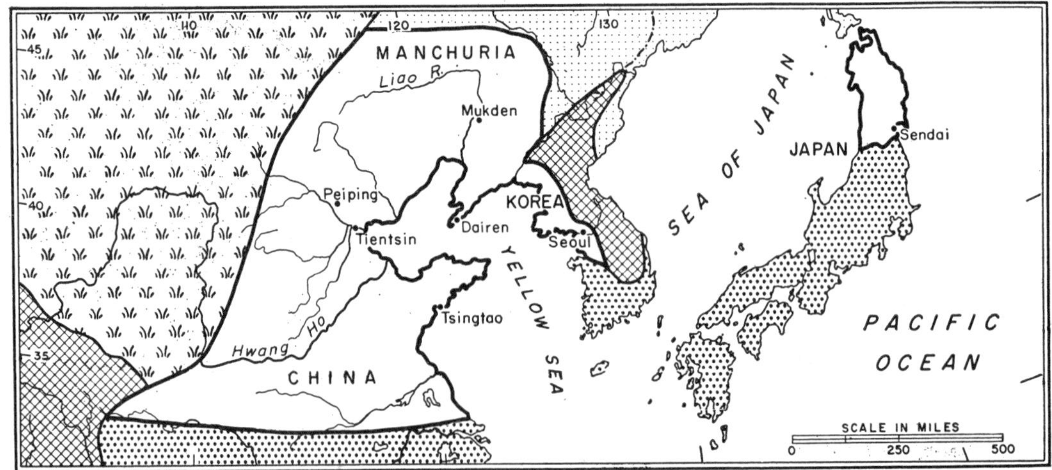

interior borders are marked by the 20 inch *isohyets,* or lines connecting points of equal rainfall, and the northern and southern borders are formed respectively by the 150- and 200-day average frost-free season lines. Long Summer Humid Continental regions occur only in North America, Europe, and Asia.

The North American region includes the tier of states extending from central Nebraska and Kansas on the west to the Atlantic coast. The European region, interrupted by mountains and seas, includes the Po Plain of Italy, the Danube Basin of Yugoslavia, Hungary, Bulgaria, and Romania, and the western portion of Ukraine in the Soviet Union. The Asian region consists of northeast China, southern Manchuria, northwest Korea, and northern Honshu.

PHYSICAL ENVIRONMENT

Climate

Cold winters are a distinctive feature of all humid continental climates—a season that distinguishes them from the tropical and subtropical regions. Annual range of temperature is large since the summer heat resembles that of the Rainy Tropics. The year is divided into four clearly marked seasons. Daily weather is highly variable and seasons differ considerably from year to year.

Cyclones and fronts. Variability is due chiefly to the position of the humid continental regions in the middle latitudes, which are the scenes of conflict between polar and tropical air masses. The boundary zone between these contrasting air masses is known as the polar front, and represents the meeting place of cold air from the poles and the warmer air masses of the westerlies. Along this zone of contact, waves are formed that develop into great eastward-moving eddies of air. Air whirls converging into a low-pressure center are known as cyclones or "lows." Anticyclones or "highs" develop when polar air dominates and winds blow out from the high pressure center. "Highs" bring cold, clear weather in winter or hot, dry conditions in summer, whereas "lows" are responsible for warm, cloudy, wet weather. Sizes of cyclones and anticyclones vary, but usually cover thousands of square miles. The storms move in a general eastward direction across North America and Eurasia at speeds between 20 and 30 miles per hour. A winter journey of a "low" across the United States takes from three to five days. Cyclonic activity is most prevalent in winter when the sun is in the opposite hemisphere and the polar front has moved south into the middle latitudes.

When air masses of different temperatures, pressures, and moisture contents meet they do not usually mix, but set up boundaries, or zones of discontinuity called fronts. Usually the boundary moves along the surface of the earth as one air mass moves and another replaces it. If colder air is replacing warmer air, the result is termed a cold front; if warmer air replaces colder air, it is termed a warm front (study Figure 9-5). No two fronts are alike in all details, but major characteristics of cold fronts or warm fronts are sufficiently similar for helpful generalizations. When cold air advances, friction retards the movement of the surface air but does not interfere with the cold air aloft. It advances with a steep or blunt front (the cold front), displacing the warmer air ahead and forcing it to rise quickly, often causing violent precipitation and sudden change in wind direction. The activity is concentrated in a rather narrow belt, 50 to 100 miles in width (called a "squall line") but extending hundreds of miles in length, usually in a northeast-southwest direction. The cold front moves at the rate of 20 to 35 miles an hour. After the passing of a cold front the weather is clear and the air, cooler and drier.

When a warm front advances the warm humid air rises gently up over the wedge of colder air lying ahead of it. In the lifting process its temperatures are lowered, condensation occurs, low clouds form, and drizzles begin. As the warm air continues up the slope, widespread rain develops and the cloud cover becomes more complete, with high clouds extending as much as 500 miles in advance of the actual front. Warm fronts generally move more slowly than cold fronts; consequently, warm fronts are frequently overtaken by cold fronts.

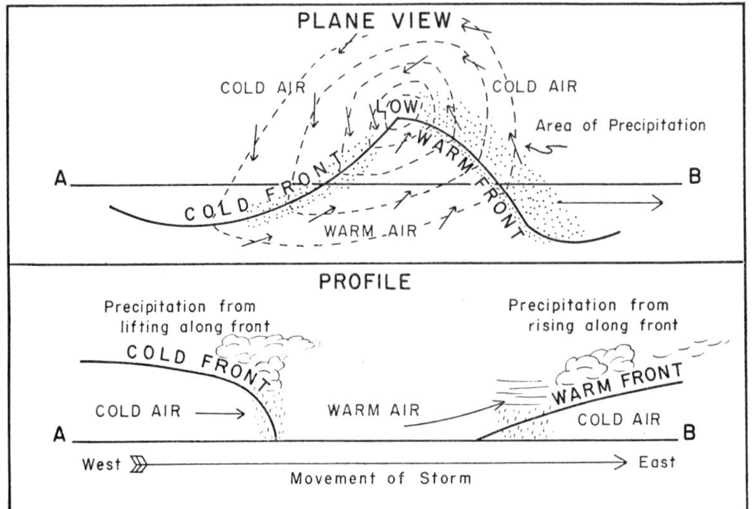

FIGURE 9-5. *The cyclonic storm.*

Temperatures. Summer temperatures are high. July averages about 75° with daily maxima exceeding those of the Rainy Tropics. Summer days are sultry and there is little relief from the heat at night. Winters are cold, with January averaging about 25°. Occasional cold waves send thermometer readings to zero and below. Location affects winter temperatures; stations deep in the interior or poleward are subject to colder winters than those located on coasts or equatorward margins.

In North America, the Great Lakes have an influence on temperatures. Cold air passing over the water bodies is tempered by the stored heat which retards fall frosts on the eastern lake shores. The spring season is also late since the cold lake waters chill the eastward-moving warm air. Annual ranges for the region are about 50°. Growing seasons range from 150 days poleward to 200 days on the southern margin.

Precipitation. Precipitation occurs throughout the year with the maximum usually in the summer season. Summer rains result from numerous convectional storms and are frequently associated with thunder and lightning.

FIGURE 9-6. *Typical climatic graphs of Long Summer Humid Continental stations.*

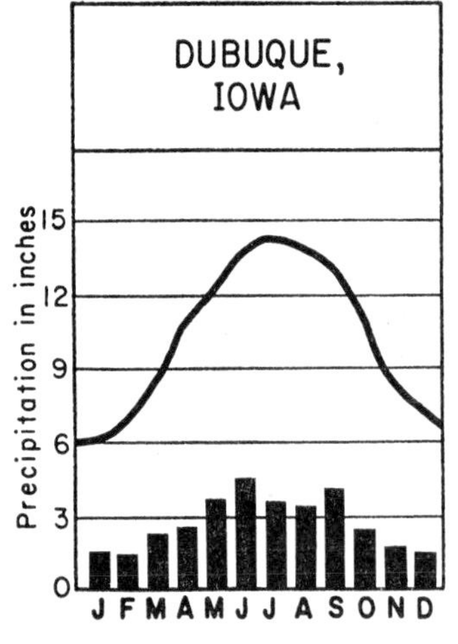

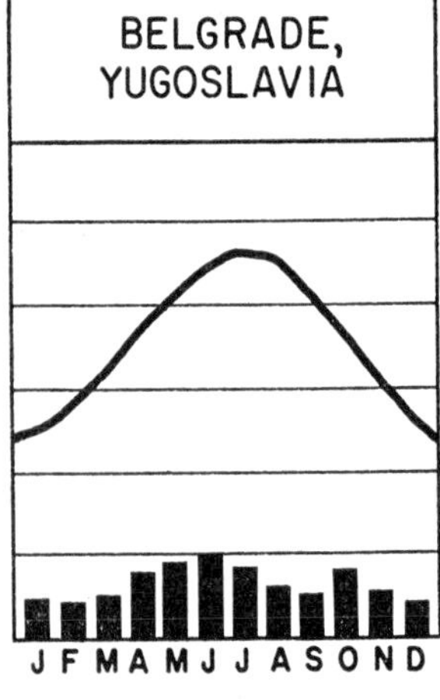

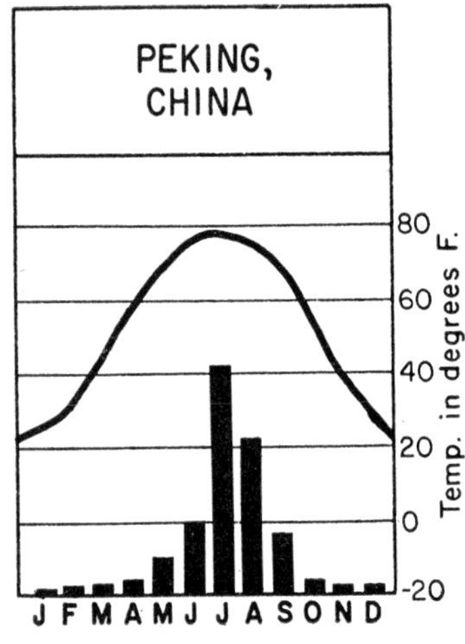

Winter precipitation is frontal (cyclonic), frequently in the form of snow although part falls as a cold, disagreeable rain.

Total annual precipitation varies greatly in these regions. In North America the eastern portion receives 35 to 45 inches. Amounts decrease westward, with 20 inches marking the sub-humid limits of the region in the west. The Danube Basin and much of North China average less than 30 inches a year. Fluctuations from year to year are considerable. Snow falls 20 to 30 days a year and amounts vary from about 10 inches on southern margins to as much as 40 inches in the north. Snow cover persists from a few weeks to several months and the visible evidence thus gives the impression that winter precipitation is greater than summer, but from 5 to 15 inches of snow are required to melt down to one inch of water. A snow cover prevents deep freezing of the earth, acting as a blanket, keeping the heat in and the cold out.

Tornadoes develop during the spring and summer in the Mississippi Valley—the states of Kansas and Iowa average 14 to 16 a year. Great loss of property and life often result from these violent storms.

Surface features

A large per cent of the land is of low relief. Plains are the most distinctive features of every region; but there is considerable diversity of surface and in no case are highlands lacking.

United States. The largest and most important plain occurs in the United States. Here the physiographic province known as the Interior Lowlands occupies the western two-thirds of the region; the Appalachian Highlands separate these lowlands from the narrow Middle Atlantic Coastal Plain. On the south, smooth terrain merges into hilly country such as the Ozark Plateau, but the smooth to gently-rolling surface continues westward through

FIGURE 9-7. *Tornado. Notice that the tornado hangs from the large cumulo-nimbus cloud like a funnel. The movements of the funnel are erratic—rising, falling, turning, and swinging in various directions. When the end of the funnel touches the earth, there is near-complete destruction.* (United States Weather Bureau.)

FIGURE 9-8. *A cross-section of the United States region.*

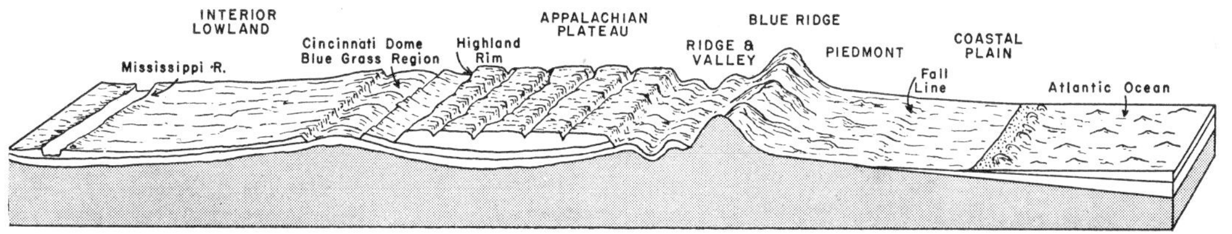

FIGURE 9-9. *The plains of Kansas. This view shows the slightly undulating topography of the western portion of the United States region. The fields have been terraced and contour listed in the fall. The snow collected in the furrows has melted and the water is staying on the contours, gradually to soak into the ground and build up reserve moisture for next summer's crop.* (United States Department of Agriculture Soil Conservation Service.)

the Great Plains. The Corn Belt, which extends from eastern Nebraska and northeastern Kansas to central Ohio, is topographically one of the finest agricultural lands in the world. It owes at least part of its uniformity to favorable glaciation during the Pleistocene Period. The ice sheets invaded most of the area several times, smoothing off the hillocks and filling in low sections.

Three broad divisions of the Appalachians are recognized: the dissected plateau on the west, a series of linear ridges and valleys in the center, and the higher Blue Ridge and Great Smoky Mountains on the east. The most significant area of lowland in the Appalachians is the Great Valley, extending from the Hudson Valley to the Tennessee Valley.

Europe. Mountains divide the European region into three distinct lowlands: the Po Plain, the Danube Basin, and the Lower Danube Lowland, including southwestern Ukraine. The Po Plain of northern Italy, formerly an extension of the Adriatic Sea, was created by sediments deposited by streams from the Alps and Apennine Mountains, and even today is being pushed seaward at a rapid rate.

Eastward from Austria, the ranges of the Alpine Mountains divide; the Carpathians, or northern branch, swing to the east then south in a broad arc to the Danube River; the southern branch extends through Yugoslavia and southern Bulgaria. The Danube Basin is thus encircled (see Figure 9-11).

Asia. Two lowlands—the North China or Yellow Plain and the southern half of the Manchurian Plain—form the core of the Asian region. The former is the largest plain and one of the most clearly defined regions of China, with highlands or sea borders everywhere but on the southeast, where it merges into the Yangtze Plain. Like the Po Plain, it has been built by river deposition, largely by the Hwang Ho or Yellow River. The same floods which originally built this lowland are now major problems. The Hwang Ho flows through vast stretches of dry land and enters upon the plain with a large load of sediments; reduced gradient and velocity diminish the carrying power of the stream and it deposits silt, raising its bed in places above the level of the plain. Natural levees keep the river within its channel except during flood-seasons. To minimize danger of inundation of fertile farmland, the Chinese have built retaining dikes, but even these are periodically breached, allowing flood waters to devastate broad areas. In contrast to this large depositional plain, the Manchurian Plain, featuring rolling topography and extensive terraces, was formed largely by erosion. Here the Liao River and its tributaries have worn down the land.

In addition to these plains, the Asian region includes: the Shantung Peninsula of North China, which is about equally divided between plains and uplands; the southern portion of the east Manchurian uplands; northwestern Korea, which is mainly hilly but has small river plains near the coast; and northern Honshu, which is largely mountainous with small alluvial coastal plains.

FIGURE 9-10. *Farmland on the west edge of the Appalachian Plateau. Here the land is more rolling and strip cropping is practiced to prevent erosion.* (United States Department of Agriculture Soil Conservation Service.)

FIGURE 9-11. *A physiographic diagram of south central Europe.*

FIGURE 9-12. *A virgin stand of yellow poplar and white oak.* (United States Forest Service.)

Natural vegetation

Hardwood forests consisting of maple, oak, chestnut, hickory, and other deciduous species characterized the original cover in the more humid areas of the United States region, which at one time contained the finest stand of hardwoods in the world. Farms have replaced the forests and only a few remnants appear in woodlots and on the more rugged slope lands. Conifers grow on the sandy coastal areas or in the cooler and higher elevations. On the sub-humid margins forests are replaced by grasses. Prairie grasses once carpeted the western portions, but much of the prairie land has now been turned under by the plow. Fields of grain cover these former grazing lands.

The Italian region has no forest cover on the floor of the plains, but conifers ascend the higher alpine slopes. Stately rows of Lombardy poplars have been planted along roads in the main part of the valley. Meadowland is common in the central portion of the plain and marshes fringe the low coastline. The Danube Basin, chiefly in the western part, has dense forests on many of its surrounding slopes and often on the hills that rise from the basin floor. Deciduous species, usually beech, are found on the lower slopes, replaced at higher levels by conifers. Marshes are characteristic in the poorly-drained areas, especially on the delta of the Danube. The boundary between forest and grass in the Danube Basin appears in eastern Romania, where trees disappear and short grass steppe vegetation becomes dominant and continues into the Ukraine.

The quest for cropland and the need for building materials and fuel have consumed almost the entire forest cover of North China. Even the hills are bare. In some areas the land has been tilled for so many centuries that there is now some doubt as to the original nature of the vegetation. The only trees are found along roads and surrounding farmsteads, where poplars and willows have often been planted. Short grass vegetation is the dominant natural cover in the more arid west. The Manchurian area, more recently settled, still contains forests on the mountain slopes. Deciduous species grow near the margin of the plain and are replaced by conifers at higher elevations. Similar forests were characteristic of the Korean area, but most accessible forests have been removed. The forest cover on the lower slopes of northern Honshu consists of broadleaf deciduous species, distinctive from the broadleaf evergreens in the warmer southern part of the island. Conifers replace birch, beech, poplars, and other hardwoods in the colder, higher elevations.

FIGURE 9-13. *A late fall scene in a hardwood forest of the United States. The animal is a white-tailed deer.* (Fish and Wildlife Service: Peter J. Van Huizen.)

Soils

The soils are generally more fertile than those of the Humid Subtropics, resulting from less precipitation, grass vegetation, and lower temperatures, with the soil often frozen during winter. Leaching is less intense and of shorter duration; organic content is usually higher. Three principal soil groups are recognized.

The *chernozems* occupy the drier margins in the United States, eastern Romania, and Ukraine. This rich black soil has been subjected to only slight weathering and leaching and is therefore high in mineral nutrients. The tall grass vegetation contributes an abundance of organic matter as a result of the death and decay of roots, stems, and leaves. The main limitation for these inherently productive soils is the relatively low rainfall which restricts crops to grass and small grain types.

Prairie soils have developed in the grasslands of higher precipitation that border the chernozems. They are only moderately leached, dark in color, and rich in organic matter. They are excellent agricultural soils and form the heart of the American Corn Belt. Even though slightly lower in native fertility, they are more adaptable than the chernozems, due to higher rainfall they receive.

Gray-brown soils predominate in the more humid portions of the regions. Developing under heavier rainfall and deciduous forest vegetation, they contain somewhat fewer plant nutrients than the other groups. The rain causes greater leaching and the forests contribute less organic matter. However, they are easily cultivated, respond to fertilization, and with good management are highly productive.

Special attention should be given to the soils of North China or the Yellow Plain. Much of this alluvial lowland, as well as the hills to the west, is mantled with wind-blown material, called *loess,* that has been carried by the strong winter monsoon winds from the dry lands of the interior. The admixture of loess and alluvium produces a highly productive soil. Its characteristic yellow color is the basis for the names Yellow Plain, Yellow River, and Yellow Sea.

FIGURE 9-14. *Firewood being hauled along a Peking street. China is still in a man-power stage.* (Theodore Herman.)

MAN IN THE LONG SUMMER HUMID CONTINENTALS

The Long Summer Humid Continental regions rate high as a home for man. Farming, mining, industry, and related commercial activity, in varied combinations, form a broad base for supporting large populations. The United States region, with its many great cities and diversity of activities, is the most densely-populated portion of the nation. In Europe, the Po Plain contains about 40 per cent of the Italian people; the Danube Basin is the economic heart of the countries it comprises; and Ukraine is part of the more densely settled section of the U.S.S.R. Although the Asian portion is overshadowed by the Humid Subtropics to the south, it nevertheless is populated to near its agricultural capacity and has the greatest numbers of all these regions.

Cultures differ markedly; there is especially great contrast between the North American and Asian regions. The former has a science and machine civilization, epitomized by a highly-developed commercial agriculture, with farm families having high standards of living and education, and by the most important and advanced industrial concentrations in the world. The region is spanned east-west and north-south by the most dense transportation net in the world. The average American thinks nothing of travelling many miles to work or play. Subsistence farming typifies activity in the Orient, buying power is small, needs and wants are few, and methods are largely those of centuries past. The Asians are still in a man-power stage. Only Japan and the Manchurian Plain approach adequate transportation facilities; most of China cannot be reached by either rail or all-weather roads. Lack of modern transportation is a major economic and political weakness in China today.

Agriculture

From the standpoint of numbers of people involved, agriculture is the leading activity. The farming scene differs materially from one region to another, and even between portions of the same region. In general, grains tend to dominate but the emphasis differs and other crops, as well as livestock, are often significant. The greatest contrasts are in the techniques and tools for production and in the sizes of farms.

United States. Commercial agriculture characterizes the United States region. On the basis of dominant farm enterprises and systems, it is common to recognize the several agricultural regions shown in Figure 9-15 (*below*). All of the Corn Belt, the eastern half of the Winter Wheat Region, the northern fringes of the Corn and Winter Wheat Belts and the Middle Atlantic Truck-Cropping Region, and a portion of the Hay and Dairy Region are included in the Long Summer Humid Continental Region. This diversity in agriculture results in part from differences in the details of surface, soil, and climate, and in part from market possibilities.

Corn Belt farming is one of the most distinctive in the world. Smooth to rolling topography, excellent soil, and a warm, moist growing season, in combination with a progressive farm population, have led to the development of a high order of agriculture in which science and machinery play major roles. A high percentage of the farms are owner-operated. They average about 160 acres, and both farms and fields are generally rectangular in pattern. Feed and forage plants dominate the crops, with corn the leader. Oats, even with the decrease in workstock, is still important, fitting well into the farming scheme—planting comes earlier than corn in the spring and value is also derived from its service as a nurse-crop for hay. The importance of the soy bean, a cash and feed crop, has increased greatly in recent years. To maintain soil fertility, farmers are employing a rotation scheme which commonly involves: plantings of corn the first year, a small grain the second, and a legume or grass the third. On the richest

FIGURE 9-15. *Agricultural regions of the United States.* (After material from the Bureau of Agricultural Economics, United States Department of Agriculture.)

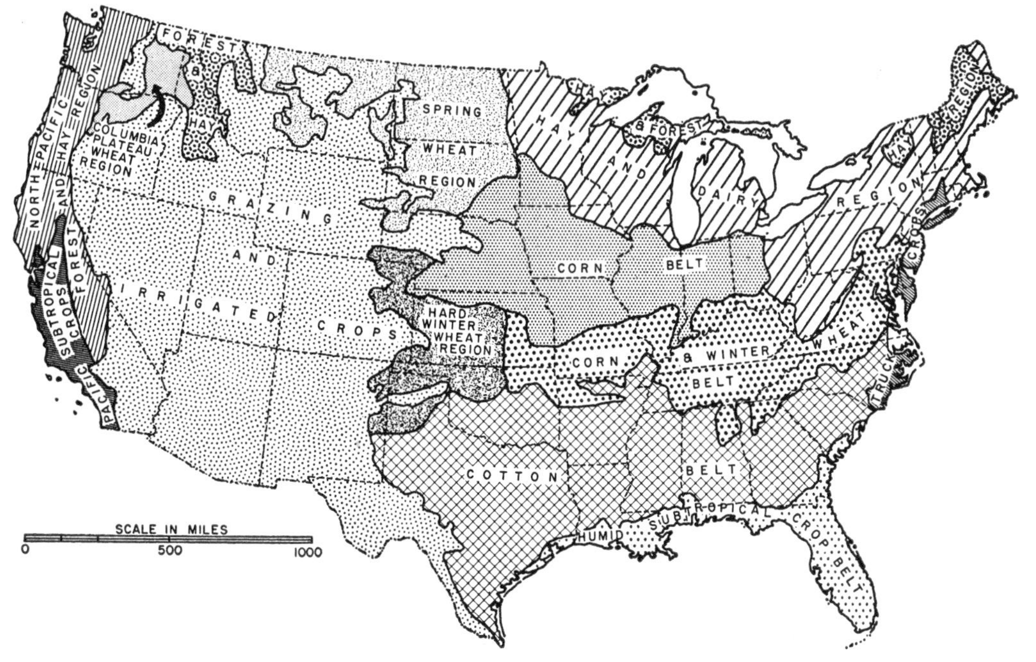

FIGURE 9-16. *Mechanical corn picker in Illinois. Farming operations in the United States Corn Belt are highly mechanized.* (Standard Oil Company of New Jersey.)

land, a five-year rotation is often followed: first year, corn; second year, corn; third year, soy beans or oats; fourth year, winter wheat; fifth year, clover or alfalfa. Hogs and beef cattle are kept on most farms, and animal-fattening is an essential part of the farmer's program, with most of the corn and oats and all of the hay being fed. Sale of animals returns about three-fourths of the farm income.

Southwest of the Corn Belt, lesser precipitation has encouraged the widespread production of winter wheat. Farms are larger, ranging from a half-section in the east to a section or more in the west. Operations are completely mechanized. Grain sorghums are frequently raised in rotation with wheat. Beef-cattle grazing is also important.

The Corn and Winter Wheat Belt, often termed the "middle country," is a transitional zone with elements of both southern and northern farming common. More rugged topography restricts arable land to about one-third of the area. Corn and winter wheat, of course, are the leading enterprises, but specialty crops are significant in certain well-defined districts. The Lexington or Bluegrass Basin of Kentucky is a leading tobacco center, ranking second in output only to the Virginia-Carolina area mentioned in the Humid Subtropics. Fruits and vegetables are local specialties in many areas, and for the region as a whole, animal industries return at least 50 per cent of the farm income.

The Middle Atlantic Truck-Cropping Region is confined between the Piedmont and the Atlantic Ocean. The land is level to gently rolling and is usually under 100 feet in elevation. Wheat, corn, and hay are grown on a large part of the land under cultivation, but vegetable production is more important. This region is one of the world's foremost producers of commercial vegetables, even though these crops occupy but a fraction of the area. The mild, marine-modified climate with a long growing season is suited to many varieties, including sweet potatoes, sweet corn, cucumbers, cabbage, peas, tomatoes, spinach, and so forth. Two, three or even four crops can be grown yearly on the same land. As soon as a harvest is completed, the land is worked, fertilized, and a new crop is planted. Under such intensive production, farms are small in contrast to other portions of the United States region. The Middle Atlantic Truck-Cropping Region benefits from good transportation and proximity to large city markets. In recent years canning and freezing have developed extensively.

The southern part of the Hay and Dairy Region extends into the Appalachian Uplands. A high per cent of land in slope, poor soils, and cool, moist climate discourage widespread crop agriculture here, but favor the growth of good quality grass for pasture and hay. These factors, plus the nearby city markets, have stimulated the development of dairying. In the more isolated sections of this region and in the adjoining parts of the Corn and Winter Wheat Belt, agriculture is backward—probably the most backward in this nation. Corn, grown on surprisingly steep slopes, and livestock have been the mainstays in the farmer's subsistence economy. Conditions, except for rising populations and depletion of soils, remained little changed from the time of settlement shortly after the American Revolution until recent years, when improved transportation eased contact with the outside. This has made possible the development of coal, timber, and recreation resources, and has allowed

FIGURE 9-17. *Self-propelled combines operating in the Winter Wheat Belt. Machines such as these have cut down the man hours required for wheat production in this region from 50 hours per acre 100 years ago to less than two today.* (Standard Oil Company of New Jersey.)

FIGURE 9-18. *Dusting cabbage on the eastern shore of Maryland* (Standard Oil Company of New Jersey.)

these isolated people to observe a more modern way of life. The Finger Lakes District, south of Lake Ontario, on the northern margin of the Appalachian Plateau, is also distinctive. In addition to dairying, the truck-farming activity here is comparable to that of the Middle Atlantic Coastal Plain. Grapes and fruit production are also important.

Europe. Grains dominate in the European region, although contrasts are found in cropping systems and crop associations. The Po Plain, the principal agricultural area of Italy, is of particular interest because wheat, corn, and rice, the world's principal grain crops, are all grown in significant quantities. Hemp, flax, and sugar beets are notable and many mediterranean-type crops were introduced long ago; there is wide distribution of vegetable gardens and vineyards, the latter found especially on sunny slopes. The sericulture industry of Italy is centered in the alpine valleys on the northern margin of the plain. In the areas of poor drainage or on uncultivatable hillsides, cattle raising, and particularly dairying, has developed.

The countries of the Danube lowlands are primarily agricultural. Wheat is the leading crop; corn is usually a poor second, except in Romania. Barley and oats are important and in some sections sugar beets, grapes, and tobacco are noteworthy. Cattle are found on most farms; sheep are numerous on the steppe. Since World War II the Danubian countries have become Soviet satellites and farming systems are being patterned after those now practiced in the Soviet Union.

Wheat has long been the crop of the Ukraine. Agriculture has been revolutionized since the communist regime took control. Two types of farms are now found in the Soviet Union, the collective farms formed by the amalgamation of former peasant holdings into large operating units, and the state farms organized from former estates or in virgin areas where agriculture had not been practiced. Machine and tractor stations are distributed through the agricultural areas to conveniently serve a number of farms; by scheduling the use of farm machinery, great advances have been made with a minimum of equipment.

Asia. The small-scale, intensive, hand-labor farming of the Asian region contrasts sharply with the large-scale, mechanized farming of the United States. Farms on the North China Plain average five acres and must support an average of six persons. Soil is fertile and productive, but relatively low and unreliable rainfall restricts the production of the heavy-yielding rice to the few areas where irrigation is possible. Moreover, two crops in one growing season can be produced only in the southern part. Wheat, more suitable to subhumid conditions, is the distinctive crop, but is not as dominant as rice in South China. Millet, corn, and the grain sorghum *kaoliang,* are widespread. Soy beans and many vegetables are grown throughout, adding variety to family diet and distributing the use of labor. Only on the Manchurian Plain is there surplus for export. Northern Honshu merits special mention—it is a transitional zone between the agriculture of traditional Japan,

FIGURE 9-19. *A view across the Connecticut Valley. This is a significant tobacco-producing area—the long buildings are tobacco barns.* (Standard Oil Company of New Jersey.)

where farming is set along subtropical lines, and that of Hokkaido or frontier Japan, which is more recently established and has many characteristics reminding one of Europe and North America. In northern Honshu farms are somewhat larger than in the south, averaging 3.5 to 4 acres; rice is still a major crop but, owing to severe weather, the fields lie fallow in the winters. Many northern boundaries of subtropical crops are reached here. Sweet potatoes and tea are grown only in the southern margins; latitude 38° N marks the northern limits of bamboo, and 39° or 40° N, the extent of significant sericulture. Other crops are added to the farming pattern, including apples, white potatoes, millet, and buckwheat.

Fishing

The waters off the Atlantic Coast offer a transition between fish species occupying warmer sea waters to the south and those inhabiting the colder waters of the North Atlantic. The fishing industry of the United States region, therefore, has characteristics similar to both areas. Shellfish, chiefly oysters and clams, are important seafoods harvested in the sheltered coastal bays. Large numbers of menhaden are netted and processed into fertilizer for the truck-farmers on the sandy coastal plain and elsewhere. A variety of species such as herring, shad, and mackerel are a part of the commercial catch for the fresh-fish markets. Inland fisheries are found in the rivers of the Mississippi Valley, where catfish, carp, and buffalo fish comprise much of the commercial catch. The fisheries associated with the Great Lakes will be discussed in the following chapter.

Fishing in the European region is confined chiefly to the coastal waters of the Black Sea and the lower courses of the Danube and Dnieper Rivers. Several species of fish, including herring, salmon, carp, and perch, are caught, but the most valuable is the sturgeon, prized for its roe—caviar in the luxury trade.

Some fishing is practiced in the waters of the Yellow Sea, but the activity is far less important than in the waters south of Shanghai. The coastline south of Shanghai is indented with small harbors, whereas the coast to the north is more regular and provides less protection for small fishing boats. The inhabitants of North China have looked more to the land than to the sea for their food. Northern Honshu lies near the boundary between north and south Japanese fisheries, and species from both grounds are harvested. Many small Japanese fishing villages line the coast—the occupants often do part-time farming.

Forest industries

The forest-clad slopes of many of the mountains in the Long Summer Humid Continental regions have stimulated small lumbering industries. A few hardwood mills operate in the rougher upland areas of the Appalachians and Ozarks of North America. Logging is most often a winter activity in the Danube Basin, when the trees are easily transported over the snow. North China's bare mountain slopes afford no opportunities for lumbering and hardly enough material for fuel. Chinese housewives burn roots, straw, and the stalks of kaoliang, the giant sorghums, for cooking purposes. The mountain slopes in eastern Manchuria, unlike North China, still contain valuable forest resources of hardwoods and conifers, especially the Korean pine. Manchuria's lumbering activity will be discussed in the chapter dealing with Short Summer Humid Continental regions. Japanese lumbermen in northern Honshu follow a forestry program similar to that practiced in the southern part of the island—small scale lumbering with the accent on complete use and careful forest management.

Mining

Minerals, particularly fuels, are major resources in several of the regions. Figure 8-37, page 170, graphically indicates the wide extent of bituminous coal in the United States region; here lie the greatest producing fields in the world. The great coal deposits of the United States directly support several hundred thousand miners, pro-

FIGURE 9-20. *A continuous mechanical coal miner. This underground mechanical marvel wraps up coal mining into one continuous operation. Cutting and loading simultaneously (eliminating drilling and blasting), the continuous miner is served only by a shuttle car that transports the mined coal directly to waiting mine cars or rubber conveyer belts. Use of this machine greatly speeds production.* (Bituminous Coal Institute.)

vide cargo for railroads, and are extremely significant in the foundation of the nation's industrial capacity. There is also considerable petroleum production within the United States region. Major lead and zinc mines are located near the southern margin of the region in Missouri.

Romania has the best mineral endowments of the European region; petroleum and coal are the most important products. Hungary ranks with France and Yugoslavia in bauxite reserves, but production has been relatively small. In Asia there are coal deposits in southern Manchuria and on the Shantung Peninsula; iron occurs near the coal in the Manchurian sector. Accessibility has led to the development of these reserves as major sources of supply.

Manufacturing

Manufacturing develops in response to certain basic requirements, including raw materials, power, labor, markets, transportation, and capital. It tends to locate at points which provide optimum access to these ingredients.

The major part of the American Manufacturing Belt lies within the boundaries of the American Long Summer Humid Continental region. A combination of favorable factors has made this belt the largest, most important, and diverse industrial area of the world. The most significant requirements of basic industry, iron ore and coking coal, are easily assembled here. Iron ore is obtained from the Great Lakes region and from foreign sources through Atlantic ports. The Appalachian coal

FIGURE 9-21. *Coal transport on the Ohio River. Waterways allowing bulk transport lessen the cost of coal.* (American Waterways Operators.)

FIGURE 9-22. *Unloading a Great Lakes iron ore boat. These great ore boats, averaging 600 feet in length, bring iron ore to coal. The huge unloading machine scoops 20 tons of iron ore from the vessel with each bite. Three such machines can unload 12,000 tons of iron ore in about three and one-half hours.* (American Iron and Steel Institute.)

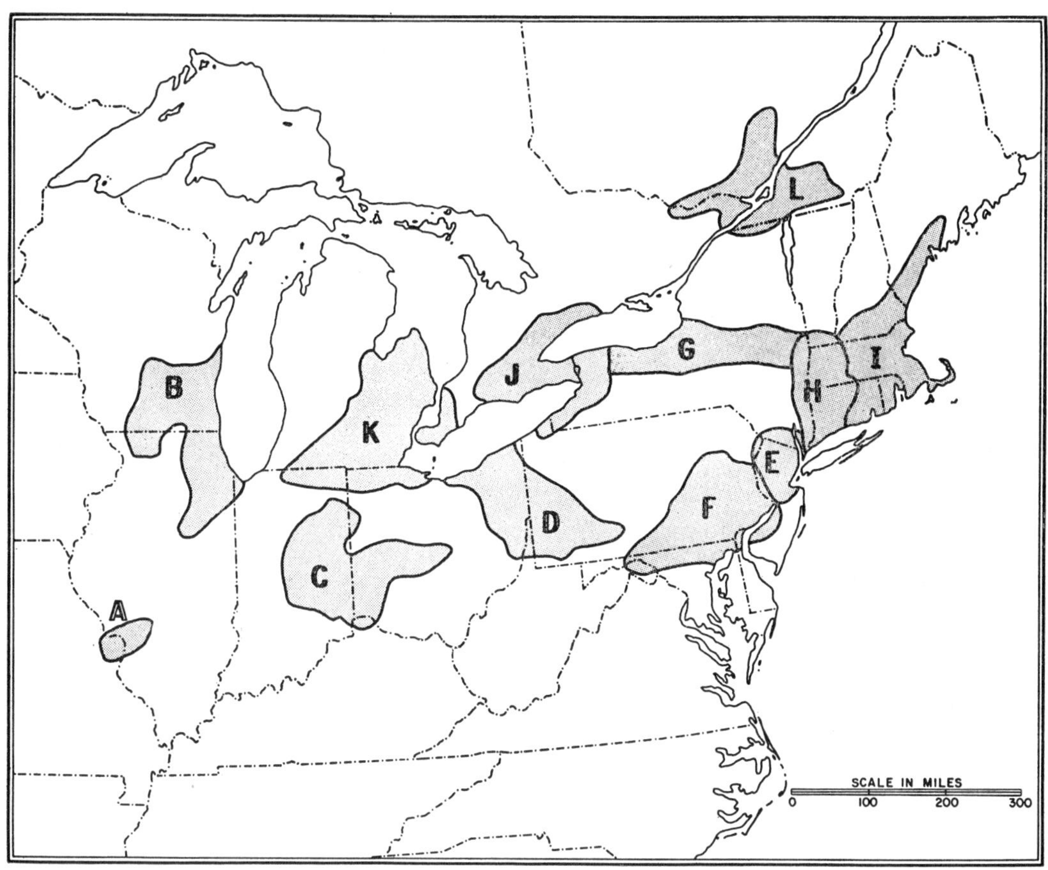

FIGURE 9-23. *The sub-regions of the American Manufacturing Belt.* (A) *St. Louis district;* (B) *Chicago-Milwaukee district;* (C) *Ohio-Indiana Inland district;* (D) *Pittsburgh-Cleveland district;* (E) *New York Metropolitan district;* (F) *Southern Pennsylvania district;* (G) *Mohawk Valley and Ontario Plain;* (H) *Southwestern New England;* (I) *Eastern New England;* (J) *Lake Erie-Ontario district;* (K) *Southern Michigan automobile district;* (L) *Lower St. Lawrence Lowland.* (After White and Foscue, *Regional Geography of Anglo-America,* Second Edition, Prentice-Hall, Inc., 1954.)

fields supply vast resources for power, and stores of petroleum are also nearby. Transportation facilities are excellent. The Great Lakes, linked by rivers and canals, provide a 1700-mile west-east waterway for the shipment of bulky raw materials to processing centers and markets. The St. Lawrence River is a water outlet to the northeast Atlantic. Rivers of the Mississippi system are utilized for barge traffic, and the Illinois waterway provides connection with the Great Lakes. Numerous harbors serve the Atlantic seaboard, which is linked to the Trans-Appalachian area by the Hudson River and the New York State Barge Canal. The densest net of railways, highways, and airways in the United States provides rapid transportation. Petroleum products are brought to the region by a network of pipe lines. The heaviest population of North America is concentrated within the belt, supplying skilled and unskilled labor, as well as large consuming markets.

The American Manufacturing Belt is not an area of continuous industrialization; it

FIGURE 9-24. *Stockyards in Kansas City, Missouri.* (Standard Oil Company of New Jersey.)

consists of a series of sub-regions. Each industrial concentration is based on special advantages of assembly, raw material proximity, labor skills, markets, early start, and other factors. The list of commodities produced is large—only a few of the major activities will be used to characterize each sub-region.

The St. Louis district (*1*) is the most westerly sub-region. Meat packing, brewing, shoe manufacture, petroleum refining, bauxite processing, and steel production are part of its diverse activities. The Chicago-Milwaukee district (*2*), bordering the south and southwest shores of Lake Michigan,[1] is outstanding for iron and steel plants, petroleum refineries, meat packers, and breweries. Clothing, agricultural implements, mining machinery, and furniture are other major commodities. The highly-diversified Ohio-Indiana Inland district (*3*), located between the eastern coal fields and western farm lands, concentrates on medium and light industry. It is the machine tool center of the world, and also manufactures electrical goods, clothing, soap, and agricultural machinery. The Pittsburgh-Cleveland district (*4*) leads in heavy iron and steel and has the leading role in the rubber industry, as well as producing electrical equipment, automobile parts, machine tools, and glass and clay products. The New York Metropolitan district (*5*) is extremely diversified, lacking mainly iron and steel production, but concentrating on clothing, chemicals, printing, and petroleum refining. Light and heavy industry characterize the southern Pennsylvania district and the contiguous areas of Maryland and Delaware (*6*), which stress textiles and chemicals, food processing, shipbuilding, and petroleum refining. This district is also noted

[1] The northern fringes of this district are actually in the Short Summer Humid Continental region.

for its tidewater steel plants which utilize imported iron ore. The Mohawk Valley and Ontario Plain (*7*), stretching from Albany, New York to Lake Ontario, contain a series of specialized industrial cities. Based on secondary raw material, products range from locomotives to cameras, electrical goods and clothing to optical equipment and chemicals. The Southwestern New England district (*8*) is concentrated chiefly in the Connecticut Valley. Manufacturing here is highly diversified, stressing products with high values, including machine tools, hardware, firearms, clocks, watches, electrical goods, high-grade paper, and a host of others. The Eastern New England district (*9*) parallels the seaboard and specializes in diversified light industry. Included are small metal goods, such as hardware, clocks, and jewelry, woolen goods, cotton textiles, especially fine fabrics, and shoes.

Outside of the United States, the Po Valley of Italy contains the largest industrial area in these regions. Here, coal and iron are lacking, therefore heavy industry is minor. Light industries, however, are favored by hydroelectricity, skilled labor, and a certain amount of raw materials. Cotton, rayon, wool, and silk textile milling is important, along with food processing. Other industries include manufacture of mechanical equipment, including automobiles, and light metal products. Chief centers are Milan and Turin.

Modern manufacturing is still in its infancy in the Danubian lands; handicraft and food processing are most typical. As the result of communist-inspired struggles to establish broader industrial bases, some development has occurred recently. For example, an iron and steel works has been established near Budapest and the Hungarian textile industry has been extended.

During the period of Japanese control (1931-1945), a significant industrial area came into being in southern Manchuria, between Mukden and Dairen. Local coal, oil

FIGURE 9-25. *Cuyahoga River ore dock and blast furnaces.* (American Iron and Steel Institute.)

FIGURE 9-26. *South Charleston, West Virginia. A congested industrial area on the Kanawha River. This is a great chemical manufacturing center.* (American Waterways Operators.)

shale, iron, limestone, soybeans for oil, and nearness to the coast were favorable factors. The Japanese created a salient industrial structure based upon iron and steel, particularly for the production of railway equipment, with other manufactures including cement, chemicals, and soybean products. Tientsin and Tsingtao, as a result of their functions as ports and commercial centers, also have some industrial development, mainly based upon the processing of agricultural products, with cotton textiles of particular importance.

Tourism

The Appalachian Mountains, the Atlantic sea coast, and the Great Lakes are resort areas for the millions of people who inhabit the American region. The sandy beaches of the Atlantic have numerous summer resort centers, led by Atlantic City. Mountains are utilized for both summer and winter sports. New York City is a leading tourist attraction in the United States, and many other cities of the American Manufacturing Belt also draw thousands of visitors.

Tourism and recreational activities in the European region are closely tied to the urban centers. Historic Venice, Vienna, Milan, Budapest, and Belgrade are but a few of the colorful cities that attract local and world travelers.

Urban centers

United States. Industry has led to the development of the largest urban concentrations in the world in the American

Manufacturing Belt. More than two score cities exceed 100,000 in size, and many more fall in the 50,000 to 100,000 class. New York, on the east coast at the terminus of the easiest route through the Appalachians, stands above all others. About eight million people live within the city limits and five million more, within the metropolitan area. It has the nation's best harbor, and is the largest port and commercial center, as well as being a leader in manufacturing and finance, and the center of styles and entertainment.

Chicago, second city of the United States, also has developed as the result of the combined benefits of commerce and industry. Its strategic situation at the south end of Lake Michigan assured the focus of land transportation routes. Philadelphia is the third city of the region. It is a great sea port and a major manufacturing center. Baltimore, Cleveland, St. Louis, Washington, Boston, Pittsburgh, and Cincinnati are all between 500,000 and 1,000,000, and a dozen more exceed 250,000. (Baltimore and Washington are close to the boundary between the Long Summer Humid Continental Region and the Humid Subtropic Region.) Manufacturing is a principal activity in all except Washington, whose principal activities are associated with the federal government.

Europe. The Po Plain is the outstanding urbanized area of the European region. At least one dozen cities exceed 100,000 population. Milan is the metropolis of the plain and second largest city of Italy with about 1.3 million. Its situation with respect to transportation routes has promoted a thriving commerce, and in recent years Milan has

FIGURE 9-27. *Port and skyline of New York City.* (American Waterways Operators.)

FIGURE 9-28. *Venice, city of canals.* (Italian State Tourist Office.)

become that country's leading industrial center. Turin, on the slopes of the Piedmont at the west end of the plain, is also an important industrial and commercial center. Venice, at the head of the Adriatic Sea, is historically the most famous of the Po Plain cities, having reached its greatest heights as a commercial center during the Middle Ages, when trade between Europe and the Orient flowed through the Mediterranean Sea. Today its fame is based upon its picturesque canals, churches, palaces, and the romance of its historic past; it has become one of the leading tourist attractions in Europe.

Three large cities dominate the Danube countries—Vienna, Austria, nearly two million, Budapest, Hungary, slightly over one million, and Bucharest, Romania, 1.4 million. Belgrade, major city of Yugoslavia, with about 500,000, is also in the basin. Each tends to dominate urban life within its respective country.

Asia. The Asian Long Summer Humid Continental region has many villages, but few cities. Tientsin and Peking are the leading population nodes—both exceed two million. Tientsin is the major commercial and industrial center of the North China Plain; Peking owes its growth to its services as the capital of the Chinese Empire. Mukden, with a population over 1.7 million, is the chief city of Manchuria. Its location on the main railway at the junction of lines to Peking and Korea has favored its growth. Tsingtao, on the south side of the Shantung Peninsula, has an excellent harbor and a population of over 750,000. Dairen, at the southeast tip of the Kwangtung Peninsula, has a fine harbor and an important function as a port.

OUTLOOK

The general patterns of livelihood appear to be established in the Long Summer Humid Continental regions. The United States region has the resource base, both natural and human, for continued advancement. The climax of industrial development is not in sight and experiments indicate major increase in crop and livestock yields.

The future of Italy is closely tied to the Po Plain, the agricultural and industrial heart of the country. Any material raising of the Italian standard of living must come largely through improvements in production there. The possibilities, however, are limited; intensive agricultural practices are already common and the major industrial assets are being used. The Danubian countries are probably destined to remain predominantly agricultural, since they lack significant industrial resources, as well as capital and technology. The outcome of the impact of Soviet Union guidance remains to be seen.

Problems and prospects in the oriental Humid Subtropics were noted in the last chapter; similar generalizations can be made for the Long Summer Humid Continental region. Here, too, populations are large and living standards are low. Agriculture is intense, secondary occupations are minor, and technology and capital low. One area, southern Manchuria, has possibilities for major industrial growth. The future of the Asiatic

FIGURE 9-29. *Budapest, Hungary. The Danube divides the city. On the west, the direction of this view, are the administrative, cultural, and intellectual institutions of the city; industrial and commercial activities are centered on the east. Budapest is a leading European flour-milling center.* (Legation of the Hungarian People's Republic.)

mainland is presently in the hands of a communistic form of government; only time will reveal the effectiveness or failure of the new policies.

SELECTED REFERENCES

Alexander, Lewis M., "The Impact of Tourism on the Economy of Cape Cod," *Economic Geography,* XXIX, No. 4, 1953, 320-326.

Atwood, Albert W., "The Merrimack: River of Industry and Romance," *National Geographic Magazine,* IC, No. 1, 1951, 106-140.

Ginsburg, Norton S., "China's Changing Political Geography," *Geographical Review,* XLII, No. 1, 1952, 102-117.

Hoffman, George W., ed., *A Geography of Europe.* New York: The Ronald Press Company, 1953.

Hoffman, George W., "The Survival of an Independent Austria," *Geographical Review,* XLI, No. 4, 1951, 606-621.

Hutchison, Isobel W., "A Stroll to Venice," *National Geographic Magazine,* C, No. 3, 1951, 378-410.

Micheal, Pauline, "Collectivization Along the Danube," *Foreign Agriculture,* XV, No. 10, 1951, 216-221.

Shen, Tsung-han, *Agricultural Resources of China.* Ithaca, N. Y.: Cornell University Press, 1951.

Steiner, H. Arthur, ed., "Report on China," *Annals of the Academy of Political and Social Science,* CCLXXVII, 1951, 1-228.

White, C. Langdon, and Edwin J. Foscue, *Regional Geography of Anglo-America,* Second Edition. New York: Prentice-Hall, Inc., 1954.

CHAPTER 10

Short Summer Humid Continentals

THE SHORT SUMMER HUMID CONtinental regions are the poleward frontiers of relatively continuous settlement; beyond lie the winter-dominated lands. In many ways these regions resemble their Long Summer neighbors. Climate differs only in intensity—summers are shorter and cooler, winters are longer and colder. Agriculture remains the dominant activity and grains, the leading crops; corn disappears and spring wheat replaces winter wheat. Hardier cereals such as rye, barley, and oats, and root crops, especially potatoes, assume important roles. Conditions favor dairying; the North American region contains America's Dairy Belt. Industry is also important; the northern margin of the American Manufacturing Belt, including the heart of Canadian industrialization, is in the

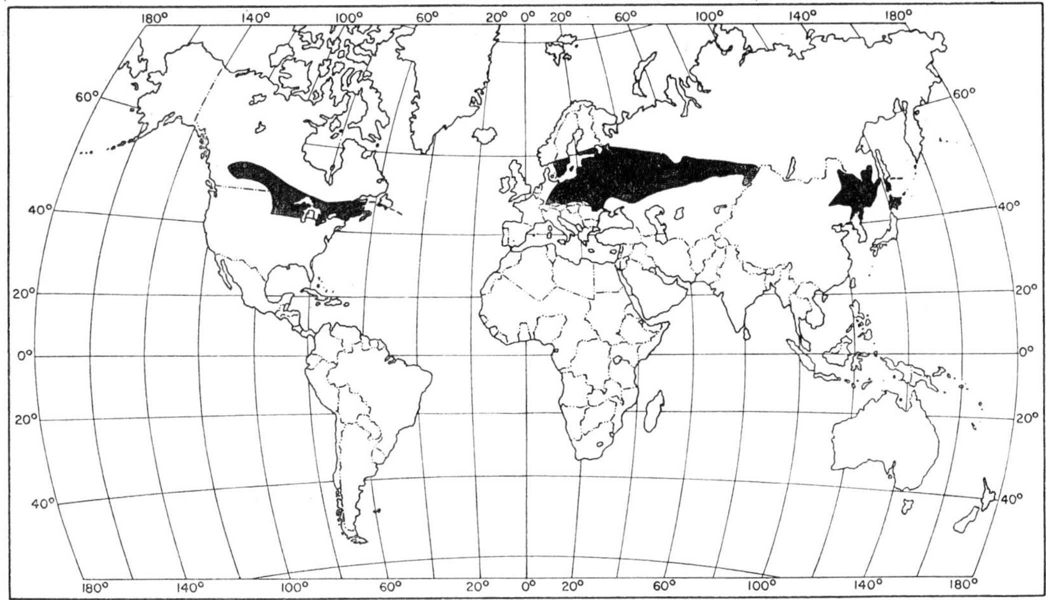

FIGURE 10-1. *The Short Summer Humid Continentals.*

North American Short Summer Humid Continental region, and there are several manufacturing districts in western Eurasia. In addition, two great world fisheries are located off the eastern coasts of North America and Asia.

Location

The Short Summer Humid Continental regions lie poleward of the Long Summer regions. The North American region extends from the Atlantic Ocean through northern New England and the Maritime Provinces of Canada westward through the Great Lakes to the vicinity of the 100th meridian in the United States; but it reaches the 120th meridian in Alberta, Canada, as the result of progressively lower heat and a lower evaporation rate, which allows an increasingly higher precipitation efficiency. The Eurasian region stretches from south Sweden and central Germany through Poland to include a major share of the Russian lowland between latitudes 50° and 60°. Beyond the Urals, a narrow belt straddles latitude 55° through the West Siberian Lowlands and terminates near the northern range of the Altai Mountains. Much of the U.S.S.R. region is bordered by steppe on the south. The third region is in east Asia, occupying northern Manchuria, northeast Korea, the neighboring portion of the Soviet Union, and the entire Japanese island of Hokkaido.

PHYSICAL ENVIRONMENT

Climate

Location in the higher latitudes and greater continentality account for climatic differences that distinguish these regions from the Long Summer regions. Cold winters, short warm summers, large annual ranges of temperature, moderate precipitation, and lower vegetative growth potentials characterize the Short Summer Humid Continental regions.

Temperatures. Winters are long and severe, with January averages ranging as much as 30 degrees lower than they do in the Long Summer Humid Continental regions. Daily

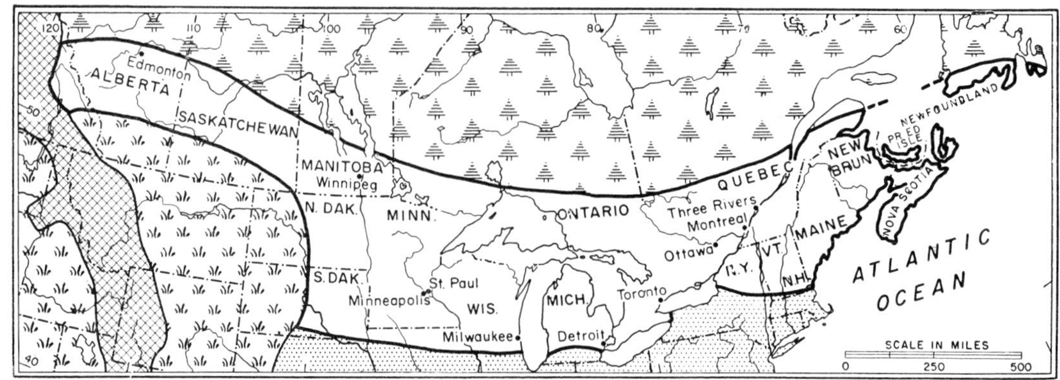

FIGURE 10-2. *The Short Summer Humid Continentals of North America.*

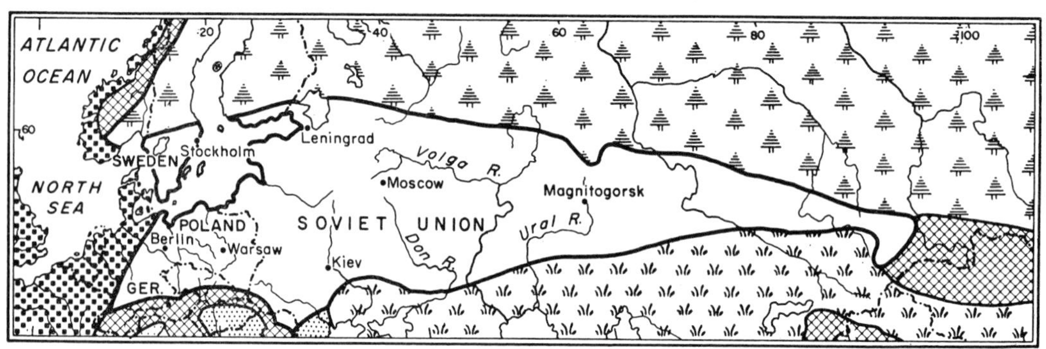

FIGURE 10-3. *The Short Summer Humid Continentals of western Eurasia.*

FIGURE 10-4. *The Short Summer Humid Continentals of eastern Asia.*

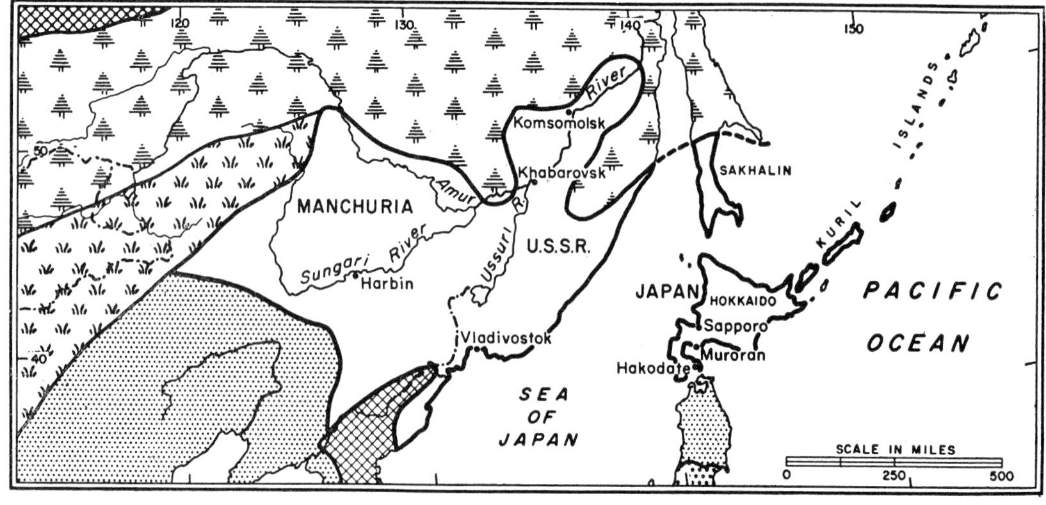

temperature fluctuations of 30 to 40 degrees are common. Winters also differ from year to year. Summers are short, but a few months are warm and the daytime maxima frequently reach 90° and above when skies are clear. July averages are generally only five to ten degrees cooler than the Long Summer Humid Continental regions. Although summers are short, the 16 to 18 hours of daylight help to compensate for the brevity of the season; nevertheless, plant growth potentials are less than in the regions to the south. Annual ranges are high. Winnipeg, Canada, for example, has a yearly average range of about 70° with an average monthly low of —3° and a monthly average high of 67°. Frost-free seasons are short, ranging from 90 to 150 days.

Precipitation. Summer is the season of maximum precipitation. Yearly totals vary from 20 to 40 inches in typical places, but northern interior areas often receive less than 20 inches. Winter precipitation is chiefly in the form of snow, and 60 to 80 days with snowfall are common. The total fall may amount to as much as 50 inches in the more humid portions. Cold weather maintains snow cover for four months or more.

Strong winds accompanied by zero weather, called blizzards in North America and *burans* in the U.S.S.R., occasionally occur in the interior portions of the regions. Powerful winds whirl snow particles high into the air and visibility is then practically zero. The combination of freezing temperatures, wind, and blinding snow is extremely hazardous to man and livestock.

Location and local differences. The oceanic influence on the leeward sides of continents is generally not strong enough to cause the development of a definite climatic type; however, there are some modifying effects of the sea on the eastern margins. Summers are cooler and winters warmer than in the interior; precipitation tends to be more evenly distributed.[1] The St. Lawrence estuary in the North American region carries maritime influences some distance inland, and the Great Lakes also produce modifications.

Cool currents—the Okhotsk off Asia and the Labrador off North America—have a cooling effect when northeast winds blow onto the continent. These, however, are not the prevailing winds. Thick sea fogs occur when moist warm air comes in contact with the chilled air above the cold currents; the neighboring littorals are frequently shrouded in fog, making coastwise navigation dangerous.

[1] These differences are sometimes used as the criteria for the recognition of a modified or New England type of climate on the eastern peripheries of North America and Asia in these latitudes.

FIGURE 10-5. *Typical climatic graphs of Short Summer Humid Continental stations.*

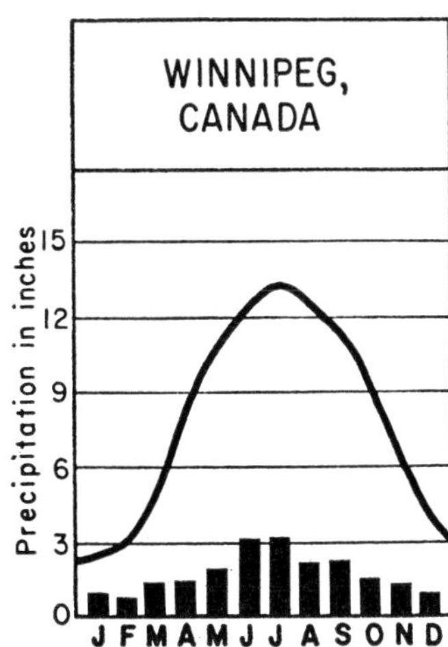

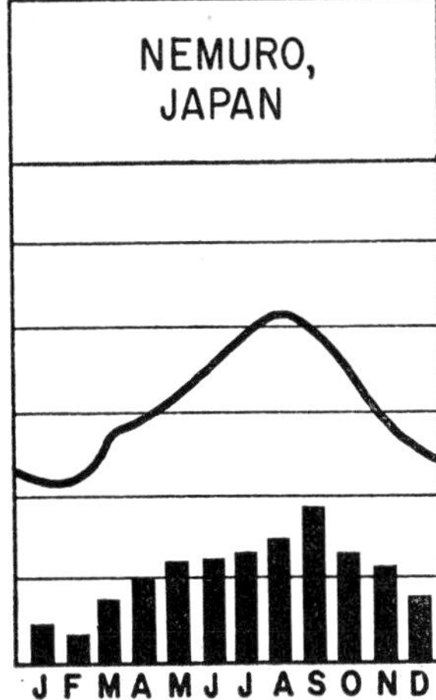

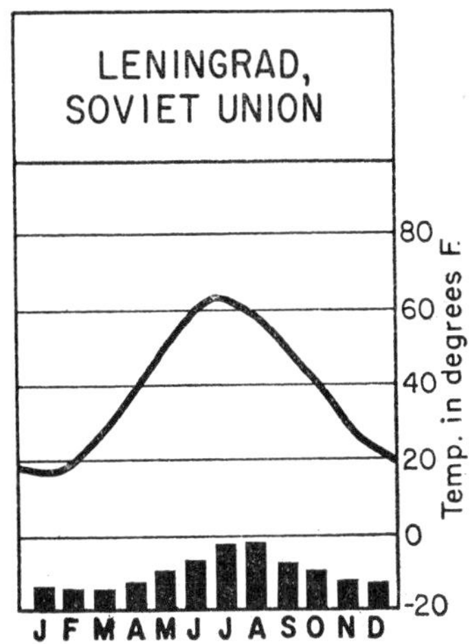

FIGURE 10-6. *Landscape in the Laurentian uplands. The streams of this region have a great power potential. This view shows the Chelsea Power plants on the Gatineau River, Quebec.* (Royal Canadian Air Force.)

Surface features

North America. The major portion of the North American region is contained in the Interior Lowland Physiographic Province, a vast expanse of nearly level land. In the west this lowland merges into the Great Plains, which are somewhat higher, but of monotonously slight relief. A fringe of the Laurentian Uplands, an area characterized by gentle hills with a few low, rounded mountains and literally thousands of lakes and extensive swamps, is included in the north. In the east there is a predominance of hills and low mountains known as the Northeastern Uplands. These subdued uplands long have been exposed to the forces of weathering and erosion, and in general summits range between 1500 and 3000 feet. Only two areas of low relief are noteworthy: the Aroostook Valley of Maine and the Annapolis-Cornwallis Valley of Nova Scotia. There are, however, numerous small stream valleys. Coastal plains are usually lacking, with slopes meeting the sea in an irregular coastline.

Most of the region was affected by continental glaciation during the Ice Age, with extensive modifications in topography, soils, and drainage. Through much of the Laurentian Upland and the Northeastern Uplands the results were adverse—in many areas the ice sheet was an eroding agent, leaving bare rock surfaces exposed. In others deposition was the principal activity. In some cases the load of material being carried by the ice sheet was dropped as a ground moraine consisting of various sized stones intermingled with clay, sand, and gravel, collectively known as glacial drift. At places where the margins of the ice were more or less stationary, with a balance between advance and melt, ridges of glacial drift accumulated as marginal moraines. Much of the glacial load was carried beyond the margins of the glacier by streams of melt waters. Like all streams, these sorted their material according to weight, depositing the heaviest first and the lightest last. In some cases these glacio-fluvial deposits were arranged in flood plain form in existing valleys, and are known as valley trains; in others they were spread in fan-like deposits about the margins of the ice to form outwash plains.

Other glacial features include eskers, kames, kettles, and drumlins (see Figure 10-8). *Eskers* are long, narrow ridges, commonly sinuous, composed of stratified drift. They range in height from a few feet to 50 or more, in length from a fraction of a mile to over 100 if gaps are included, and in breadth from 20-40 to 300-500 feet. *Kames* are low, steep-sided hills with a knoll-like form, consisting of stratified drift. *Kettles* are small depressions that occur in drift, usually stratified. Few exceed a mile in greatest diameter, and most are no more than 20 to 30 feet deep. *Drumlins* are low elliptical hills of glacial drift, streamlined in form. They average nearly a mile in length, 1200 to 1800 feet in width, and 60 to 100 feet in height. Usually drumlins occur in groups or "fields" running into the hundreds.[2]

Glaciation in the Interior Lowlands portion of the region was more beneficial, with resulting conditions similar to those described for the Corn Belt. Several sub-divisions, however, should be recognized. The Great Lakes district is mantled with recent glacial deposits in which there are thousands of lakes, ponds, and swamps. Bordering the Great Lakes, there are lacustrine plains that have resulted from deposition of sediments into water and their eventual exposure by shrinking of the lakes.

[2] For more detail on glacial geology and landforms, an outstanding text is Flint, Richard Foster, *Glacial Geology and the Pleistocene Epoch*. New York: John Wiley and Sons, Inc., 1947.

FIGURE 10-7. *The Aroostook Valley, Maine. The village is Limestone, Maine, an important shipping point for potatoes.* (United States Department of Agriculture Soil Conservation Service.)

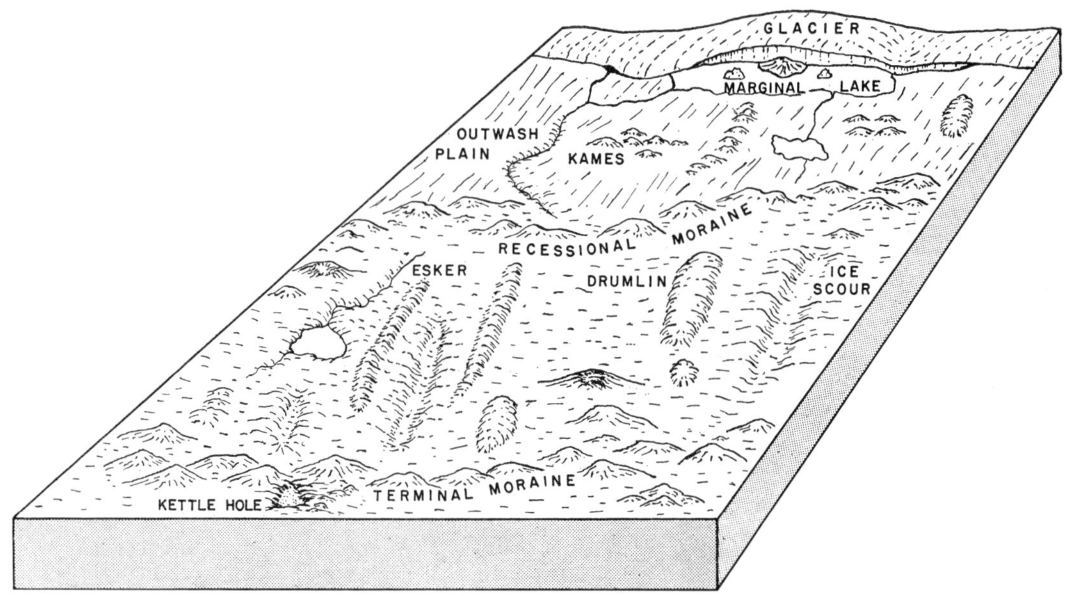

FIGURE 10-8. *Glacial features.*

FIGURE 10-9. *A view across the Red River Valley of the North.* (United States Department of Agriculture Soil Conservation Service.)

FIGURE 10-10. *A virgin hardwood stand in the Nicolet National Forest, Wisconsin. All the trees shown in this view are maples.* (United States Forest Service.)

The Driftless Area, lying largely in southwestern Wisconsin, is particularly distinctive since it was not covered by the ice sheet and thus not favorably smoothed.

The northwestern portion of the lowlands is also mantled with recent glacial deposits and has numerous lakes and ponds. Many more lakes and ponds existed immediately after the shrinkage of the continental ice sheet than are present today; some drained naturally and others were drained by man and converted to farmland. The most famous, former glacial Lake Agassiz, is evidenced by a large lacustrine plain and the present-day Lake Winnipeg. The tremendous prehistoric lake was formed during the waning stages of the Ice Age; as the ice retreated poleward, northward-flowing melt water was blocked and covered the extensive and fertile plain that is today drained by the Red River of the North. When the ice retreated into Hudson Bay, the present-day drainage by way of the Nelson River was established.

Europe and the U.S.S.R. The European region is part of the North European Plain. In the entire expanse there are few elevations that rise to 1000 feet. The most notable exceptions are the Central Russian Uplands west and south of Moscow, which in general rise in low hills of 600 to 1000 feet elevation and do not break the continuity of the plain except where steep slopes face the west bank of rivers. The Ural Mountains are the only real break in the topography and, although they separate the western plains from the flat Siberian Plain, they are not a significant barrier.

Like the North American region, most of the plain was affected by continental glaciation, which disrupted drainage and covered the surface with glacial and glacio-fluvial deposits. Three north-south zones are apparent: the *ground moraine* which dominates in south-

FIGURE 10-11. *Leatherleaf bog in the Hiawatha National Forest, Wisconsin. The smaller islands support red pine. Poor drainage conditions in this area impede normal soil development.* (United States Forest Service.)

FIGURE 10-12. *A farmstead in the Prairie Provinces of Canada surrounded by wheat.* (National Film Board of Canada.)

ern Scandinavia; the Baltic *terminal moraine,* which attains elevations up to 900 feet, forming a long zone of sandy hills paralleling the Baltic Sea from the Jutland Peninsula of Denmark into the Soviet Union; and a great *outwash plain,* built by the melt waters pouring from the Baltic Moraine, extending across Germany and Poland into the Soviet Union. Much of the outwash plain is poorly drained, with large swampy areas and soils that are frequently sandy. In contrast, the southern fringe of the North European Plain is mantled with fertile loess, presumably brought by winds that blew across the material deposited by the glacial melt waters.

East Asia. The east Asian region is dominated by uplands. On the mainland notable lowlands do occur in the Sungari Plain of north Manchuria and the adjacent Ussuri Valley and Middle Amur Lowland of the U.S.S.R., but elsewhere mountains often descend to the sea with little or no coastal plain. There are three sizable lowlands in Hokkaido, of which the Ishikari Plain, extending north-south through the west-central part of the island, is the most significant. The others are the Tokachi Plain on the southeast coast and the Nemuro Plain on the east coast.

Natural vegetation

Forests are the natural cover in the wetter portions of the North American region. Pine, spruce, hemlock, and fir dominate the evergreen species, and a mixture of birch, aspen, beech, poplar, maple, and other deciduous trees occur on the warmer southern margins. The foliage of the hardwoods during the fall season adds brilliant splashes of color to the landscapes. The virgin forests have been cut in many of the areas, especially around the Great Lakes and in the

Northeastern Uplands. Second growth and rotting stumps now cover thousands of acres of forestland that at one time appeared inexhaustible and as impenetrable as the forests of the humid tropics. Grasses gradually supplant the forest in the drier, western interior.

Forests constitute the typical cover of the western portion of the Eurasian region, where the land is either too rough or too infertile for agriculture. Conifers are most common in the higher elevations, but are also scattered throughout the sandy areas of the glaciated plains. Heath and moor are usual in the poorly-drained lands. A belt of mixed forest stretches into the U.S.S.R., forming a distinctive vegetative zone between the colder coniferous forest lands in the north and the drier grasslands in the south. Marshes occur along the flat east banks of Siberian rivers that are flooded during the spring thaw.

The mountains in the Far Eastern section of the Asiatic region are covered with dense stands of conifers made up of spruce, fir, larch, and Korean pine. Broadleafs grow at the lower elevations. Broadleaf forests compose the vegetative mantle of southern Hokkaido; there is a gradation into coniferous forests northward.

FIGURE 10-13. *Wheat elevators in Saskatchewan. Such grain storage facilities are a common sight throughout the wheat lands.* (National Film Board of Canada.)

Soils

Soils show transitional characteristics paralleling the change in climate and vegetation. Gray-brown soils like those of the more humid phase of the Long Summer Continental region prevail on the warmer mixed-forest margins. Poleward with lowering temperatures and a change to coniferous forest, *podzol* soils occur. This group, as its Russian name indicates, is ash-gray in color, acid, and low in soluble salts and organic matter. The forest cover takes little and returns little to the soil, but the surface drainage water continually carries away nutrients. More fertile soils are found in the interior; paralleling the lowering precipitation and the transition to grass vegetation there is a gradation from gray-brown or podzol soils through prairie soils to chernozems.

Effects of glaciation have in places interfered with the natural soil-building processes. Poor drainage, frequently indicated by swamps and marshes, has restricted normal development in a number of areas. Excessive drainage occurs in stony ground moraine and coarse, sandy glacio-fluvial deposits—particularly in the European region. Adverse effects also result from scouring, which has produced bare rock surfaces in some northern, hard-rock areas. On the other hand, the lacustrine deposits, such as those of old glacial Lake Agassiz and the borders of the Great Lakes, are excellent agricultural soils. The wind-deposited loess also is usually high quality soil.

MAN IN THE SHORT SUMMER HUMID CONTINENTALS

The Short Summer Humid Continental regions mark the northern limits of the world's major zones of relatively dense and continuous population. Within each region, population density tends to thin out both

FIGURE 10-14. *Dairy farms in Wisconsin. Pastures, barns, silos, and cows are typical features of most Wisconsin landscapes.* (Wisconsin Department of Agriculture.)

poleward and toward the drier interior. The nature of the topography also affects distribution, with rough upland sections discouraging settlement. The greatest concentrations are found along the southern margins of the north European plain, where fertile soil and mineral deposits have favored agriculture and industry, and in the eastern portion of the North American region, part of the manufacturing belt, including many cities and the industrial heart of Canada. Northern Manchuria and the Japanese island, Hokkaido, are the most densely populated purely agricultural areas. Unlike the regions to the south, the Manchurian sector and Hokkaido are the oriental frontierlands and are not yet crowded to capacity.

The agricultural possibilities are not as promising here as in the Humid Subtropics and Long Summer regions, but when fish, minerals, and forests are added to the base, the foundations for supporting comparatively large numbers of people are strong.

Agriculture

Farming is the most widespread activity. Dairying and small grain and root-crop production comprise the major enterprises best suited to the climatic and soil conditions. The emphasis varies considerably in response to differences in detail of environment as well as in culture.

North America. Two distinct agricultural regions are found in the North American area. The Spring Wheat Region occupies the western, lower-rainfall portion, and the Hay and Dairy Region, the more moist eastern portion. In the Spring Wheat Region commercial agriculture prevails, and the bulk of the production is consumed elsewhere. Farms are fully mechanized and are commonly 400 acres or more in size. Rural population is sparse and dispersed. Long, cold winters, with a relatively slight snow cover to offer protection to a crop, require that wheat be planted in the spring rather than the fall. Wheat overshadows all other crops and gets first choice of the land; barley, hay, and flax for seed are the common rotation crops. The growing season is too short and the nights too cool to mature corn for grain; however, some corn is grown for silage use on the southeastern margin.

To the east, cooler, more moist climate, poorer soil and rougher surface restrict profitable grain production but favor forage crops and pasture. The large concentration of urban centers provides markets for milk products. These factors have induced a large portion of the farmers to become dairymen; the area is known as America's Dairy Belt. Farming here is an intensive, year-around activity. Farm units are smaller, usually 100 to 125 acres, and are devoted to raising the feed and pasture for an average of 20 to 40 dairy cows. The typical farm has fields of hay, oats, and corn, a silo in which the corn is preserved as silage, and a large barn to house the stock and store

FIGURE 10-15. *Mechanical potato digger in the Aroostook Valley near Caribou, Maine. In this area the potato is the "king" crop.* (Standard Oil Company of New Jersey.)

FIGURE 10-16. *A farming community on the north shore of the St. Lawrence River. Cool climate, adverse slopes, and podzol soil restrict farming opportunities and make dairying one of the best and most profitable uses of the land.* (National Film Board of Canada.)

winter hay. The nature of the dairy products sold depends upon location with respect to markets and cost of transportation. Near cities fluid milk is sold, but manufactured products such as butter, cheese, and condensed milk are more important in the areas distant from cities.

Within the dairy belt, city markets have encouraged some vegetable and fruit production in a number of favored areas bordering the Great Lakes and in New England. Aroostook County, Maine, is one of the major potato-producing areas of the United States; the Cornwallis-Annapolis Valley of Nova Scotia accounts for an important share of Canada's commercial apple crop.

Europe and western U.S.S.R. Agriculture is more diversified in the European region. Rye, well-adapted to cool climate and sandy soils, replaces wheat as the chief grain and breadstuff. The North European Plain, including its extension into the western portion of the Soviet Union, is the great rye-producer of the world. Potatoes thrive under similar conditions, hence this is also the world's major potato region. Potatoes are used for food, feed and industrial purposes. Sugar beets are grown extensively and flax is important in the Russian sector. Throughout, livestock are usually part of the farming systems, with the dairy and swine phases most significant.

Since the late 1920's, through the Russian planned economy, spring wheat acreage has been increased in the southern margins of the region in European Russia. Moreover, east of the Urals many millions of acres of virgin lands, not previously used for crop agriculture because of their marginal character, have been developed for spring wheat production.

Eastern U.S.S.R. and Asia. In northern Manchuria, spring wheat and soy beans are the main crops. Farms and fields are somewhat larger than those of the North China Plain. Yields per person are also higher and a surplus is available for export. Development in the Amur and Ussuri Valleys has been recent and includes both agriculture and other activities. Since the early stages of World War II strategic reasons have prompted the Soviet Union to concentrate major effort on this Far Eastern appendage over 5000 miles from the heart of the nation. Only one railroad, the Trans-Siberian, provides land contact with the west. Large scale, mechanized state farms have been established for the production of wheat, rye, oats, barley, and sugar beets. Some of the poorly drained, low-lying areas are devoted to hay crops and livestock rearing, including both herds of dairy and beef cattle.

The agriculture of Hokkaido differs markedly from that of Humid Subtropical Japan. The former presents a pioneer landscape—farms average ten or twelve acres in size and are usually in single, rectangular plots. Many of the crops of the south are not grown; instead more adaptable species are planted. Beans have the greatest distribution and rank first. White potatoes and sugar beets are prominent cash crops. Rice, specially developed for more restricting climatic conditions, is the most widespread grain, but it does not dominate land utilization as elsewhere in Japan. A considerable acreage is given over to forage crops for dairy cows and for horses, which are used for draft purposes. Hokkaido has the most important dairy industry of Japan. During the early stages of settlement, the Japanese government brought agricultural experts from New England to Hokkaido to help plan the development of the island. The influence is noted in the rectangular survey patterns, and in the New England style of

FIGURE 10-17. *Harvest time in the south of Sweden. The typical Swedish farm contains 25 to 50 acres.* (Swedish Travel Information Bureau.)

FIGURE 10-18. *Autumn plowing on a Polish state farm.* (Polish Embassy.)

some of the houses, barns, and silos, as well as the crops. Despite early planning, many elements of old Japan are present in the form of conventional southern house types, crops, and methods. The blending that results has given Hokkaido a cultural landscape distinctive from the rest of the Orient.

Fishing

One of the major fishing grounds of the world is in the coastal waters off northeast North America. Physical conditions here are extremely favorable for the growth of an abundance of plankton, minute plant and animal organisms, the basis of fish food. A series of submarine elevations called banks are located on the wide, shallow continental shelf which extends from southern New England to Newfoundland. Three banks are most important: the Georges Bank east of Cape Cod, the Sable Island Bank southeast of Nova Scotia, and the largest, the Grand Banks, southeast of Newfoundland. The shallow water of the banks, 300 feet or less, allows an abundance of light to penetrate to the ocean floor, and this stimulates the growth of plankton. The depths are aerated by contrasting currents—the cold Labrador Current and the warm water from the Gulf Stream—and by tides and general storminess which renew the supply of oxygen necessary for life.[3] The indented coastline provides many excellent harbors for the numerous fishing vessels, and the smooth bank bottoms favor the use of otter trawls or dragnets for capturing demersal, or bottom-feeding, varieties. Cod, haddock, and flounder are among the important commercial species, taken chiefly by use of otter trawls.

[3] One author suggests that without the circulation of water all but the uppermost layer of the sea would become an empty waste. See Bigelow, Henry B., *Oceanography, Its Scope, Problems and Economic Importance*. Boston: Houghton Mifflin Company, 1931, 119.

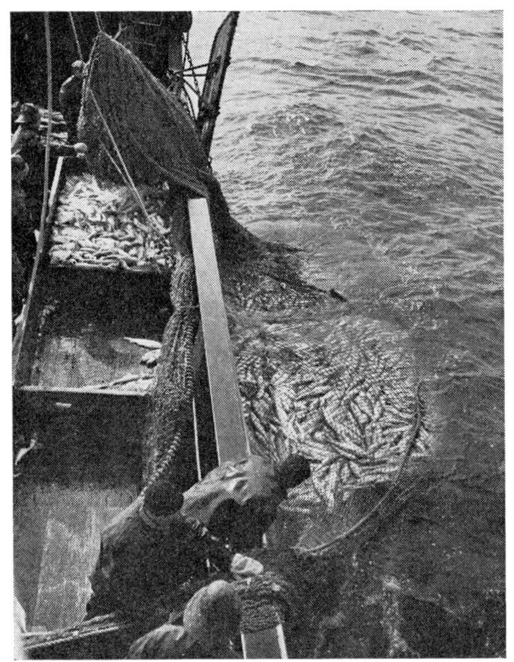

FIGURE 10-19. *Fishing operation on the Grand Banks off Newfoundland.* (National Film Board of Canada.)

Large quantities of herring and mackerel constitute the catch of pelagic species, or surface feeders. In addition this area has a valuable shellfish industry based on lobsters, clams, oysters, and scallops. The Great Lakes, led by Lake Erie, contain the most important United States and Canadian fresh-water fisheries. Blue pike and lake herring make up the largest portion of the commercial catch, but other species, particularly white fish, perch, and carp, are also taken. Many of the Canadian lakes, such as Winnipeg, Winnipegosis, and Manitoba, have important winter commercial fisheries.

The Baltic Sea fisheries are so overshadowed by the rich fishing grounds of the North Sea that their importance is often minimized. However, the presence of cod, mackerel, and especially small herring, as well as oyster beds, along the west coast have stimulated a fishing economy among the Baltic shore countries. The highly-indented coastline of Sweden and Finland furnishes numerous harbors for fishing craft. Finnish fishermen are particularly active in the Baltic and the Gulf of Finland, and also make important catches in their numerous streams and lakes. The major Finnish fishing grounds are in the coastal waters lying between Helsinki and Hangö.

The shallow water over the continental shelf contiguous to eastern Siberia and Hokkaido is a major world fishing ground. Conditions favoring a fishing industry are similar to those found off northeast North America. Species include herring, cod, mackerel, and salmon; crab is the most important shellfish. Approximately one-fifth of the total Japanese catch comes from waters near Hokkaido.

FIGURE 10-20. *Ladder Fishing. When fishermen from the tiny village of Minudie, Nova Scotia, clear their nets, they drive a team of horses and a wagon three miles from shore. They take a ladder along to gather in the fish. The tremendous tides of the Cumberland Basin, which have a range of 22 to 28 feet, make this operation possible. At times the shad, caught by their gills, stick stubbornly.* (Imperial Oil.)

FIGURE. 10-21. *Finnish fishermen marketing brined herring in Helsinki.* (Finnish National Travel Office.)

Forest industries

Lumbering in the United States had its beginning during the colonial era along the northeastern seaboard, especially in the present State of Maine. After the peak of lumber production was reached here, the loggers moved westward to the forests of the Great Lakes states. In the early decades of the present century, the saw timber was cut. Today the logging emphasis is on trees for pulp, most of which are harvested from stands of second growth. Lumbering in the southern margins and more accessible areas in the Canadian portion of the region has had a similar history and the best saw timber has been cut. The smaller trees and the forests avoided earlier now furnish raw material for pulp mills. Logging in both countries is chiefly a winter season activity—the snow cover and frozen ground facilitate log transportation. The lakes and rivers are utilized for moving logs to the mills in the spring and summer. Pulp and paper mills, situated on water sites, are scattered throughout the Great Lakes area and the northern New England states. Canadian pulp and paper mills are found from the lower St. Lawrence River westward to the province of Manitoba.

The tapping of sugar maple trees for the manufacture of maple sugar and syrup is unique in the North American region. The province of Quebec accounts for most of the Canadian supply and New York and Vermont produce two-thirds of the United States' total. The demands of city-dwellers for Christmas trees have stimulated a small but profitable forest industry during the months of November and December.

There is little contrast between the components of the forest industries in the Eurasian and North American regions; however, the forests are more carefully managed and the waste is nil, with even smallest branches gleaned for fuel. Trees are felled mainly during the winter, natural waterways are signifi-

FIGURE 10-22. *Floating newsprint. This log harvest is floating down the Gatineau River to the mills where it will be processed into newsprint.* (Malak, Ottawa.)

FIGURE 10-23. *Canadian Paper Company, Cornwall, Ontario. Water for transport, hydroenergy, and the process are attractions at this site.* (Malak, Ottawa.)

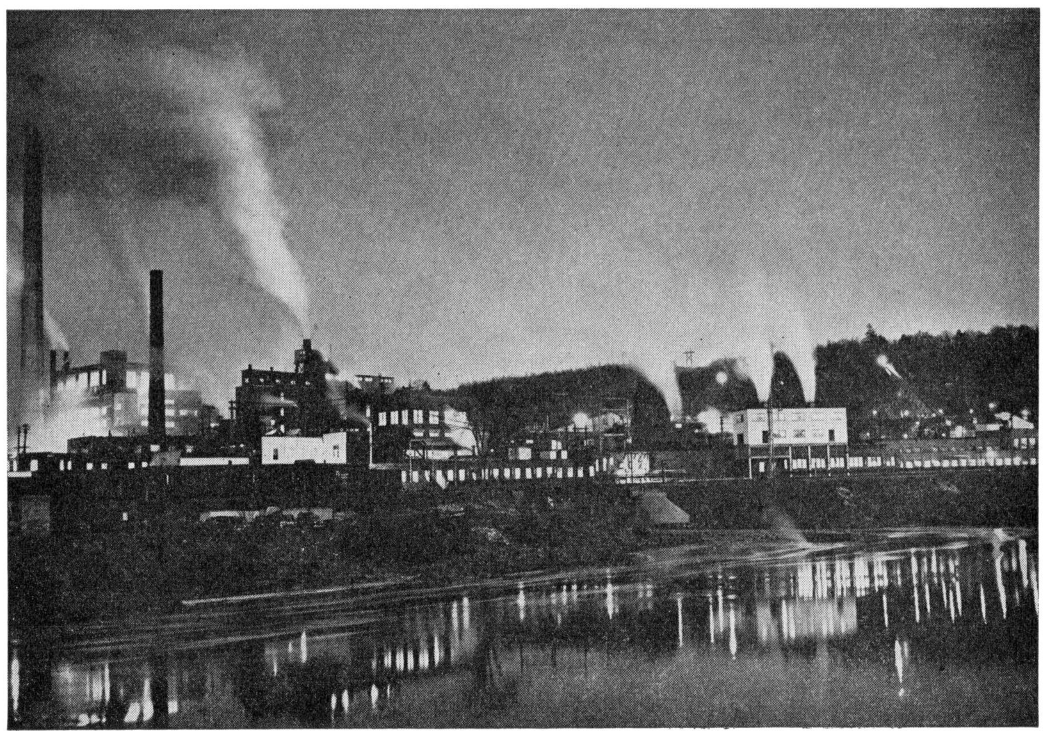

cant in log movement, and pulp and paper mills utilize much of the softwood cut, especially in Sweden, Finland, and the western U.S.S.R. The emphasis on pulp and paper is not as strong here as in North America since the forest must also furnish logs for lumber and large quantities of wood for winter fuel.

Mining

North America. Some of the most significant iron ore deposits in the world occur in the Lake Superior District, which includes parts of northern Minnesota, Wisconsin, Michigan, and southern Ontario. Eight distinct ore bodies, known as iron ranges, are present. The Mesabi Range of Minnesota is outstanding—it is the most productive iron ore deposit yet known. Mining here has been favored by the richness and size of the deposit, its accessibility, and the ease of working. The overburden of glacial drift is easily removed. The ore, mined with power shovels, is loaded directly into railway cars for haulage down to the lake ports of Duluth and Superior. In the other ranges a portion of the ore is mined from underground seams. This district has a fortunate relationship to the American Manufacturing Belt, with the Great Lakes providing the highway for the low-cost transport of bulky iron ore to the margins of the coal fields in huge, specially-designed ore boats. The major portion of the steel industry of the United States depends upon the Lake Superior district for its ore. The rich deposits, drawn upon for more than half a century, are being depleted, but there are enormous reserves of lower-grade ores which can be used in the future.

FIGURE 10-24. *Oil well in a wheat field in the Prairie Provinces. This is now a common sight in the Edmonton-Leduc area.* (National Film Board of Canada.)

Tremendous lignite, or brown coal, and sub-bituminous reserves are found in the Prairie Provinces of Canada. A huge new petroleum field, recently opened in Alberta, has major developments centered in the Edmonton-Leduc area. Highest quality Canadian coals are mined in Nova Scotia. The world's largest nickel deposit and production occur in the Sudbury area of Ontario; platinum and copper are also mined there. Large deposits of asbestos are worked near Quebec. Building stones have long constituted a noteworthy product of New England. The abundance of high quality granite, marble, and slate near to large urban centers has made this area a leader in the stone industry.

Eurasia. Upper Silesia is an important coal-producing area in Central Europe and also contains small iron deposits, giving rise to a significant industrial development. Large deposits of sub-bituminous coal and lignite occur in the Moscow basin, and there is also lignite near Leningrad. One of the large iron ore districts of the Soviet Union is found in the Southern Urals. The greatest coal reserves of the U.S.S.R. occur near the Tom River, a tributary of the Ob, in an area known as the Kuznetsk Basin. An oil-producing field is located between the Volga River and the western flanks of the Urals, especially on either side of the Kama River; the large reserves there have prompted the name "Second Baku," after the great oil field near Baku on the western shores of the Caspian Sea. In the

FIGURE 10-25. *Rock crusher north of Lake Ontario. Throughout the glaciated areas road building and concrete construction are facilitated by an abundance of rock.* (International Harvester Company of Canada.)

Far East, one of the two largest coal deposits of Japan is located on the Ishikara Plain of Hokkaido. One of the principal iron deposits of Korea occurs near the northeast border.

Manufacturing

Several subdivisions of the American Manufacturing Belt are located in the North American region: (*1*) The Lake Erie-Ontario district in western New York and adjacent Ontario contains the industrial centers of Hamilton, Toronto, Buffalo,[4] and Niagara. Iron and steel, flour-milling, electrochemical, and metallurgical industries are dominant. (*2*) The Southern Michigan Automobile District is centered at Detroit-Windsor, with a ring of tributary cities in the lower Michigan peninsula and northern Indiana and Ohio. About 90 per cent of the automobiles and automobile parts of North America are produced in this area. (*3*) The Lower St. Lawrence Lowland, with its manufacturing cities of Ottawa, Montreal, and Three Rivers is the eastern Canadian manufacturing center. An abundance of water power and timber has stimulated aluminum production and paper industries—Three Rivers is one of the world's largest paper-manufacturing centers. Other manufactures include flour, iron and steel, clothing, and textiles. In addition to the subregions of the manufacturing belt, there are numerous centers which specialize in proc-

[4] Buffalo is in the previous region but it is mentioned here because of its association with this industrial subregion.

FIGURE 10-26. *Open pit iron mining in the Lake Superior District. Huge equipment in use from mines to mills, the great reserves of iron, ease of mining, the downhill rail grade to lake ports, the ore boats, and loading and unloading equipment are responsible in a large measure for America's industrial strength.* (American Iron and Steel Institute.)

essing raw materials from their hinterlands such as wheat, fish, wood, and dairy products.

In response to coal deposits, as well as other factors favoring industrial location, several significant manufacturing districts are distributed throughout the European and Asian regions. Sweden is the industrial leader among the Scandinavian countries. Although the nation is rich in iron ore, heavy industry is not particularly characteristic, since coal is lacking. Products are diverse, ranging from expensive glassware to the fine steel cutlery, bearings, and other articles manufactured at Eskilstuna and nearby centers; billions of matches are produced at Jönköping. Germany has a number of large and small industrial concentrations whose products are infinite. Prior to World War II, Berlin was the largest manufacturing city in Germany. Saxony, with centers at Leipzig, Zwickau, Chemnitz, and Dresden, is a significant central German industrial area. Chemicals, textiles, optical goods, and porcelains are the characteristic specialties. Bavaria has a number of specialized manufacturing centers such as Nürnberg and Stuttgart. The Silesian Coal Basin is the industrial heart of Poland; in addition to one of the great European coal reserves, iron and other metal resources are nearby. Manufacturing accents are on iron and steel, but chemicals and textiles are significant. The adjacent section of Czechoslovakia, together with the Bohemian Basin, contains the concentrations of that country's industry. Ostrava is the leading iron and steel center; the Skoda munition works are at Pilsen. Foods, beer, shoes, and fine glass are notable Czechoslovakian products.

The U.S.S.R. has its share in the industrial developments of this region. Leningrad is a focus of ship-building, machinery, wood products, chemicals, and electrical equipment. The Central Industrial District around Moscow is one of the great Russian industrialized areas. Products range through textiles, autos, agricultural machinery, precision equipment, and a score of others. Eight major industrial cities are situated in the Urals, dominated by the steel and machine centers at Magnitogorsk, Sverdlovsk, and Chelyabinsk. Relatively recent is the industrial rise of the Kuznetz Basin. Factory growth in the past quarter-century has made the district the fourth largest in the country, with important centers at Stalinsk, Leninsk-Kuznetskiy, Kemerovo, and Novosibirsk. Komsomolsk and Khabarovsk, on the lower Amur, and Vladivostok on the coast are the industrial centers in the Far East, specializing in steel and ships, with some general manufacturing. Hokkaido has a steel plant at Muroran where ore and scrap are imported to use with coal from the Ishakari deposits.

FIGURE 10-27. *An assembly line in a Canadian truck manufacturing plant.* (National Film Board of Canada.)

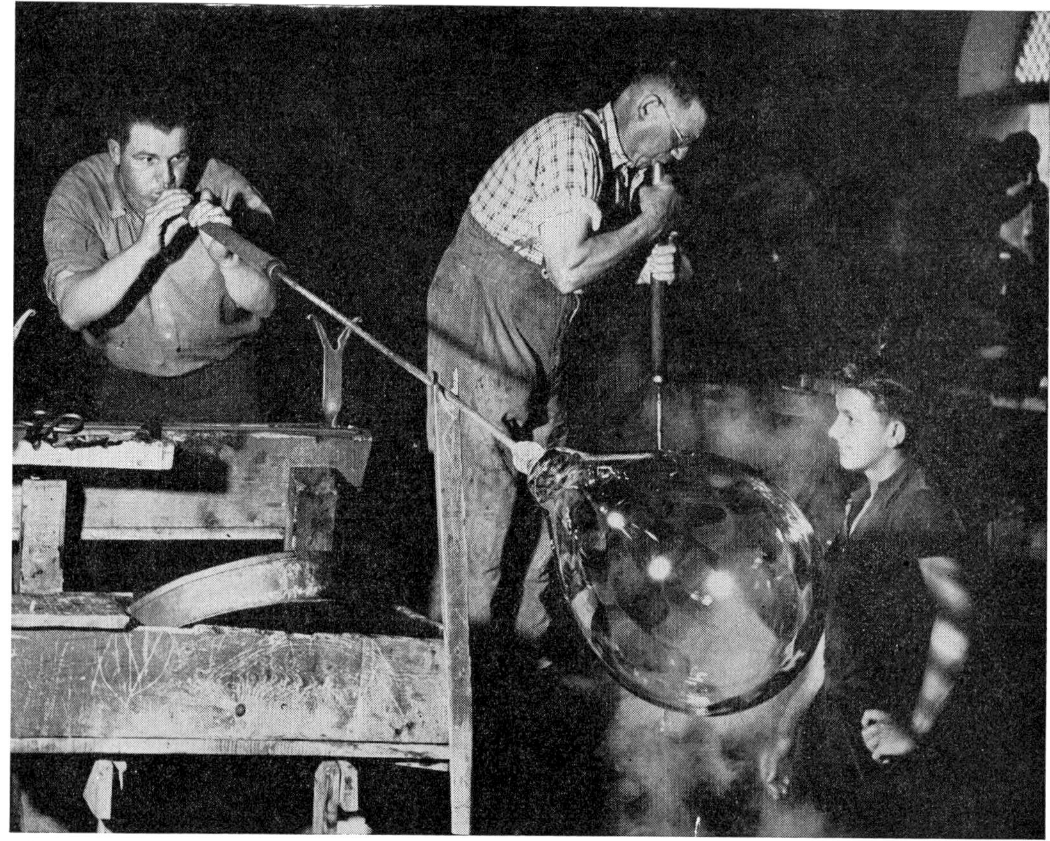

FIGURE 10-28. *In the European manufacturing region the artisan still has an important role in industry. The picture shows German glassblowers at work.* (German Tourist Information Office.)

Tourism

Tourism is well established as one of the major economies of these regions. Charming rural landscapes, historic attractions, mountains, streams, lakes, and a picturesque coastline provide recreational outlets for the densely-populated areas of the eastern United States and Canada. Scenic beauty and sports opportunities attract thousands of tourists, vacationists, hunters and fishermen. Summer resorts and homes are scattered along the coastline and many of the lake shores. Tourism is less developed in the Eurasian regions, although Sweden and Finland draw many visitors from Western Europe as well as the Americas.

Urban centers

A surprising number of large commercial and industrial cities are found within the Short Summer Humid Continental regions. Principal concentrations in the American region occur in (*1*) the Toronto to Windsor sector of Ontario, the leading industrial district of Canada, (*2*) the St. Lawrence Valley between Lake Ontario and Quebec, and (*3*) the Detroit area of Michigan. The population of Detroit, the automobile capital of the world, is about two million. Montreal, the head of navigation on the St. Lawrence River, has nearly 1.25 million people and is the leading city of Canada. Cities such as Milwaukee and Buffalo benefit from splendid situations with respect to transportation routes and derive considerable importance from commerce as well as industrial activity. Ottawa is dominantly a political center, serving as the capital of Canada. The western cities have grown largely as the result of favorable transportation and are bulk-breaking, assembly, and distribution points. For example, the east-west railway lines, as well as the main north-south lines of central Canada, pass through Winnipeg. The twin cities, Minneapolis-St. Paul, have a somewhat similar situation that has led to flour milling and meat packing. Edmonton, oil center, capital, and major commercial city of Alberta, benefits from its position on the main line of the Canadian National Railroad. Calgary, on the Canadian Pacific Railroad, serves the urban needs of the southern farming and ranching district of Alberta, and is also an oil center.

There are many cities in the North European Plain. The two outstanding centers are Moscow, with about five million people, and Berlin, with more than three million. Both cities benefit from transportation, commerce, and industry in addition to their political functions. At least twenty cities in Germany exceed 100,000 population, most deriving their significance from industrial activity and transportation. Nearly as many are found in Poland with Warsaw, the capital and largest city, exceeding 600,000. Leningrad, with over three million people, is the second largest city of the Soviet Union. There are a number of industrial centers within the Soviet area; especially important are those of Northern Ukraine, Volga Valley, Southern Urals, and Kuznetsk Basin.

The main city of the Far East region is Harbin, Manchuria, at the point where the Chinese Eastern Railway crosses the Sungari

FIGURE 10-29. *Ottawa, capital city of Canada.* (Royal Canadian Air Force.)

FIGURE 10-30. *Helsinki, Finland. Looking down on the South Harbor and marketplace.* (Finnish National Travel Office.)

River and makes junction with the rail line southward. The present population is more than 750,000. Khabarovsk and Vladivostok are the principal cities in the Soviet Union portion. Khabarovsk has a favorable situation on the banks of the Amur River just below the confluence of the Ussuri River, where the Trans-Siberian railroad bends southward to Vladivostok, which is the Soviet Far Eastern port. More than one-quarter of the population of Hokkaido are urban dwellers, half of which live in Sapporo, the capital, and Hakodate, the main seaport.

OUTLOOK

Generalizations for the outlook of the Short Summer Humid Continental regions are difficult to make because of complexities of cultures, standards of living, political ideologies, and the aftermath of World War II. The American region, divided between two progressive nations, should experience further development; it has the land, resources, and technology, and is not overburdened with redundant populations. The stage of careless resource exploitation has probably passed and the era of scientific management and utilization is beginning in forestry, agriculture, fishing, and mining. The St. Lawrence Seaway, a long-discussed project to improve navigation from the Atlantic to the Great Lakes, soon will be constructed through the joint efforts of the United States and Canada. This will be an industrial asset, allowing easier movement of raw materials and finished goods. The basic supports of the North American region are definitely improving.

The European region, torn by war and disrupted by political realignments, has a clouded future. In any event there are physical limitations in arable land and other resources that will hamper major growth.

During the past quarter-century the Soviet Union has advanced from a backward agrarian nation to the number two world power. Agriculture has been socialized and modernized and a large industrial capacity has been established, although these accomplishments have been at the expense of the personal freedoms of the peoples. Many of the components of Soviet strength are found in the Short Summer Humid Continental region. The European portion has likely witnessed its greatest growth; continued development will more and more be based upon the resources of Siberia. The greatest future weakness is in agriculture since much of Soviet territory is plagued with low rainfall and short, cool growing seasons. Mineral and forest endowments are more favorable and the planned economy should bring greater industrialization.

The oriental frontierlands of Manchuria and Hokkaido, with room for people and underdeveloped resources, offer some promise.

SELECTED REFERENCES

Cressey, George B., "Changing the Map of the Soviet Union," *Economic Geography,* XXIX, No. 3, 1953, 198-207.

Deasey, George F., "The Tourist Industry in a 'North Woods' County," *Economic Geography,* XXV, No. 4, 1949, 240-259.

Green, John D., "There is Plenty of Iron," *Steelways,* No. 14, January, 1948, 1-5.

Gregory, J. S. and D. W. Shave, *The U.S.S.R.; A Geographical Survey.* New York: John Wiley and Sons, Inc., 1946.

Jorré, Georges, *The Soviet Union, the Land and Its People.* New York: Longmans, Green & Company, 1950.

Kemeny, George, "Eastern Europe: Development in Social and Economic Structure," *World Politics,* VI, No. 1, 1953, 67-105.

Lincoln, Freeman, "Battle of the St. Lawrence," *Fortune,* XLII, No. 6, 1950, 84-90.

Shimkin, Demitri, B., *Minerals, a Key to Soviet Power.* Cambridge, Mass.: Harvard University Press, 1953.

Smith, J. Russell, and M. Ogden Phillips, *North America.* New York: Harcourt, Brace and Company, Inc., 1942.

Volin, Lazar, *A Survey of Soviet Russian Agriculture.* Washington, D. C.: U. S. Department of Agriculture, Monograph No. 5, 1951.

Zimmerman, Erich W., *World Resources and Industries.* New York: Harper and Brothers, 1951.

CHAPTER 11

Dry Continentals

THE DRY CONTINENTAL REGIONS are lands of variety. Great stretches of middle latitude grasslands and deserts occupy seemingly endless expanses of plains and plateaus. Climate from region to region differs greatly in yearly temperatures, due to variations in latitude, but scanty rainfall is the common denominator. Risk and failure haunt the croplands of semi-arid portions, where farmers attempt practices common in the humid lands. Low rainfall raises the land-man ratio—holdings change in size from acres to sections or square miles and in name, from farm to ranch or station. Crops are restricted to drought-tolerant cereals. Grass is the chief resource in many areas and there, grazing is the basic activity. The pastoral economy varies in complexity from that of the

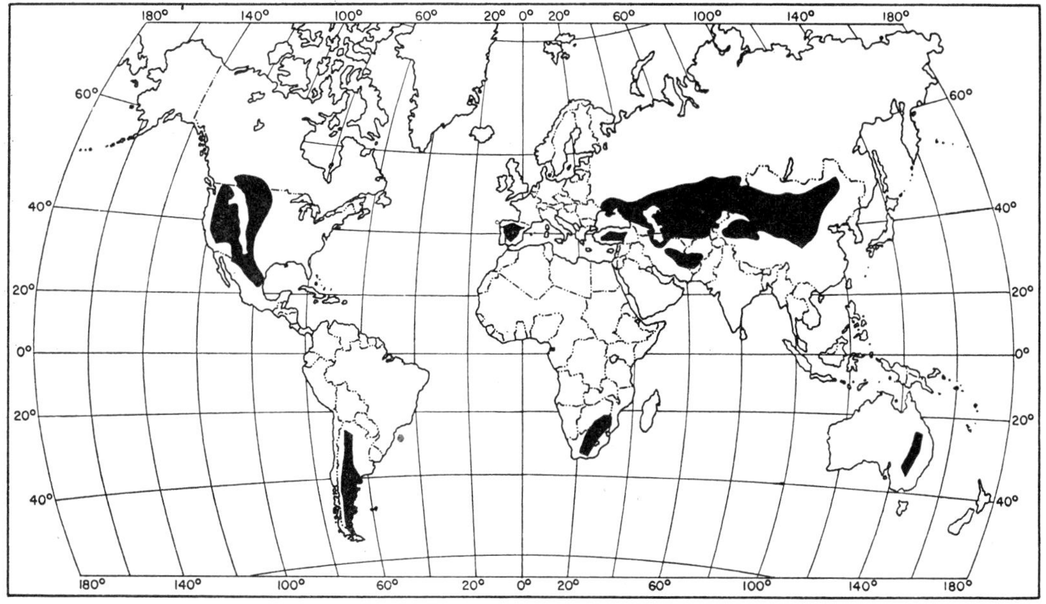

FIGURE 11-1. *The Dry Continentals.*

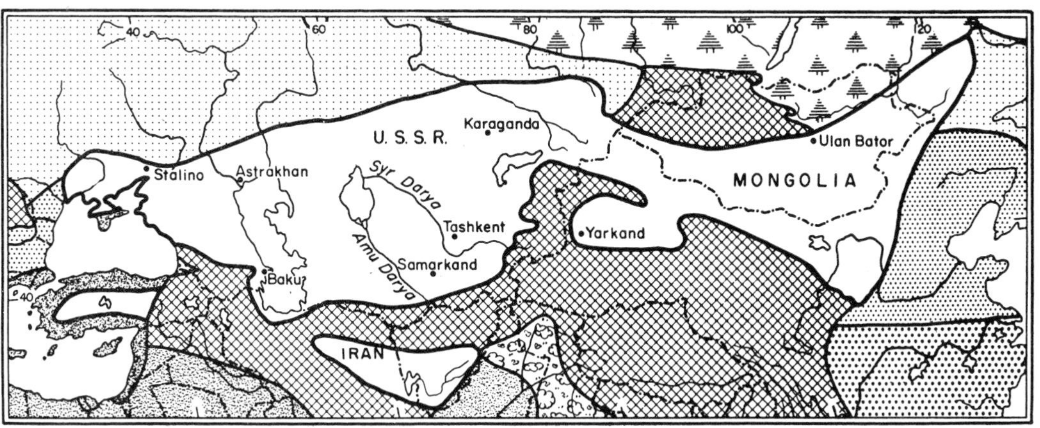

FIGURE 11-2. *The Dry Continentals of Eurasia.*

wandering nomad of central Asia to large commercial livestock ranches with huge herds of beef and bands of sheep in other regions. Settlements are widely dispersed, having developed mainly near mineral deposits and in oases where dependable supplies of water stimulate irrigation and intensive agriculture. Man and his works are almost obscured by the immensities of space in all of the Dry Continental regions.

Location

The Dry Continental regions have two characteristic types of locations: one, deep in the interior of the large continents, distant from the oceans, the principal sources of atmospheric moisture; the other, in the dry shadows on the lee side of high coastal mountains. These locations account for scant precipitation. Regions are

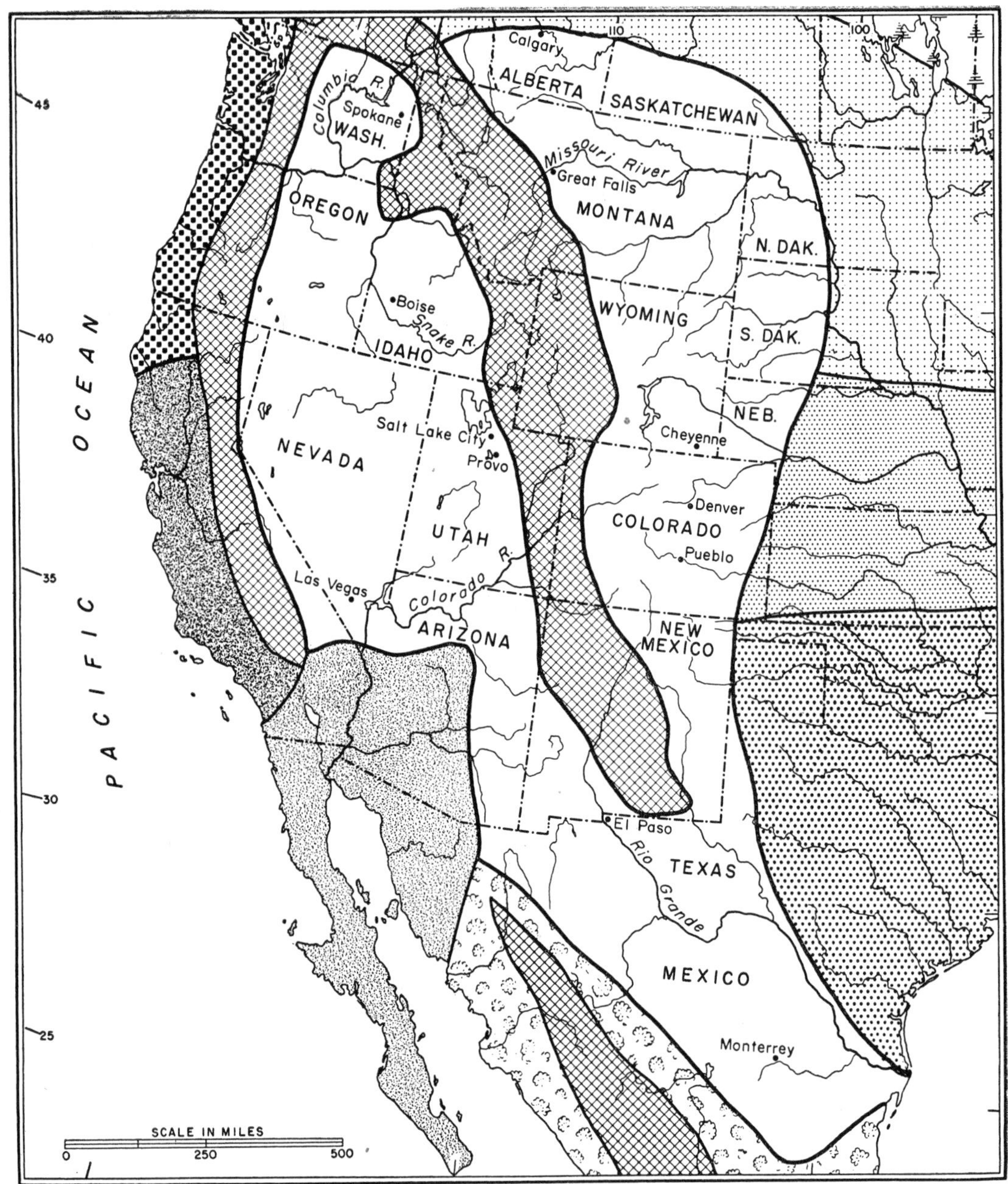

FIGURE 11-3. *The Dry Continentals of North America.*

found on all the continents, but the widest distribution is in the great land masses of the Northern Hemisphere.

The largest region is found in the heart of Eurasia, filling the vast space that extends from western Ukraine and the Caspian Sea to the Loess Highlands of northwest China. Distance from the Atlantic Ocean and the barrier of the earth's major highland system place the entire area out of the range of normal rain-bearing winds. Smaller Eurasian regions include the interior plateaus of Turkey

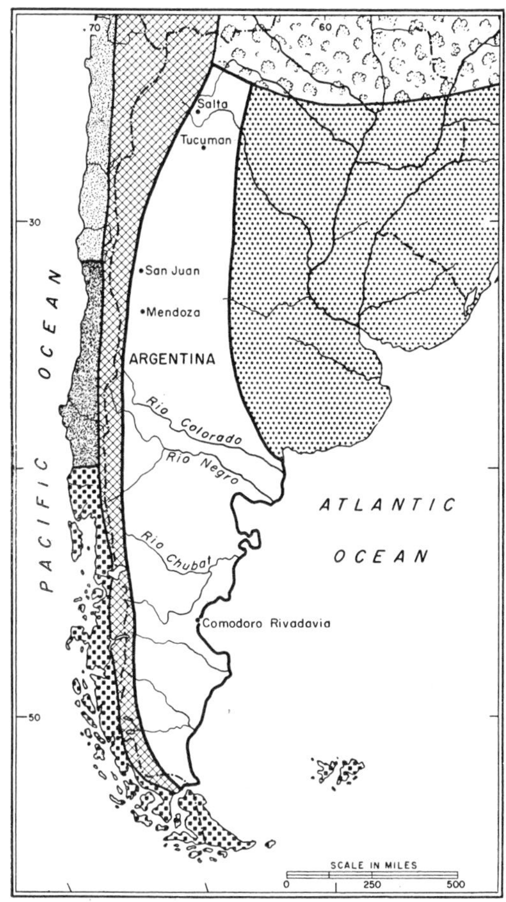

FIGURE 11-4. *The Dry Continentals of South America.*

and Spain—the Anatolian Plateau and the Spanish Meseta.

The Dry Continental regions of North America occupy a major portion of the middle latitudes between the hundredth meridian on the east and the Sierra Nevada-Cascade Mountains on the west. The Rocky Mountains separate two divisions—the Great Plains on the east and the Intermontane Province on the west between the mountains.

South America contains the only land mass in the Southern Hemisphere that extends far enough into the middle latitudes to develop extensive Dry Continental climate. A region lies in the lee of the Andes Mountains in Argentina. Owing to the narrowness of the continent, the entire area known as Patagonia is in a dry shadow and the region reaches the sea along its eastern border. Limited land extensions into the middle latitudes restrict the size of the Dry Continental regions in Africa and Australia. In Africa a region lies west of the Drakensberg Mountains, and in Australia a small region occurs west of the Eastern Highlands in New South Wales.

PHYSICAL ENVIRONMENT

Climate

The Dry Continental climates are lacking the homogeneity characteristic of the previous regions. Temperature contrasts are the major differences. The regions fringe mild, subtropical lands in nearly all cases. In Asia and the Americas, the great north-south extent of the regions through more than 20° latitude results in cold winters poleward. Narrow Patagonia faces the south Atlantic and is marine-modified. Only during the summer months do all the regions have temperature similarities; however, they all have extremes of heat and cold. Aridity and its environmental influences are the unifying factors.

Temperatures. There is no typical temperature for any one Dry Continental region as a whole. The mean July temperatures range from about 60° in the poleward margins to over 80° near the subtropics. Maxima exceeding 100° occur throughout all regions. Winter temperatures show even greater contrasts. The January means for stations near poleward margins range from below 30° to as low as −16°, at Urga, Mongolia. Blizzards and non-periodic cold spells drive thermometer readings far below average. Stations in the northern Great Plains record lows of −40°. In contrast, winters are mild on the subtropical margins. In Africa and Australia coldest months are usually above 50°. Two stations in Patagonia indicate the influence of latitude on temperature: Santiago de Estano in the north has a January average of 83.1° and a June average of 55.9°, while Santa Cruz,

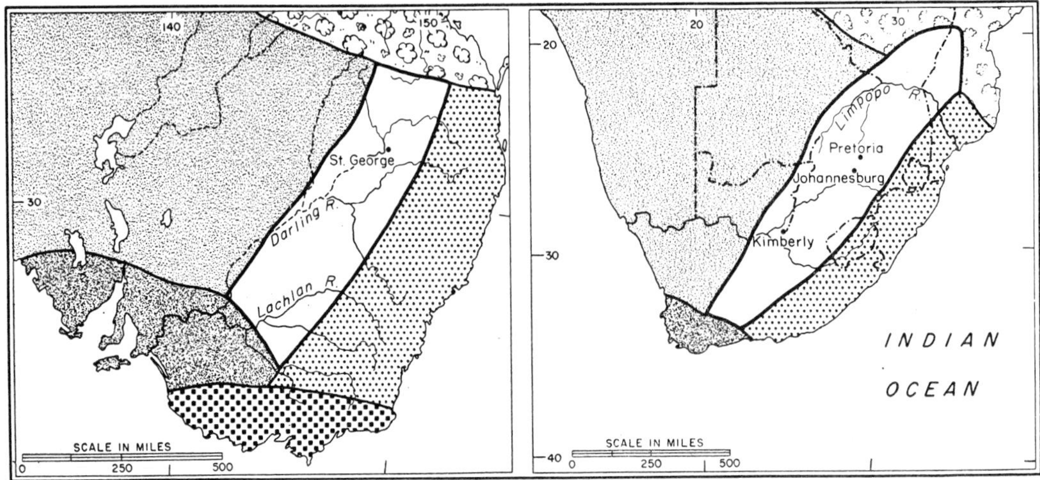

FIGURE 11-5. *The Dry Continentals of Australia and Africa.*

32 degrees farther south in latitude, has a January average of 58.6° and a June average of 35.2°.

Sunshine is abundant, especially during the summer. Clear skies promote both rapid daytime heating and nocturnal cooling, causing high diurnal ranges. Relative humidity is usually low, especially in summer. Frost-free periods range from all year in parts of Australia and South Africa to about 90 days in poleward areas of North America and Asia.

Winter temperatures in the lands bordering the eastern foothills of the Rockies are modified by foehn or Chinook winds. These winds develop when an air mass is forced up and over a mountain range. The air, becoming cooler as it rises, causes water vapor to condense and the release of latent heat retards cooling. When the air mass descends on the lee side of the mountain, it is heated by compression. Consequently the descending air is relatively warm and dry, raising lee-side winter temperatures appreciably. This warm wind is sometimes called the "snow eater," as its warming effect rapidly melts the snow cover exposing the grass. Temperatures have risen from below zero to 40° or 50° in a few hours. The Chinook is especially welcomed by cattlemen with stock on the range. Strong winds are common in the deserts during summer, filling the air with dust and sand; in the U.S.S.R. the desert casts its spell beyond its boundary and dry, scorching winds play havoc with crops in the middle and lower Volga Valley.

Precipitation. Precipitation characteristics of low amount, irregularity, and undependability are common in all areas. On the basis of amount two phases can be recognized: the steppe or semi-arid lands, on the humid margins such as are found in the Great Plains of North America and grasslands of western Asia, and the desert, such as the Takla Makan and Gobi of Central Asia. Semi-arid areas receive between 10 and 20 inches of precipitation. Evaporation rates, however, must be considered in measuring precipitation effectiveness. Where temperatures are high during the season of precipitation, evaporation rates are also high; therefore, 20 inches of rain on subtropical margins are much less effective than the same amount poleward. In fact, 20 inches of precipitation poleward often place an area within the humid limits—such is the case in the Prairie Provinces of Canada discussed in the Short Summer Humid Continentals. Middle latitude desert precipitation is practically the counterpart of the Tropical Desert—10 inches and under.

Precipitation is concentrated chiefly in the summer half of the year, except on Dry Summer Subtropical margins where winter maxima are the rule. Elsewhere, winters are relatively dry, due to the presence of high pressure air masses; some snow falls, but the cover is usually light. Convectional showers, accompanied by thunder and lightning, are usual in summer, and destructive hail storms often occur. In the desert, some years are almost rainless and in others, sudden violent rainstorms drench the land. Irregularity is also typical of the semi-arid phase and often several wet years are followed by several years of drought. During the humid years farmers and stockmen prosper, but they suffer great economic loss during years of drought.

Surface features

Surface features are very similar to those of the tropical dry regions. The same types of weathering, degradation, and aggradation are at work; there is the same grass-shrub vegetation, and the general absence of permanent streams.

Eurasia. Extensive plains, basins, and plateaus characterize the great Eurasian region. Three major landform divisions comprise the Soviet Union segment: the plain of southern Ukraine, the Turan Lowland, which includes the plains between the Caspian Sea and the central Asiatic mountains, and the Kazakh Uplands, an ancient mountain mass worn down to rolling hills and plains that separate the Turan Lowland from the West Siberian Plain. Mountains divide the drylands of Inner Asia into several distinct units. The almost rainless Tarim Basin lies north of the Plateau of Tibet between the Altyn Tagh and the Tien Shan Mountains. The Dzungarian Basin, which forms a lowland corridor between Mongolia and Soviet Middle Asia, is located between the Tien Shan Mountains and the Altai ranges; both basins are in Sinkiang. The largest unit is the Gobi Desert of Mongolia, the world's most northern desert. Surrounded by mountains, this broad basin-like depression appears as a rather featureless plain with many areas of desert pavement and shallow hollows without exterior drainage.

The Loesslands, one of the most unusual areas in the world, form the transition from the Gobi Desert to the sub-humid North China Plain. This region of hills, mountains, and valleys is mantled with wind-laid silt or loess. The fine powdery loess, varying from a thin film on the steepest slopes to depths of 300 feet, has apparently been carried by the strong winter monsoons from the Ordos Desert which lies to the west. Many people here live in caves cut into the loess walls of the valleys. Such dwellings are cool in summer and warm in winter, but disastrous when earthquakes occur, as they sometimes do.

North America. Two broad physiographic provinces may be recognized in North Amer-

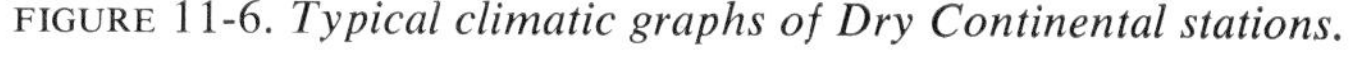
FIGURE 11-6. *Typical climatic graphs of Dry Continental stations.*

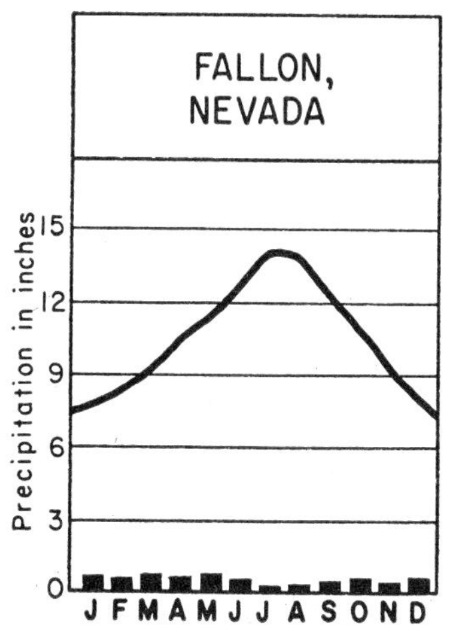

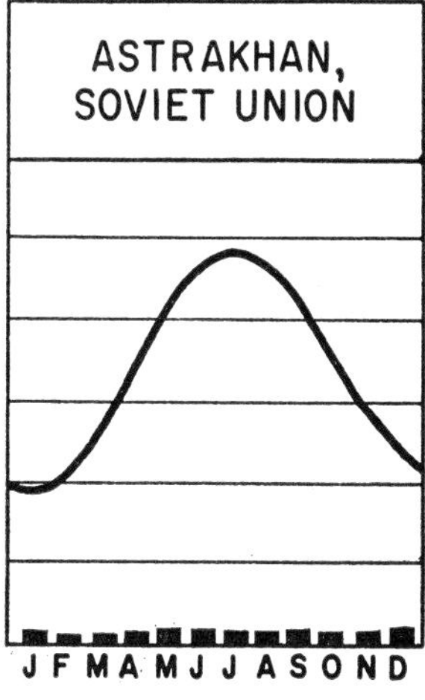

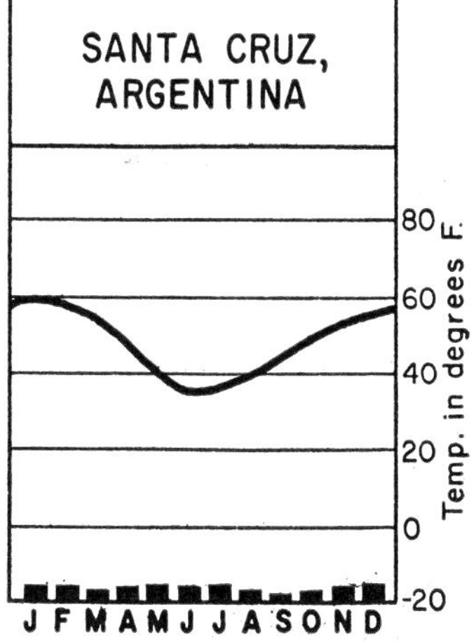

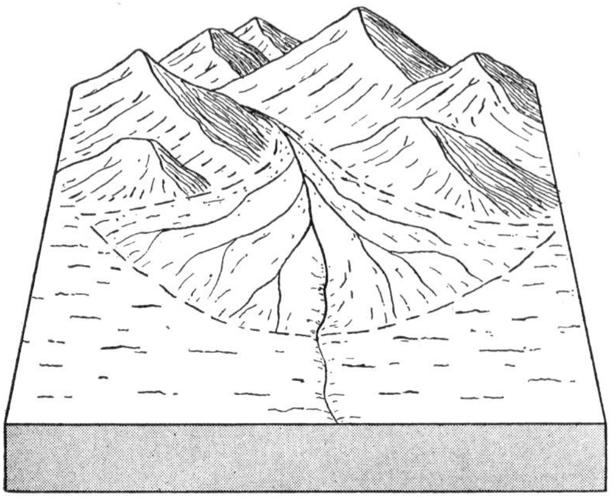

FIGURE 11-7. *An alluvial fan.*

ica: the Great Plains east of the Rocky Mountains, and the Intermontane Plateaus and Basins between the Rockies and the Sierra Nevada-Cascade Mountains. The former stretches northward from the Rio Grande to the Mackenzie River in Canada, a distance of 4600 miles, with an average width of about 400 miles; however, as Figure 11-3 indicates, not all of this area is included in the Dry Continental region. The general surface is remarkably flat, but the elevation declines gently from 5500 feet at the eastern base of the Rockies to 1500 feet at the western border of the Central Lowlands. There are local variations in surface. For example, in northwestern Nebraska there is a hilly sand dune belt; in Wyoming and the Dakotas there are extensive areas of bad-land topography where minute dissection has produced exceedingly rough surfaces with very complex forms; there are also several mountain outliers, such as the Black Hills of South Dakota and Wyoming. Terraces are present in the major stream valleys, indicating several uplifts of the region, causing rejuvenation of downward erosion.

The Intermontane Province is much more complicated than the Great Plains. The Mexican Plateau occupies the southern portion; this large expanse of arid land is characterized by many isolated ranges rising 2000 to 3000 feet above the general surface. These mountains are usually asymmetrical fault blocks, formed by upward thrusts along zones of fracture in the earth's crust. Among the ranges there are alluvial fan-fringed basins of interior drainage with playa lakes (see Figures 11-7 and 11-8). These basins have been termed *bolsons,* from the Spanish word meaning purses. On the north, the Colorado Plateau occupies a major part of New Mexico, Arizona, and Utah. This great area of some

FIGURE 11-8. *A bolson and ranges.*

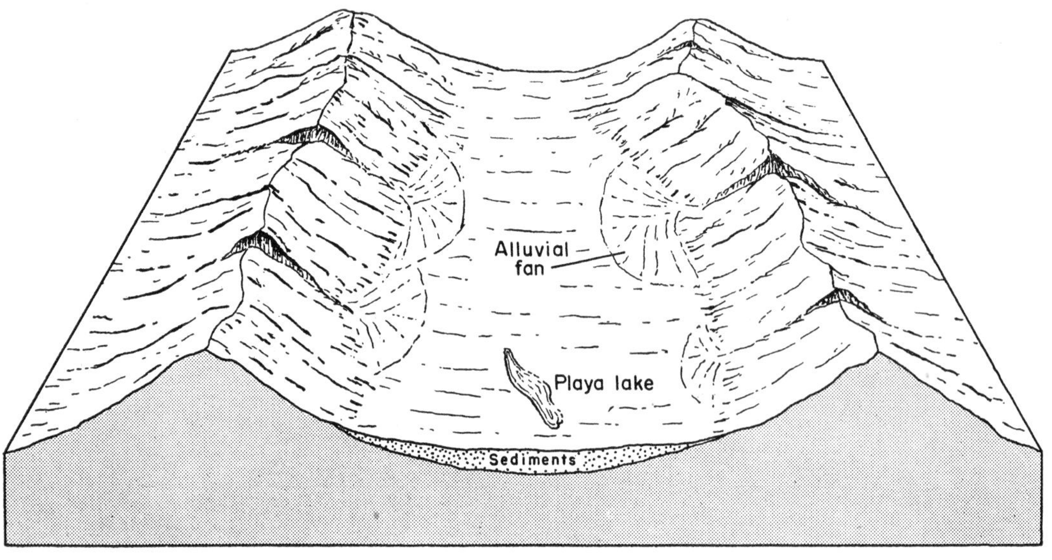

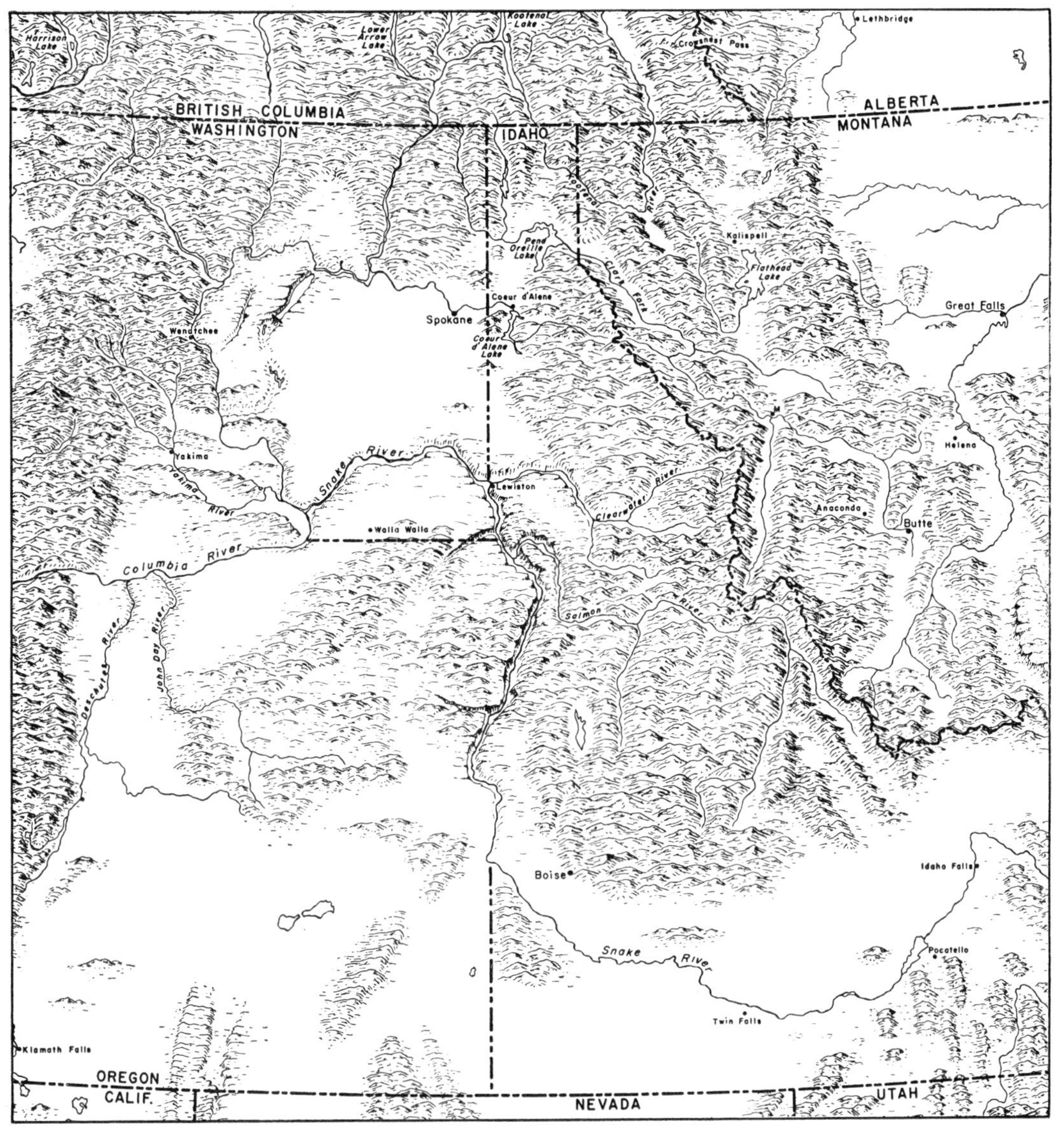

FIGURE 11-9. *Physiographic diagram of the Intermontane Province of the Pacific Northwest.*

130,000 square miles is made of brilliantly-colored and nearly-horizontal sedimentary strata. The work of running water has carved fantastic landscapes, including many vertical-walled canyons, the most magnificent of which is Grand Canyon of the Colorado River. Northwest of this plateau is the Great Basin, an area of interior drainage and mountain and bolson topography. The characteristic features are numerous basins separated by block mountains which trend north-south. The ranges are commonly 50 to 75 miles long and rise 3000 to 5000 feet above the basin floors. The surface of the Great Basin grades almost imperceptibly into the Columbia Basins and Plateaus in the northern part of the region.

FIGURE 11-10. *Aerial view of the Grand Coulee Project. This great man-made structure has a generation capacity of nearly two million kilowatts and is a key to the irrigation of a million acres of arid land which are being developed in the central plains of the Columbia Basin. The water is lifted by giant pumps 280 feet from Lake Roosevelt into an equalizing reservoir that occupies the northern portion of the Grand Coulee, the great ice age melt-water channel of the Columbia River. From the southern end of this reservoir a system of canals and laterals is being constructed to carry water to the land.* (United States Bureau of Reclamation.)

FIGURE 11-11. *Grass is the dominant vegetation in areas with 10 to 20 inches of annual precipitation.* (United States Forest Service.)

The unifying features of the Columbia Basins and Plateaus are the extensively-distributed surface of lava and the common drainage by the Columbia River system. Actually there is a variety of land forms. The Blue-Wallowa-Seven Devil Mountains roughly divide the province into the Columbia Basin in the north and the High Lava and Snake River Plains on the south. The northern part of the Columbia Basin was considerably altered by glacial meltwaters which poured across it to rejoin the Columbia River, and in so doing carved many channels, the most famous of which is Grand Coulee.

Southern Hemisphere. In Argentina, the plain of the north part of the Dry Continental region gives way to plateau topography in Patagonia, that extends southward from latitude 38° or 39°. This southern sector slopes eastward from an elevation of about 5000 feet near the base of the Andes to a few hundred feet along the coast. The regions of Africa and Australia also occupy piedmont positions. The former, an area known as the High Veld, slopes westward from the Drakensberg Mountains; the Australian region occupies a similar position to the west of the Eastern Highlands.

Natural vegetation

Low precipitation largely restricts the natural vegetation to grass, scrub, and desert xerophytes. Trees appear only on slopes of higher elevations, where precipitation

FIGURE 11-12. *Subtropical vegetation in the Intermontane Province of the United States. In this Nevada scene are blackbush and the Joshua tree. Notice that the minute detail of the landforms is clearly visible.* (United States Forest Service.)

FIGURE 11-13. *Sagebrush in the Columbia Basin.* (United States Bureau of Reclamation.)

is more abundant or where they grow along water courses.

Steppes. Grass, the vegetative cover in semiarid lands of nearly all the regions, varies in height and density of stand with precipitation and available soil moisture. The Great Plains of North America is a short-grass region, dominated by buffalo and grama grass in the north and central portions, and by mesquite grass in the warmer south. Bunch grass is found west of the Rockies. The grasslands of South Africa are known as the *veld.* Short grasses form much of the cover in Eurasia and Australia. Northern Patagonia is distinctive for its large number of low shrubs; farther south the country appears as a vast treeless moor with grass tussocks.

Deserts. Grasses are gradually replaced by low shrubs on the drier margins with varieties differing latitudinally and to some extent from continent to continent. Sagebrush is the usual vegetation in the North American deserts, and yuccas and cacti appear on the subtropical margins. Other species include greasewood, creosote bush, mesqüite, and shadscale. The scanty desert vegetation is xerophytic, utilizing all the protective devices of nature to fight aridity and high rates of evaporation.

FIGURE 11-14. *Buck pronghorn antelope.* (United States Fish and Wildlife Service: E. P. Haddon.)

Native animal life

The grasslands are the habitat of a variety of herbivorous animals as well as carnivores, rodents, reptiles, and birds. Insect life is common in all regions; grasshoppers and locusts are the greatest pests, doing considerable damage to range and crops. The steppes of Asia are inhabited by antelopes, wild asses and horses, bactrian camels, and wolves. In North America there are wolves, coyotes, antelope, and smaller animals such as the jack rabbit, gopher, and prairie dog. The bison at one time was the dominant animal of the North American region; today only a few small protected herds exist. Patagonia has many small rodents but few large animals. On the veld of South Africa, the animals are quite similar to those inhabiting the savanna to the north. Marsupials, typified by the kangaroo, are common in Australia and the emu and the dingo, or wild dog, also range the Australian steppe. Rabbits, introduced during early settlement, are extremely numerous and constitute a problem for stockmen.

Soils

The soils fall into the major division of zonal arid or pedocal—soils in which carbonates accumulate, usually in the B horizon. In response to lowering precipitation and decreasing vegetation cover, several groups are formed. The chernozems and the brown soils are found in the semiarid grasslands. Chernozems develop in the higher rainfall margins under tall, deep-rooted grass. Precipitation is not great enough to produce leaching and as a result this group is high in mineral plant food as well as organic matter supplied by the extensive root

FIGURE 11-15. *A native dwelling in the Orange Free State. Cultures differ greatly in the Dry Continentals of South Africa. This simple thatched-roof hut contrasts sharply with the modern farm home of the Europeans in the region.* (Union of South Africa Government Information Office.)

systems. These black earths are high in fertility and excellent agricultural soils; the major limitation is the low precipitation which restricts their normal crop adaptability. There are two large areas of chernozems: one stretches through southern Ukraine and across the southern margin of the West Siberian Lowland, the other occupies the eastern margin of the Great Plains of the North American region. The brown soils have developed on the margins of the chernozems under slightly lower precipitation and shorter grass. The soluble salt accumulations are nearer to the surface and the grass roots provide less organic matter, hence the lighter color. These soils are fertile, but are strictly limited for crop agriculture, owing to deficiencies in rainfall, and are used dominantly for livestock grazing.

The soils of the Middle Latitude Deserts largely fall into the gray desert soil group, although parent material may result in other light colors. The content of organic matter is low. Lime and other soluble substances accumulate near or even on the surface; usually concentrations are not sufficient to be harmful to plants. However, alkali areas do occur where the surface accumulations of soluble salts are so great as to be injurious to plants.

The fertile loess merits special mention because the semi-arid phase has the greatest distribution of this wind-laid soil of any of the regions of the world. The middle-latitude deserts, with little protective vegetation, are easy prey for the winds. Silt-laden winds from these arid lands, blowing across the bordering grassland, deposit their load to be held by the more complete vegetative cover. In addition to the Loess Highlands of China, extensive areas occur through central Ukraine into the steppe lands of western Siberia, in the Palouse Hills of eastern Washington, and in the Missouri-Mississippi Valley. The Palouse Hills are unusual. Viewed from the air they are like a billowy sea. Despite a high percentage of slope land, deep, rich soils have encouraged almost complete utilization for cropping.

MAN IN THE DRY CONTINENTALS

The Dry Continental re- ·e frontiers of modern settlement; but upancies of some are very old. The ›wns of the deserts of Inner Asia are and the neighboring steppes have lized by Mongol nomads for centuries ng. Major development in other re- relatively recent, and in many cases, lving. Much of the progress has been the twentieth century, resulting from d transportation, mechanization of better techniques, large-scale irriga- jects, and growth in markets. Apparently even the Inner Asian region is also undergoing some modern development under Soviet direction.

Agriculture is the principal activity—three phases are significant: dryland grain farming, irrigation crop production, and livestock grazing. The first and last are extensive types with dispersed settlements supporting relatively few people. The densest populations occur in the irrigated districts. The Loesslands of China support the largest population; despite the semi-arid character of the climate, there are more than forty million farmers. In contrast, extensive areas of the Gobi Desert are entirely without people and this is also true in many other portions of the arid regions. Mineral discoveries have added to the importance of

FIGURE 11-16. *Modernization of agriculture is under way in Turkey. This method of cutting wheat is a vast improvement over the old hand sickle. Notice this Caterpillar Diesel was manufactured in Peoria, Illinois.* (Turkish Information Office.)

FIGURE 11-17. *A view of wheat fields in the north central Oregon plateau. Notice that the fields occupy only the level to rolling lands on the interstream areas. The slopes are avoided because of erosion danger and the difficulties of utilizing machinery.* (United States Department of Agriculture Soil Conservation Service.)

the U.S.S.R. region, making possible the development of a major industrial area in eastern Ukraine and in several scattered, lesser centers.

Dry farming in the semi-arid lands

There is some crop production in all the major semi-arid regions, and this phase of agriculture has been increasing in significance. The climate is best suited to grain and grass-type plants. Wheat is the chief cultivated crop and, together with the bordering sub-humid lands, these regions constitute the wheat granaries of the world. The Chinese, Soviet Union, North American, and Australian regions are especially important, and parts of the plateaus of Turkey and Spain are also cultivated. The Soviet region contains much of the better farmland of that nation.

One, two, three, or even more sections of land commonly comprise the farm units in all but the Chinese region. Operations are fully mechanized, with tractor-powered equipment worked in gangs so that 20 to 60 feet of land can be cultivated or seeded in one swath around a field. In those areas where precipitation is between 10 and 15 inches, crop production usually requires a summer fallow rotation. On alternate summers the land is cultivated and kept free of weeds but no crop is produced; the soil thus has an opportunity to store moisture and nitrogen for the following year. In the areas of 15 to 20 inches of precipitation, a crop is often produced each year. Several crops other than wheat are also grown in the semi-arid regions. Some cotton is found in southern Ukraine and in the southern part of the Great Plains. Sorghum, kafir corn, and millet locally replace wheat as the principal grain or are sometimes used as a rotation, especially in areas with hot, dry winds. Large acreages of sunflowers are grown in the Ukraine.

The Loesslands of North China are the most distinctive semi-arid region. Despite adversities of climate and slope, population densities rival those of other areas in the Orient. Methods are necessarily more intensive but crops are similar to those of other semi-arid regions. Millet, winter wheat, and kaoliang lead the food crops with cotton, tobacco, and opium the major cash crops. The ratio of population to cultivated land, nearly 1200 per square mile, has made this one of the most serious famine areas in the world; a slightly drier-than-normal year results in lower crop yields for the farmer and insufficient food for all.

Farming can be treacherous business in any of the semi-arid regions because droughts appear to be part of the normal climatic cycle. A series of wet years may encourage extensive modifications of natural conditions that may lead to disaster. The United States Great Plains serve as an excellent example of man's struggle with nature in these regions.[1] Fol-

[1] For a detailed discussion of the physical characteristics of the Great Plains and the evolution of their use and misuse, see *The Future of the Great Plains,* Report of the Great Plains Committee. Washington, D. C.: U. S. Government Printing Office, 1936.

FIGURE 11-18. *The raw desert before irrigation. This barren ground near Moses Lake, Washington, on the Columbia Basin Project, marks the site of the Moses Lake Development Farm on November 1, 1946.* (United States Bureau of Reclamation.)

FIGURE 11-19. *The desert blooms. This view is of the same area shown in Figure 11-18. High-yielding croplands have replaced the low-quality grazing lands.* (United States Bureau of Reclamation.)

lowing the War between the States, a major wet period, coinciding with the building of transcontinental railroads and an increase in westward population movement, encouraged settlement on the Great Plains. The 160 acres allowed by the Homestead Act was far too small to support a family by grazing; settlers were required to put this land under the plow, regardless of its suitability. Not until 1909 was the homestead tract enlarged to 320 acres; and although in 1916 grants of 640 acres were authorized, a provision was made that they be used solely for grazing. Thus the homesteader often had to plow when plowing was harmful to the land and was sometimes forbidden to plow when plowing might have been profitable and unharmful. Much of the land remained in grass because of these limitations. Large herds of cattle grazed on what was practically one great open pasture, extending from Texas to Montana. Drought began in 1886 and continued until 1895 and the "cattle barons," faced with financial disaster, almost faded from the scene.

Farming during the nineteenth and early twentieth centuries expanded in wet years and contracted somewhat in dry years as farms were abandoned. On the whole, however, cultivated land expanded at the expense of the range. After 1910, the advances in mechanical equipment and the high prices paid for wheat became powerful influences. Large acreages were turned by the plow—including lands with a history of drought. If sufficient rain fell there was a harvest, if drought supervened there was not. Dry years characterized the climate of the plains in the early thirties and severe drought conditions burned the plains in 1934. Scores of farmers and cattlemen lost their land and livestock. Just as overgrazing impaired the natural pastures, so wrong tillage methods injured what had been considered tillable land. Soil exposed to the winds was lost in great quantities, especially in the south. Only now is man beginning to learn that he must work with, rather than in opposition to, nature if he is to live permanently in this region.

Similar problems have long plagued the Russians. Much of their agricultural area is periodically subject to drought. The Middle and Lower Volga Valley and adjacent areas constitute the principal portion with recurring dry years. In the period 1891 to 1937 there were only 11 years of good moisture supply; 22 had partial droughts and 15 had full-fledged droughts. More or less extensive droughts were also recorded in 1938, 1939, 1946, and 1948.[2]

Finding ways to combat these calamities has been of special concern to the Soviet Government. In 1948 they announced a fifteen-year program that includes moisture-conserving practices, some local irrigation, and an ambitious program of tree-planting. The most important phases of the latter scheme involve the planting of national forests in the southwest European region on the watershed

[2] Volin, Lazar, *A Survey of Soviet Russian Agriculture,* Agriculture Monograph, No. 5. Washington, D. C.: U. S. Department of Agriculture, 1951, 8.

FIGURE 11-20. *Siphoning water from irrigation ditches to the fields. Plastic tubes convey water to the corrugations between the sugar-beet rows.* (United States Bureau of Reclamation.)

FIGURE 11-21. *A view of the Naches Valley, part of the Yakima, Washington, project. The fruit orchards occupy the sloping lands on the margins while the bottom lands are devoted to annual crops and pasture.* (United States Bureau of Reclamation.)

divides and on river banks such as the Volga, Ural, and Don, and the establishment of tree shelter belts on the collective and state farms. The forests would have a double purpose. First, to help retain the snow more uniformly spread on the ground—this would protect the fall-sown grain and become a significant source of moisture with the spring melt; second, to reduce the soil erosion and soil moisture evaporation produced by the winds off the Asiatic desert. The success of these projects cannot yet be predicted; much depends upon whether or not the trees can be grown—experience has shown that unless good care is given the young trees, especially during the critical first three years, they will usually die.

Irrigation agriculture in the dry lands

Irrigation was the earliest basis for crop agriculture in the middle-latitude drylands. Works for the collection and distribution of water were established in ancient times in the dry heart of Asia. Today in this vast region, people are permanently settled only at the small and scattered oases. Most of these developments are in the Tarim Basin of Sinkiang, and are situated on the upper margins of the alluvial fans which border the mountain. The ancient kanat system of underground tunnels is still the most widespread technique for water distribution.

The southern Turan oases, together with

those on the north flanks of the Caucasus and in the lower Volga Valley, are extremely important to the economy of the Soviet Union. The longer growing season in these areas makes possible the growth of crops that could not be produced in other sections of the country. Cotton is the chief crop, occupying two-thirds of the irrigated acreage in the Turan oases. Wheat and rice are the principal grains, and sugar beets and a variety of fruits are important. About 20 million acres are being supplied with water. Irrigation techniques vary from the small ancient kanats to large-scale projects of modern design developed by the Soviet regime.

Irrigation development in the North American region is limited largely to the United States West, including the California regions discussed in the Tropical Deserts and the Dry Summer subtropics. The total exceeds 25 million acres. Much of the acreage is in large-scale projects developed by the United States Government. The projects are too numerous to mention since almost all of the permanent streams provide some irrigation water. Alfalfa, potatoes, sugar beets, and a host of horticultural crops constitute the main enterprises; cotton is a leading crop in the southern areas. Some projects have become famous for their specialties, but in most, agriculture tends to be diversified and livestock production is usually of some importance. Alfalfa and by-

FIGURE 11-22. *A mechanical hop picker operating on a Yakima Valley farm. Hops are well adapted to dry climatic conditions and a large percentage of the United States production now comes from irrigated lands.* (United States Bureau of Reclamation.)

FIGURE 11-23. *Good living is reflected in this scene on a mature irrigation project in the United States West. Notice the high quality buildings. The farmer is cultivating a field of sugar beets.* (United States Bureau of Reclamation.)

FIGURE 11-24. *Loading alfalfa hay in Africa. Draft animals are still important in the farming scheme.* (Union of South Africa Government Information Office.)

products of other crops, such as sugar-beet tops and pulp, are used for feed.

In Argentina a number of oases have developed along the piedmont of the Andes, diverting water from mountain-fed streams. Since they extend through about 15 degrees of latitude, a variety of crops is produced, but there is some local specialization. Mendoza, with about one million acres under irrigation, is the largest, and together with the San Juan oasis to the north produces the bulk of Argentine wine grapes. Tucumán, farther north, is perhaps the most famous oasis; it is synonymous with sugar, producing more than three-quarters of the nation's supply.

FIGURE 11-25. *The world-famous goat from which Angora wool is obtained. This animal can turn the low-quality forage of the Anatolian Plateau into a high-quality, salable product.* (Turkish Information Office.)

Grazing

The Dry Continental regions contain the most significant grazing lands of the world and are the centers of the

FIGURE 11-26. *Fall roundup in the Intermontane Province. Twenty owners have a share in this herd of 2000 Herefords.* (Standard Oil Company of New Jersey.)

FIGURE 11-27. *A view across the grazing and dry farming area of the Orange Free State. The Drakensbergs are in the background.* (Union of South Africa Government Information Office.)

range livestock industry. Land use is dominated by grazing except where precipitation is sufficient for dry farming or where sufficient water is present for use in irrigation agriculture.

Pastoral nomadism in Mongolia stands in sharp contrast to the commercial livestock industries which prevail in other regions. On the steppe lands of Inner Asia, the Mongol nomads keep horses, sheep, goats, yaks, and camels. Animal specialties differ with nomad tribes and from area to area, but sheep are preferred. Animals furnish meat, milk, hides, fleece, fuel, are used for barter, and have social as well as economic significance. The Mongols have no permanent homes but follow their animals along regular grazing routes. Living is much the same as in the days of Ghengis Khan, but the Soviet government is doing much to settle permanently these groups.

State livestock farms have been established by the Soviets in the U.S.S.R. steppe, operated by herdsmen who were former nomads. The collective farms also raise sheep, cattle, horses, goats, and camels. Many improvements have been made in the traditional system; pasture rotation is practiced, breeding stock has been improved, and provisions made for winter feeding. The area is noted for the fat-tailed Khirghiz sheep and for the karakul sheep which produce Persian lambskins.

The range livestock industry of the Great Plains and Intermontane Province of North America is based on beef cattle and sheep. Hereford is the main type of beef cattle, and sheep are Merino or dual-purpose crossbreeds. Cattle are most widely distributed, whereas sheep are chiefly concentrated in the cooler northern sections and the more rugged and arid areas. Sheep are able to utilize steeper slopes and have the ability to subsist on shorter grass than cattle. The greatest concentration of Angora goats in the United States is found on the Edwards Plateau of southwest Texas. Ranches are large, usually over 2000 acres, with some exceeding 100,000 acres. Sizes increase with decreased precipitation, which necessitates more land per animal unit. The isolated ranch sites are usually determined by the presence of water. Buildings consist of the ranch home, bunkhouses for the ranch hands, barns, and corrals. Irrigated hay fields for winter supplemental feeding are often maintained near the ranch headquarters.

Spring and fall roundups are the busiest times for cattlemen; calves are branded and marketable cattle segregated from the herds at that time. The balance of the cattle is scattered in small units over the range, supervised by cowboys. Spring, the lambing and shearing period, is the busy season for the sheepmen. Sheep are maintained in bands, about 1250 ewes plus lambs, and cared for by a lone sheepherder and his dogs. In the Intermontane Province and on the western edge of the Great Plains, livestock are often driven into the mountain pastures during the summer. Texas cattlemen shuttle livestock seasonally between

FIGURE 11-28. *A band of sheep in New South Wales. Australia normally has about 120 million sheep and is a principal producer of the world's finest wool.* (Australian Department of Information.)

humid and dry portions of the plains. Such movement of herds, practiced by grazers in all parts of the world, is known as *transhumance,* which denotes a seasonal movement of flocks or herds of domestic animals between two areas of different climatic conditions.

The Southern Hemisphere Dry Continental regions are especially noted for sheep. Patagonia is one of the great sheep-producers of the world and grazing of these animals is the major utilization of the land. Large *estancias* are maintained by sheepmen of British ancestry. These holdings average 22,150 acres in size, but many are larger—some embrace as much as one million acres. Isolation has made wool the specialty and this product must be moved great distances by truck. Australia is the leading world wool-producer and the principal sheep areas are located in the semi-arid lands. Here huge ranches, known as stations, also specialize in the Merino breed for quality wool. Some stations keep herds of cattle. Australia's semi-arid region is favored for grazing by mild winters, artesian water supply, and a scarcity of animal diseases. In both South Africa and Australia, drought often is a serious problem, causing a scarcity of water and grass. Predators, too, take a toll; in Australia an abundant rabbit population competes for forage and dingos kill many animals; jackals and other wild beasts kill thousands of sheep in Africa.

Fishing

South America is the only continent having a Dry Continental region whose boundaries have an extent of ocean shoreline—the regions in the other continents are landlocked. Fishing is almost a non-existing means of livelihood in these regions—with one major exception.

The Soviet Union has several interior seas, lakes, and lower river courses where important fisheries exist. These are the Black, Azov, Caspian, and Aral Seas, and Lake Balkhash,

FIGURE 11-29. *A washing and crushing plant in the Witwatersrand District.* (Union of South Africa Government Information Office.)

and the Don, Volga, and Ural Rivers, which drain into these water bodies. The catch includes carp, herring, salmon, and sturgeon. The shallow water around the north shore of the Caspian, where the Volga and Ural rivers empty large quantities of organic matter into the sea, is one of the Soviet Union's richest fishing grounds.

Mining

Mining has become an increasingly important activity in the Dry Continental regions in recent decades. The Soviet Union and American areas are especially important now, and the Loesslands of China have possibilities. The latter region has large coal deposits but, owing to the difficulties of transportation and limited industrial development, these reserves have as yet contributed little to China's economy.

Large and diversified deposits in the Soviet region have made possible its rise as a leading mineral-producer. The largest high-quality iron deposit of the nation is found at Krivoi Rog, immediately west of the bend of the Dnieper River. The Donetz Coal Basin, long the outstanding producer, lies about 200 miles to the east. A manganese deposit is located at Nikopol lower down the Dnieper. The leading petroleum production is at Baku on the Apsheron Peninsula, which juts into the Caspian Sea from the west; other fields occur around the eastern and northeastern shores and to the north of the Caucasus Mountains. The principal metallurgical coal source for the Ural steel industry is the Karaganda deposits in the midst of the Kazakh Upland. Near the north shore of Lake Balkhash is a great copper mine, at Kounrad. Salts, common to most deserts, are taken in large quantities in several localities, but particularly from Kara-Bogas Gulf on the eastern side of the Caspian Sea.

Copper, petroleum, and salts are major mineral products of the American region. Copper is mined in a number of localities in the Intermontane Province of the United States, with the Bingham Canyon open-pit mine in Utah the most famous. Petroleum and natural gas deposits are being worked in west Texas, New Mexico, Utah, Wyoming, and the recently-opened field in northwestern North Dakota. Newly-discovered fields are also being developed in Alberta, Canada, as noted in the discussion of minerals in the Short Summer Humid Continental region. Salts are reclaimed from the deposits of Searles Lake, a remnant of an inland sea in the Mohave Desert of California, as well as from the Great Salt Lake of Utah.

Southern Hemisphere regions, except for Africa, are comparatively unimportant in the world picture of mineral production. There is a small output of petroleum in Patagonia. Gold, diamonds, coal, and iron are mined in the South African region; Witwatersrand is the outstanding gold deposit in the world.

Manufacturing

Manufacturing has its greatest emphasis in the Eurasian region, with the second major industrial district of the U.S.S.R. centered in the eastern Ukraine. This district is well situated with respect to resources and markets. The large coal deposits of the Donetz Basin, iron ore of Krivoi Rog, and the supplies of manganese from Nikopol have stimulated an iron and steel industry. The products of the steel mills are manufactured into a variety of commodities, ranging from farm machinery to locomotives. Other activities are associated with chemicals, cement, aluminum, sugar-refining, wheat-milling, leather goods, textiles, and shipbuilding. Hydroelectric power generated on the Dnieper and Volga Rivers and petroleum piped and tanked from the Caucasus and Caspian districts are added industrial attractions. Farther east, Stalingrad, on the Volga, specializes in iron and steel, agricultural machinery (especially tractors), oil refining, and food processing. Southeast of the Aral Sea, modern industrialization has come to many of the ancient oases towns long noted for handicrafts, such as Samarkand, Tashkent, and Fergana, in the form of cotton and silk textile mills, food-processing plants, and a modest steel industry.

In comparison to the great American Manufacturing Belt, the North American region is not a major industrial area, but manufacturing does play a role in the overall economy. Industries rely chiefly on the products of agriculture and include meat-packing, the processing of fruits and vegetables, flour-milling, and refining of beet sugar. Others have been established to take advantage of local minerals, hydroelectric power, or strategic advantages of space and relative isolation. Many smelters operate near mining areas; one-third of United States' domestic copper is smelted at Garfield, Utah. Pueblo, Colorado, possesses a small iron and steel industry and Provo, Utah, produces almost two million tons of steel annually. Aluminum plants are located at Spokane and Wenatchee, Washington, in response to hydroelectric power. Atomic energy projects are found at Hanford, Washington, Amarillo, Texas, Los Alamos, New Mexico, and near Denver, Colorado.

Industry in the Southern Hemisphere is represented by the African region. The major area of development extends from Vereeniging northward through Johannesburg to Pretoria. Johannesburg has steelworks and the other two centers have blast furnaces as well; their combined output has made South Africa nearly self-sufficient in steel. The former city also processes gold and has developed subsidiary industries including chemicals, engineering works, and plants for the processing of agricultural products.

Tourism

The Intermontane Province of the United States is rich in resources favoring recreation and tourism. Resources include natural wonders, desert landscapes,

FIGURE 11-30. *The Boulder Canyon Project. Hoover Dam and Lake Mead are major tourist attractions.* (United States Bureau of Reclamation.)

Indian ruins, and a variety of other scenic and interesting attractions. Many of the spectacular wonders of nature have been preserved for the public in National Parks and Monuments such as the Grand Canyon of the Colorado, Bryce Canyon, Zion National Park, the Petrified Forest, Painted Desert, and Carlsbad Caverns. Although the region is distant from large population centers, excellent highways and rail facilities bring thousands of visitors during the vacation season. It also derives advantages from being a "passing-through-land" for east and west bound traffic; many of the small cities depend in part on the itinerant trade and some are especially geared to draw tourists. Many Americans are attracted by the experience of crossing a foreign border and by the old world flavor of Mexico. As a result there is a notable flow of tourists into the Mexican portion of the region.

FIGURE 11-31. *The Grand Canyon of the Colorado River. Located in northwestern Arizona, this great chasm is 217 miles long, 4 to 18 miles wide, and a mile deep.* (Santa Fe Railway.)

Urban centers

Through the bulk of Dry Continental regions, city-forming factors are absent. In Inner Asia cities are small and usually related to favorable positions on trade routes or in oases. In all the area of Sinkiang no city has as many as 100,000 people; Yarkand is closest, with 60,000. Urga, capital of the Mongolian People's Republic and center of Lamaism and trade, has about 100,000. The Loesslands of China support many towns and at least six cities of 100,000 or more, led by Sian, Lanchow, and Taiyuan.

It is only in the Soviet Union that a cluster of cities is found. There are at least a dozen over 100,000 in the steppe portion of the Ukraine; Stalino, chief city within the Donetz Basin, has over 500,000. Heavy industry, mining, and processing of agricultural crops have stimulated this growth. Oil exploitation and refining are responsible for the development of Baku into a city of the million class, and industry has caused Tashkent to become the metropolis of Soviet Middle Asia, with a population approaching 750,000.

Ankara, on the Anatolian Plateau, was established as the capital of Turkey in 1922, supplanting Istanbul. Since that date it has become a modern city of about 300,000 people. It is centrally located, but otherwise has little to offer as a capital. Madrid, capital

FIGURE 11-32. *Street scene in Ankara, modern capital of Turkey.* (Turkish Information Office.)

of Spain, occupies a similar position on the Meseta. Despite isolation and lack of resources, it has grown to about 1.7 million people; it functions as center of government, banking, and commerce.

Despite the large size of the North American region, there are but four cities above 100,000. Denver, Colorado, at the eastern base of the Rockies, is the largest and is the principal financial and commercial city between the Missouri River and the Pacific Coast. It is a leading livestock and packing center, a market for a large irrigated area, as well as mining headquarters and chief resort focus for the Rocky Mountain area. El Paso, Texas, has prospered as a result of its location on the middle Rio Grande where the river breaks through the mountains from New Mexico. Albuquerque, New Mexico, in the upper Rio Grande Valley, is rapidly approaching 100,000, and Lubbock and Amarillo in western Texas are both over 70,000 and experiencing accelerated growth. The two largest cities of the Intermontane Province are Salt Lake City, Utah, and Spokane, Washington. Their advantages for assembly and distribution are somewhat better than at other centers of the Province. Spokane has developed a significant amount of manufacturing; flour milling, forest products, and aluminum are the leading industries. Salt Lake City is one of the best planned cities in the nation and is the center of the Mormon religion. It should also be noted that although Calgary, Alberta, falls within the limits prescribed for the Short Summer Humid Continental region, it is closely associated with the Dry Continental region, serving as the urban center for the Canadian portion.

Few cities are found in the Southern Hemisphere regions. Tucumán and Mendoza, centers of major irrigation districts of the same names, are the only major cities in Argentina. Johannesburg, a gold-mining, industrial, and commercial metropolis, and Pretoria, an iron and steel center, are the important cities of the South African region.

OUTLOOK

Nature has placed stringent limitations on the possibilities for future development in the Dry Continental regions. Low, erratic rainfall and lack of sufficient water are the universal problems that have restricted settlement in the past and will restrict settlement in the future. The best parts are being utilized—a glimpse at the population map indicates that the areas of close settlement are few and far between.

In the future, as in the past, the bulk of the Dry Continental regions will be best suited to grazing. In most, range management practices must be improved to maintain present levels of the livestock industry; carrying capacities have been impaired and soil resources endangered by overgrazing in many localities. The possibilities for extending dryland farming with present techniques are very limited; in fact, the switch from plow agriculture to grass and livestock production would improve the land-man relationship in many areas.

Extension of irrigation may locally add to the population-supporting base, notably in the U.S.S.R. and the United States. The Soviet Union has grandiose plans for increasing the arable area in her desert land. In the United States a large project is being developed in the Columbia Basin that will ultimately irrigate one million acres, and the Bureau of Reclamation has estimated that an additional 16 to 18 million acres could be feasibly developed for irrigation under present economic conditions.

Mineral exploitation may be extended and additional manufacture may result from increased mining, new hydroelectric power generation, increases in agricultural products or advantages of climate and space. In recent years, many military air bases have been established in Dry Continental United States because the climate provides excellent flying conditions and there is room for air fields, hangars, barracks, and other installations.

SELECTED REFERENCES

Bowman, Isaiah, *The Pioneer Fringe.* New York: American Geographical Society, 1931.

Grattan, C. Hartley, ed., *Australia.* Berkeley, Calif.: University of California Press, 1947.

Hedin, Sven, *The Wandering Lake.* New York: E. P. Dutton & Co., Inc., 1940.

Huntington, Ellsworth, *Pulse of Asia.* Boston: Houghton Mifflin Company, 1907.

Johnson, Vance, *Heaven's Tableland.* New York: Farrar, Straus and Company, 1947.

Schwartz, Harry, *Russia's Soviet Economy,* Second Edition. New York: Prentice-Hall, Inc., 1954.

Scott, Peter, "The Witwatersrand Gold Field," *Geographical Review,* XLI, No. 4, 1951, 561-589.

Tannehill, Ivan, *Drought, Its Causes and Effects.* Princeton, N. J.: Princeton University Press, 1947.

"The Volga–Don Irrigation Project," *Foreign Agriculture,* XVI, No. 10, 1952, 175-178.

Volin, Lazar, "Russian Agricultural Potential," *Foreign Agriculture,* XVII, No. 10, 1953, 175-180.

Zierer, Clifford M., "Tourism and Recreation in the West," *Geographical Review,* XLII, No. 3, 1952, 462-481.

CHAPTER 12

Marine West Coasts

MARINE WEST COAST REGIONS ARE aptly named; in no other lands is the sea such an active force in creating climatic homogeneity. The cyclonic westerlies flowing over vast ocean bodies import a constant supply of marine air that brings ample precipitation, and keeps summers cool and winters mild. Moderate temperatures and liberal rainfall are reflected in nature's landscapes. Greens dominate the color scheme, interrupted only briefly by the yellows and browns of late summer and the bright hues of fall.

Whereas climate provides a salient element of regional similarity, other natural endowments, cultural features, and stages of development have created great contrasts from region to region. Western Europe, the "heritage land"

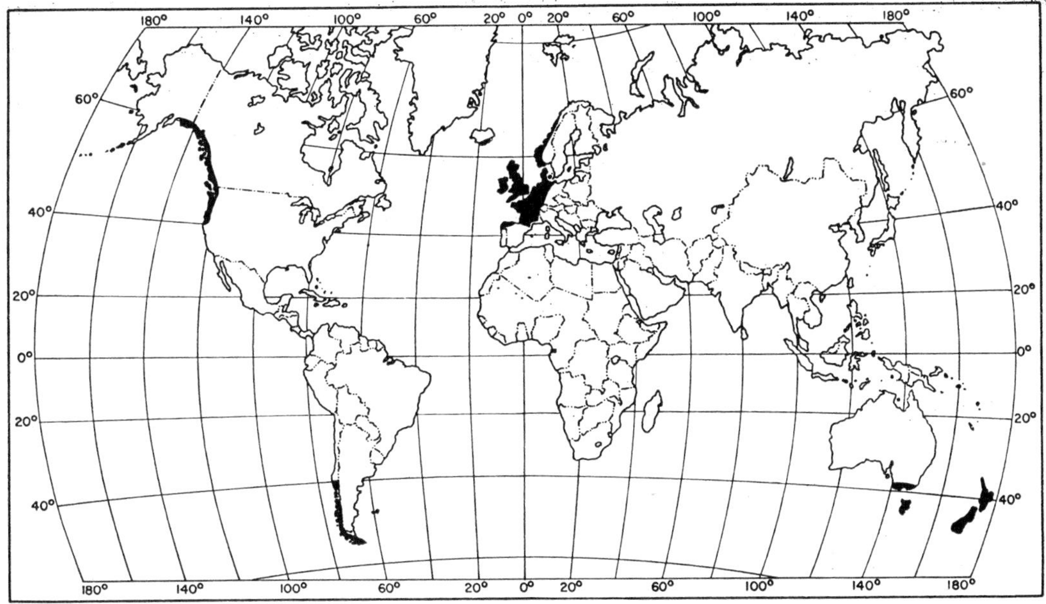

FIGURE 12-1. *Marine West Coasts.*

of most of the peoples of the United States, Canada, Australia, and New Zealand, represents maturity. Here energetic men, utilizing their rich resource base and geographic position, have created a most significant segment of the cultural and industrial world; Western Civilization and the Industrial Revolution epitomize their accomplishments.

The other Marine West Coast regions, less endowed, count their white settlement in years, not in centuries. In contrast to western Europe, their occupancy is immature. The Pacific Northwest of North America shows the most promise, based on its land, water, and forest. Isolation from the great world communities is the major handicap of the regions in the Southern Hemisphere.

Location

The Marine West Coast regions are located poleward of the Dry Summer Subtropics on the western margins of the continents, in the heart of the cyclonic westerlies. The greatest region is in western Europe, extending from northwest Spain to northern Norway. Included in the bulk are the British Isles, western France, western Germany, the Low Countries, and Denmark. The North American region, known as the Pacific Northwest, includes northwestern California, the Pacific slopes of Oregon, Washington, and British Columbia, and the southern fringe of Alaska. The South American region is confined to the southern one-third of Chile. Australia, with a limited area influenced measurably by the cyclonic westerlies, has only a small region that includes most of Victoria and all of the neighboring island of Tasmania. New Zealand, 1200 miles southeast of Australia, is an isolated island marine region.

PHYSICAL ENVIRONMENT

Climate

Marine West Coast regions owe their climate chiefly to continent-margin locations in the path of the cyclonic westerlies. The eastward streams of air are modified by passage over the sea, therefore the atmosphere

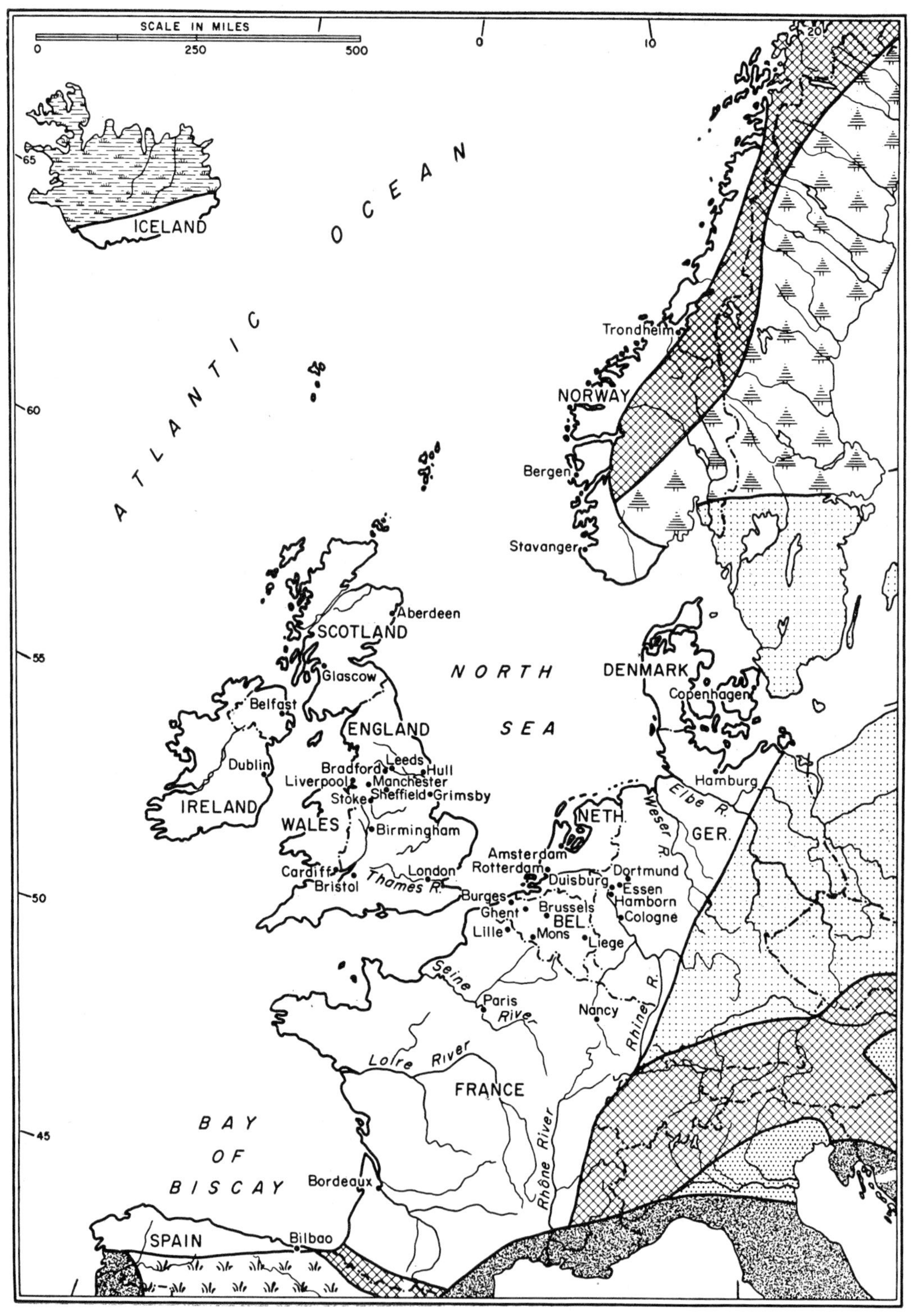

FIGURE 12-2. *Western Europe.*

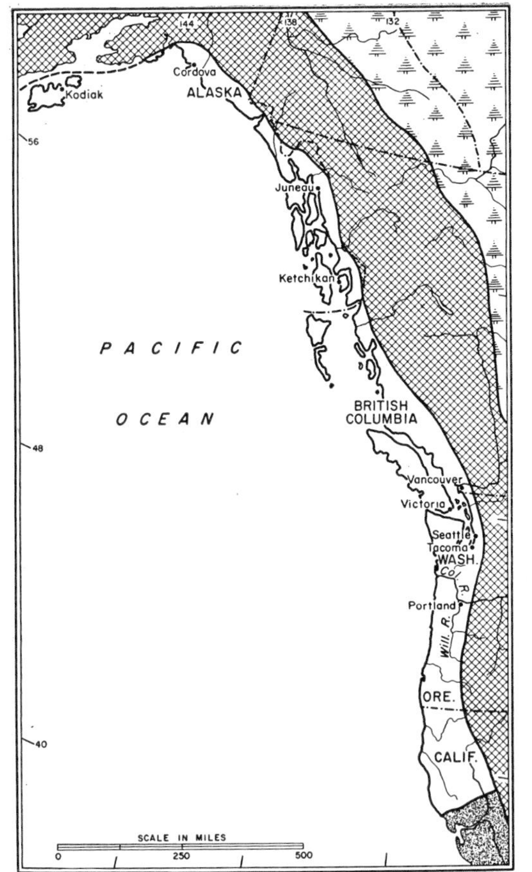

FIGURE 12-3. *The Pacific Northwest.*

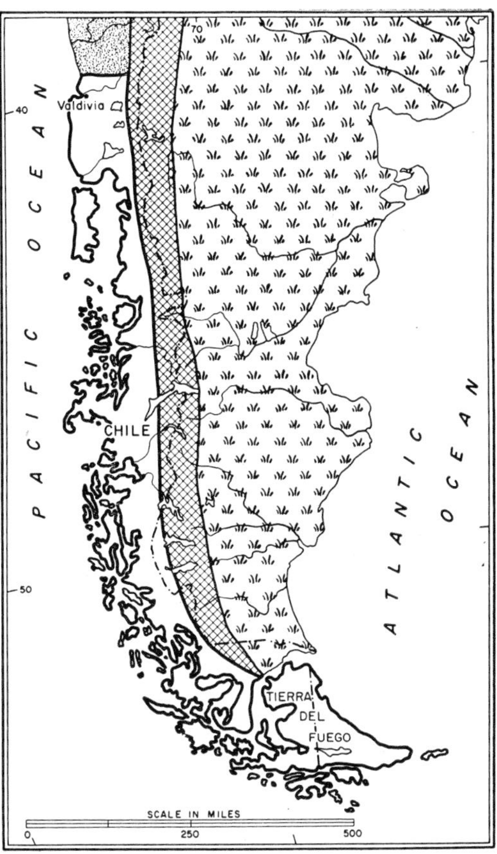

FIGURE 12-4. *Southern Chile.*

FIGURE 12-5. *Australia–New Zealand.*

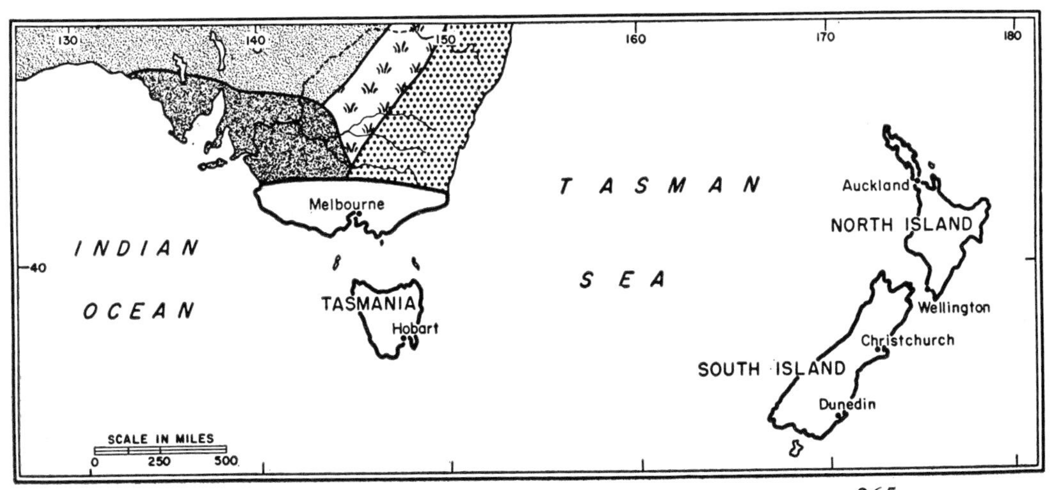

FIGURE 12-6. *Juneau, Alaska. Along the Panhandle of Alaska the mountains drop sharply to the sea, restricting the Marine West Coast climate to the lower seaward slopes.* (Pan American World Airways.)

over the land is ruled by marine air masses. Temperatures are mild for the latitude and annual extremes are small. Clouds and rain are typical for many months of the year, but considerable sunshine occurs during summer and early fall, especially on subtropical margins.

The modifying effect of the comparatively warm ocean on the incoming air masses explains why marine climates extend beyond 60° N. latitude in Norway and Alaska. The shoestring shapes of the Marine West Coast portions of Norway and Alaska, as well as that of the region in Chile, are due to mountain ranges which closely parallel the coast and restrict marine modification inland.

Temperatures. Summers are cool with average July temperatures usually about 65°. Portland, Oregon, has a July average of 67.2° and London, England, 62.7°. Weeks of hot weather are rare, but maxima occasionally reach 90° and above. Summer nights are seldom too warm for sleeping, and blankets are often needed for comfort. Winters are mild, with January averages in the neighborhood of 40°. Seattle, Washington, records a January average of 39.8° and Dublin, Ireland, 42.1°. Two factors account for winter mildness: the stored heat in the offshore ocean bodies, and warm ocean drifts, which bring tropical heat from equatorial waters. Thus the incoming air is warmed, causing winter temperatures to average about 25 degrees higher than inland areas of Europe in similar latitudes. W. G. Kendrew writes, "The air over the ocean west of Norway is more than 50 degrees warmer than the average for the latitude, the greatest anomaly of temperature

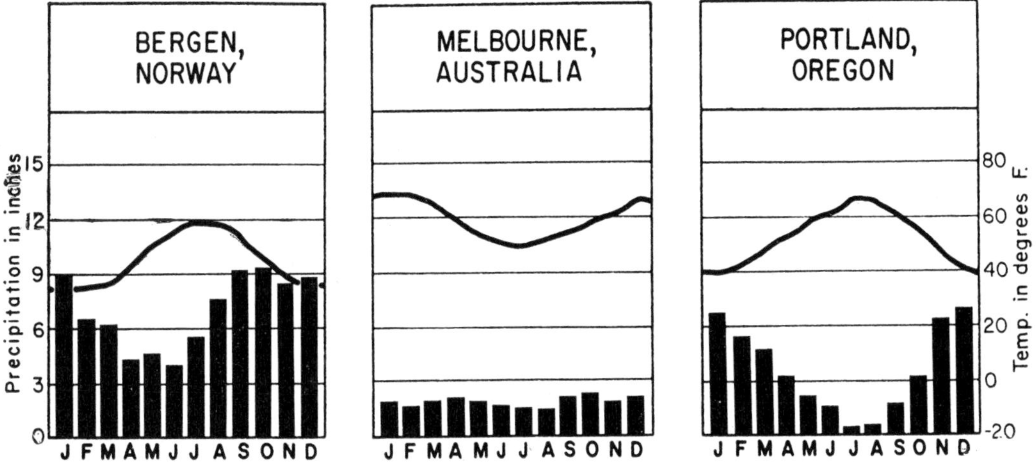

FIGURE 12-7. *Typical climatic graphs of Marine West Coast stations.*

known."[1] Vancouver, on the coast of British Columbia, has a January average of 35.6°, 38 degrees warmer than the −3° recorded at Winnipeg, Manitoba, in the interior, but less than one degree higher in latitude. Although winter temperatures are mild, one may feel uncomfortable due to the high relative humidity. Sensible temperatures at 40° are chilly, raw, and penetrating, whereas in the interior of the continent 40° would be considered fairly comfortable. There are few spells of cold weather, especially in regions where mountains block out cold continental air; but in western Europe, where high protecting mountain ranges are lacking, the area is subject to cold waves from the Eurasian interior. Winter diurnal ranges are low because clouds and water vapor retard nocturnal cooling. The atmosphere operates on the same principle as the panes of glass on a greenhouse and the process is sometimes called the "greenhouse effect." Incoming short wave radiation passes through the atmosphere but long wave earth radiation is largely absorbed and only a small part is lost directly into space. The earth's radiation absorbed by the atmosphere is re-radiated and therefore earth heat is retained in the lower atmosphere. Yearly ranges of temperature are from 15 to 25 degrees. Length of growing seasons is from about 150 days near poleward margins to as high as 300 days equatorward.

Precipitation. Mild, extended rain and

[1] Kendrew, W. G., *Climates of the Continents.* New York: Oxford University Press, 1942.

FIGURE 12-8. *Topography and precipitation.*

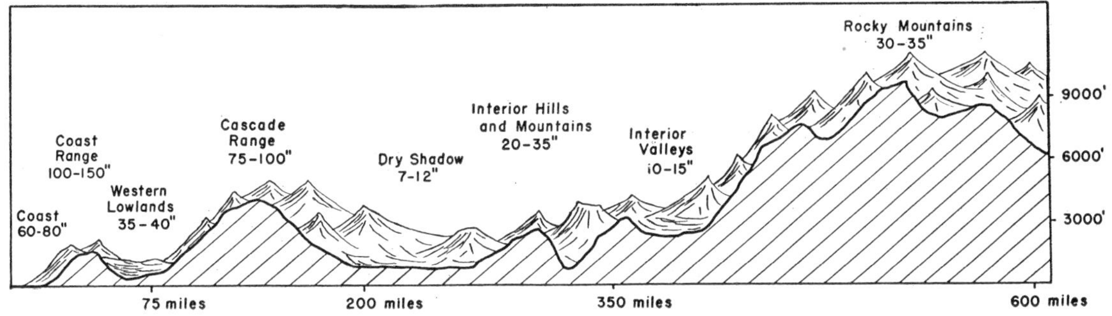

FIGURE 12-9. *Scene in the Tillamook Burn, Oregon, Coast Range. The Burn, which encompasses 355,397 acres of forest land, is the most famous fire-killed timber area in western North America. Twenty years ago it contained one of the finest stands of growing timber in the Douglas fir region, and loggers were only beginning to harvest the prime crop. Then came the great fire of 1933. This and subsequent fires during the summers of 1939 and 1945 killed an estimated 12 to 13 billion board feet of timber.* (Oregon State Board of Forestry.)

cloudy weather are truly Marine West Coast characteristics. Averages are difficult to state since amounts vary with relief, exposure, and distance inland (see Figure 12-8). Windward slopes near coasts receive from 80 to over 100 inches a year while leeward locations commonly receive from 30 to 40 inches. For example, 200 inches of rain falls annually on a small windward area near the south end of Vancouver Island, but the city of Victoria, a few miles to the east, has only 30 inches. Where coastal mountains are lacking, as in western Europe, moderate precipitation is carried well inland. Precipitation occurs during all seasons but many areas tend to have winter maxima. Cyclonic disturbances are most active at this time and severe storms often lash the seacoast.

Toward the eastern margin of the Marine region in Europe, the continental influence becomes stronger and there is a tendency for precipitation to become more concentrated in the warmer half of the year. Precipitation is chiefly cyclonic in origin, falling in long continuous drizzles. Thunderstorms are infrequent, ranging from three to ten a year. On the lowlands there are only a few days with snow, which seldom remains on the ground for long. Highlands, however, have deep snow covers. There are a large number of rainy days; Seattle, Washington, has 151 days with rain while Valencia, on the west coast of Ireland, has 252. The intensity is low as illustrated by Seattle with a total precipitation of only 32 inches. There is much cloudy weather, which gives these regions the distinction of being the cloudiest on earth. Fogs are prevalent, especially along the coast; Great Britain averages 50 foggy days a year. Average relative humidities are high and on the littorals the air is nearly always damp. During summer, however, humidities are occasionally so low in the Pacific Northwest (30 per cent and under) that logging operations are stopped to prevent forest fires.

Precipitation has a high degree of reliability; drought is infrequent. Subtropic margins, particularly in North America, have fairly dry summers reminiscent of mediterranean regions. Sprinkler irrigation during the summer has become a common sight in the Puget Sound-Willamette trough; even in the coastal valleys of Oregon, where yearly averages are about 90 inches, supplemental irrigation is increasing.

Surface features

A maximum of rough topography and highly irregular coastlines are characteristic features of most of these regions. The coasts of Norway, Scotland, British Columbia, Alaska, southern Chile, and southern New Zealand are similar. All are fringed with islands and deeply indented with long, steep-walled, narrow arms of the sea known as fiords. These features were produced by

FIGURE 12-10. *Sprinkler irrigation in the Nestucca River valley of western Oregon. This area receives about 90 inches of precipitation annually, but only about three inches fall during July and August, despite a high degree of cloudiness. Dairymen have found supplemental irrigation of pastures profitable during these months.* (United States Department of Agriculture Soil Conservation Service.)

FIGURE 12-11. *Spectacular fiordic scenery of Norway.* (Norwegian Information Service.)

the submergence of ice-scoured mountain valleys that fronted on the sea. Such coastlines have numerous harbors and beautiful scenery, but leave little room for man; the limitations are indicated by the fact that less than four per cent of Norway is arable (see Figure 12-11).

Most Marine West Coast regions are favored with an abundance of water resources resulting from the combination of mountain watersheds in their backgrounds and the persistent precipitation. Hydroelectric power sites are available in many areas, and the obtaining of industrial water supplies is relatively easy. In addition, streams such as the Rhine, Elbe, and Thames in Europe, and the Columbia in the United States, are excellent transport arteries.

Western Europe is the most favorable of the regions. The North European Plain begins at the Pyrenees Mountains and swings northeastward through the Aquitaine and Paris Basins of France, and continues through the Low Countries into Germany. Throughout the greater part of the plain, elevations seldom exceed a few hundred feet, and in the Netherlands about 35 per cent of the country is actually below the mean level of the sea and is protected by sand dunes and dikes.

The Puget-Willamette Lowland in the Pacific Northwest is the only other major area of low relief. Even here the Puget Sound Lowland, as a result of glaciation, has an irregular surface; glacial and glacio-fluvial deposits are widespread and often consist of sterile sand and gravels, the finer materials having been washed free. The Willamette Valley in Oregon is more favorable, floored with alluvial materials carried down from the bordering mountains by the Willamette River and its tributaries; only in the middle and northern portion do hills break the continuity of the flat or undulating surface.

Southern Chile is virtually without level land. The forested slopes of the rain-drenched Andes descend sharply to the sea. Glacial erosion and deposition in the past created numerous lake basins, which are kept brimming full by the abundant precipitation. In contrast to middle and northern Chile, which is without a single good natural harbor, the south has a highly-indented coastline; however, the limited development of the back country provides little commerce to stimulate use of the excellent harbors.

In Victoria, Australia, the continent's mountain divide bends westward and forms the northern boundary of the Marine West Coast region. The coastal strip is somewhat broader than that of the Humid Subtropic region in the east, and is altered slightly in character. The Great Valley of Victoria, separated from the sea by low hills, is the major lowland. The Great Valley is divided into two parts by Port Phillip Bay. Tasmania, essentially an outlier of the Eastern Highlands, is a mass of mountains and hills with small fertile valleys. New Zealand is largely a mountainous country; less than one quarter of its surface is below the 650-foot contour. The two large islands are divided by a main mountain

FIGURE 12-12. *A view of the rugged terrain of the Alaskan Panhandle. Forests and water are two important resources in the future of the area. Note the sharp demarcation of the tree line.* (United States Forest Service.)

axis which extends from Fiordland in the south to East Cape in North Island. On either side of the highlands, small areas of level land occur. These are very limited in extent and are not continuous.

Natural vegetation

Forests, favored by the temperate rainy climate, comprise the typical natural vegetation. Uniformity of cover, however, is lacking and each region has differences in species whose qualities for use vary. Similarities occur mainly in densities of stands and sizes of trees. The luxuriant growth of many forest areas makes them comparable to the selva of the Rainy Tropics.

The forests of western Europe fell prey to the cultivator and were cleared years ago. Oak and beech were the principal species; conifers were scarce and confined chiefly to the higher elevations. Areas with poor soils and drainage were covered by marshes and moors, many of which remain today. With the exception of Norway, many of the forests existing in western Europe have been planted. Some areas, too rugged or with soils too poor for agriculture, now maintain stands of commercial trees. Southwest France has a planted pine forest in the sandy Landes area along the Bay of Biscay. Lowland landscapes viewed from a distance in England and France appear forested due to the many English hedgerows and ornamental trees on estates, and in France, because of the trees and hedges planted for

FIGURE 12-13. *The Netherlands, lowest of the Low Countries. If it were not for the rampart of coastal sand dunes and dikes, much of this nation would be under water. This scene shows a Friesland canal south of Sneek. Barge transportation is an important means of bulk movement in western Europe.* (Standard Oil Company of New Jersey.)

screens and farm and pasture boundaries by the peasants of the *bocage* country (See Figure 12-15, page 274).

The Pacific Northwest contains the most valuable coniferous forests in the world. Thick stands parallel the coast from northern California to Alaska. The redwood is the outstanding species in the hills and coastal valleys on the south margin, with a major concentration in the Eel Valley of northern California. This tree is magnificent, reaching a height of 300 feet with a diameter exceeding 10 feet; a redwood forest is one of the most majestic sights on earth. Dense stands of Douglas fir dominate the conifers in Oregon, Washington, and southern British Columbia. Mature trees attain heights of 200 feet and more with diameters ranging from six to nine feet. Douglas fir constitutes the most important lumber tree of the region. Other large conifers include the western hemlock, western cedar, and spruce. In the Alaskan Panhandle hemlock and Sitka spruce are the major species.

The Chilean region is clothed with rain forests from the coast to the treeline of the Andes. Unlike the Pacific Northwest the forests are dominated by less valuable broadleaf evergreen beeches; however, conifers are found in the higher elevations. Luxuriant forests in the Australian region contain tall, straight eucalyptus which reach heights of 300 feet. Beautiful understories of tree ferns cover the forest floors. Prior to white settlement, approximately three-fourths of New Zealand was covered with broadleaf and coniferous forests. Scrub forests and grass grew on areas of less precipitation. Today nearly half of the forest cover has been cleared for crops and

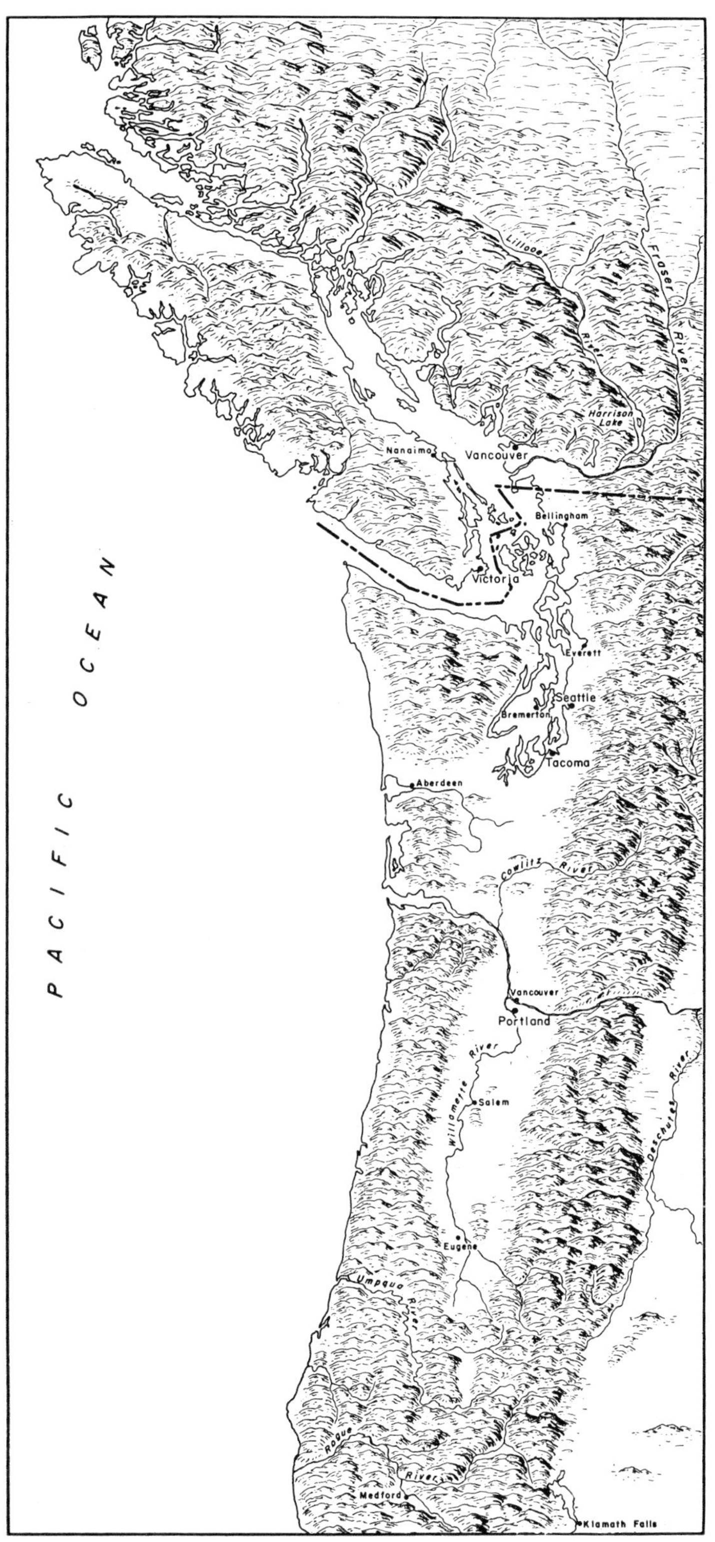

FIGURE 12-14. *Physiographic diagram of the Pacific Northwest.*

FIGURE 12-15. *Hedgerows enclosing farmlands in Somerset, England.* (British Information Services.)

pasture. The remaining broadleafs are chiefly species of beech. Among the conifers, the Rimu or red pine is the principal timber tree. The Kauri, the largest tree of New Zealand, is prized for timber and a valuable resin called kauri gum. Similar to Australia, tree ferns form the understory in many of the forests.

Soils

The soils of the Marine West Coast regions do not fit the world classification scheme as well as those of other regions. The diversity of surface, variations in vegetation, glaciation, and alluvial deposition have produced many local differences. In general, most are leached of their soluble elements and are acid in reaction. Podzols prevail in the poleward areas with conifers, and gray-brown soils are common in those portions that have deciduous forests. In many of the mountainous districts severe glaciation left bare rock exposed at the surface; at the other extreme, youthful alluvial soils of valleys are frequently very fertile, with drainage the main agricultural limitation.

MAN IN THE MARINE WEST COASTS

The Marine West Coast regions, for their size and limitations of surface and soils, support surprisingly large numbers of people. Western Europe has one of the great population blocks of the world. The United Kingdom alone has more than 50 million people, and average densities of 735 and 825 persons per square mile are found in Belgium and the Netherlands. The Pacific Northwest, in contrast, presently supports relatively few people; nonetheless, it is in a stage of rapid development and rather large concentrations are forming in the Willamette-Puget Lowland, including the Frazer River floodplain and delta of British Columbia. A major share of the two million people of Victoria, Australia, dwells within this realm and there is a similar number in New Zealand. South Chile is the only region with a small population; heavy and persistent rainfall, lack of level land, and remoteness have made it unattractive.

Primary production—agriculture, forestry, and fishing—dominates the activities of most regions, but western Europe ranks with east-central North America as a manufacturing belt and preceded that area in industrial development.

FIGURE 12-16. *Virgin redwoods near Crescent City, California.* (United States Forest Service.)

Agriculture

Marine West Coast regions are not endowed with the best conditions for farming. Frequently surface, soils, and the moist, often cloudy maturing season place restrictions on the crops that can be grown. In western Europe there is competition from other forms of land use, especially from industries and urban centers. Fortunately the major plains are located towards the equatorward margins, where summers are warm and not excessively wet. Grass, root crops, vegetables, and certain fruits do well. Of the small grains, oats are best adapted, although barley is grown extensively and wheat is found in the areas with relatively dry summers. The long, cool frost-free season and the mild winters favor pasture production, allowing a long grazing season, and animal industries are usually major enterprises.

Western Europe. The European region leads in agricultural development. Farming here is an old activity but its nature has undergone basic changes in the modern era; today it is often secondary to industry and no country approaches total self-sufficiency. The majority of countries have tended to specialize or stress those enterprises for which their environment is best suited and for which markets are readily available; all seek to avoid major imports. Only Denmark is mainly agricultural; more than 50 per cent of the Danes are farmers. Science, industrious people, standardization of high quality products, and elimination of the middle man by cooperative buying and selling organizations have made their agriculture profitable. They have geared their farming activities to the market needs of the neighboring industrial countries, specializing in dairy products, particularly butter, lean bacon-type hogs which utilize much of the available skimmed milk, and poultry, mainly for eggs. Farms, averaging 25 acres, are intensively managed and devoted to raising pasture, feed, and forage crops. Dairying is the chief phase of agriculture throughout the European region. Beef cattle and sheep are also raised in large numbers, especially in the United Kingdom.

FIGURE 12-17. *Forests for the future. The young stand of Douglas fir in the foreground will be ready for thinning in about 35 years. This selective harvest will provide materials for poles and pulpwood. Approximately 50 years later, the stand will be ready for a complete harvest.* (Weyerhaeuser Timber Company.)

Generally at least one-half of the land is given over to pasture and hay. Many fine breeds, now important in other parts of the world, were developed in the area bordering the North Sea. Crops other than oats, barley, and root crops are important in the drier areas. For example, wheat is grown extensively only in eastern England and the Paris Basin of France.

The Pacific Northwest. Agriculture in the North American region is confined largely to the Puget-Willamette Lowland and small plains scattered along the coast. General farming is common, but enterprises are similar to the European region. Dairying and poultry production are widespread, but are especially important around Puget Sound and in the coastal valleys. Tillamook County, Oregon, has gained a national reputation for quality cheddar cheese. The Willamette Valley is the outstanding agricultural area; favorable gentle surface, fertile soils, and warm dry summers allow the production of a wide range of crops and animals, including grains, hay, grass and forage seeds, a variety of fruits, walnuts and filberts, other horticultural crops, poultry, and livestock. Development of supplemental irrigation by taking water from shallow wells or surface sources with small pumps, and using portable pipes and sprinklers, has increased the possibilities greatly; improved pastures and a significant growth in the acreage of processing crops, such as sweet corn, beans, carrots, and beets, have resulted.

Southern Hemisphere. The Southern Hemisphere's basic limitations are small local populations and great distances to major consuming centers. Agriculture is further restricted in south Chile by excessive rainfall and ruggedness of terrain; here a scant population is engaged in sheep-raising and lumbering. Agriculture, however, is the primary means of support in Victoria, Australia, and New Zealand. In both, the pasturing of animals is the leading phase of land utilization; sheep raising and dairying are the main farm enterprises. Both are admirable adjustments to environmental conditions and at the same time provide products which can be exported—butter, lamb, wool, and cheese comprise the greater part of the items entering foreign trade.

FIGURE 12-18. *The wealth of Denmark in a large measure is related to its livestock. This herd of red Danish cows is on its way to be milked. There are more than one and one-half million dairy cows in Denmark.* (Royal Danish Ministry for Foreign Affairs.)

Fishing

The Marine West Coast region of western Europe possesses one of the world's major fisheries. Rich fishing grounds extend from northern Norway to the Bay of Biscay, but the concentration of the activity is in the waters of the North Sea. Halfway between England and Denmark are the Dogger Banks, one of the most productive fishing banks in the world. A combination of factors has favored the development: plankton is abundant on the shallow continental shelf; smooth bottoms favor the use of otter trawls; aeration of water is provided by tides and currents; rivers bring in large amounts of fish food; warm ocean drifts keep seas open through the winter; drowned river mouths and fiords serve as excellent ports; and a high per capita fish-consuming population provides excellent markets. Cod, haddock, herring, and mackerel constitute the principal commercial species taken.

All the countries of western Europe are engaged in fishing, but the British Isles and Norway are the leaders. Numerous fishing villages border the east coast of Great Britain; Aberdeen, Hull, and Grimsby are the major centers. About seven per cent of the Norwegian adult male population is engaged in commercial fishing; many divide their fishing occupation with farming or lumbering. Bergen, Trondheim, and Stavanger are Norway's most important fishing ports.

Important commercial fisheries are located along the North Pacific Coast of North America from California to Alaska. Salmon are the most valuable species and comprise the major portion of the catch. This anadromous fish is caught in rivers or near river mouths. The Columbia River is the major salmon stream of the region. Halibut and tuna are other significant fish. An oyster industry has been developed in some of the sheltered bays of Oregon and Washington with Willapa Bay of Washington outstanding. Many of the coastal

FIGURE 12-19. *A French farmstead. The French farmer often attempts to produce as many of his daily necessities as possible. French women are not excluded from heavy manual farm labor. Brick is a common building material throughout western Europe.* (French Embassy Press and Information Division.)

FIGURE 12-20. *Hothouses near Brussels, Belgium. In the crowded Low Countries, hothouses make possible the production of out-of-season vegetables and fruits.* (Belgian Tourist Office.)

FIGURE 12-21. *A Willamette Valley landscape south of Salem. Complete utilization of the fertile valley awaits further population growth and expanded markets for agricultural commodities.* (Oregon State Highway Commission.)

cities are fishing ports; Seattle on Puget Sound is the leader.

Fishing in the Southern Hemisphere regions is a minor activity in comparison to the Northern Hemisphere regions; however, both Australia and New Zealand have become increasingly aware of the sea's potential and some fishing activities are being accelerated.

Forest industries

The forest contributes to the economies in all the regions. The Pacific Northwest, however, leads in reserves, production, value, and quality of saw timber. The extensive forests are its greatest natural resource.

The forest industry of the Pacific Northwest is firmly based upon the dense stands of large conifers—Douglas fir, redwood, western hemlock, western cedar, and Sitka spruce. The Douglas fir is the most prevalent and most valuable tree. Its high quality wood is excellent for both lumber and plywood. Western hemlock, the second ranking tree, and Sitka spruce are used mainly for pulp for paper and rayon stock, and western red cedar is used for shingles. Logging operations are highly mechanized. Specially-designed, diesel-powered crawler tractors do much of the heavy work in the woods, but the high lead system employing spar poles, cables, and donkey engines is needed to assemble logs at landings in areas of rugged terrain. From these landings, the logs are transported by truck or rail to sawmills or to rivers for further movement. Power saws are used for much of the tree felling that was formerly accomplished by man-operated crosscut saws. Logging is usually possible through-

FIGURE 12-22. *Fishing is a major industry in Brittany, France. Its many ports facilitate the exploitation of this natural resource. This view of the harbor at Concarneau can be duplicated at many of the small coastal centers.* (French Embassy Press and Information Division.)

out the year, but the woods are sometimes closed by winter snow or by low summer humidities.

Logging in western Europe occurs mainly in Norway. Large stands of Scotch pine and Norway spruce are concentrated near Trondheim and in the southeast. The trees are small in comparison to those in other regions and are cut mainly for the pulp and paper industries. Many Norwegian farmers become loggers during winter.

Logging in Chile, presently a small industry, has little correlation with the large forest area. Several factors have discouraged this industry: the rough and rain-drenched terrain makes logging operations difficult; many of the species are inferior for lumber and give low yields per acre; furthermore, Chile is remote from good markets.

Logging is an active industry in New Zealand—in fact timber demands are depleting present stands so rapidly that it has been necessary to create forest plantations of fast-growing non-indigenous species, as well as to import lumber from North America and Australia. Rimu or red pine and Pinus radiata (an introduced species) constitute about 75 per cent of the cut. Both are used chiefly for building purposes. There is some activity in Australia and Tasmania based on eucalypti.

Mining

Minerals have played major roles in the industrial growth of western Europe. This region is favored with both coal and iron, but all the industrial countries of the region do not have sufficient quantities of these necessities and must trade with neighbors.

Great Britain was the first major coal-mining nation, and the large reserves of this fuel have been a major factor in her industrial growth. Coal has provided not only the basic power source, but also a valuable item of exchange that has been hauled as ballast in British ships to many lands, to trade for raw materials and food. The large and excellent coal deposits of the Ruhr area have in a large measure accounted for Germany's great industrial development. Coal also occurs in the Sambre Valley of France and the seams continue into Belgium and the Netherlands. The major iron ore deposits of western Europe are in the Lorraine District of northeast France and Luxembourg, and lesser deposits are found in Germany, Great Britain and in northern Spain, at Bilbao; the ores of the latter, some of the best in Europe, are exported almost wholly to other countries. Germany and France rank first and third as world potash-producers, with centers around Strassfurt and Mulhouse.

FIGURE 12-23. *Cod is the attraction for settlement of the Lofoten Islands. The barren islands of Lofoten are the center of some of the world's greatest fishing activity. Drying is one of the principal means of preserving the catch.* (Norwegian Information Office.)

FIGURE 12-24. *Ketchikan is one of the leading fishing centers on the Alaska coast.* (Pan American World Airways.)

FIGURE 12-25. *Harvest scene in the Douglas fir region: the accepted method of logging, which brings about continuous production. Patches of the uniformly-mature crop are clear cut, leaving strips and blocks of seed trees for natural re-forestation.* (Weyerhaeuser Timber Company.)

FIGURE 12-26. *Mechanical chain saw being used in the felling of a huge Douglas fir.* (Weyerhaeuser Timber Company.)

Other Marine West Coast regions are largely without minerals. A few small coal deposits occur in the Pacific Northwest, but their low quality has restricted major use. Copper is produced on Howe Sound, British Columbia; a small deposit of nickel is being worked at Riddle, Oregon, noteworthy principally because it is the only primary nickel mine in the United States. New Zealand has several small coal fields and several lignite deposits; there are also a number of lignite fields in Victoria, Australia.

Manufacturing

Western Europe. Western Europe is almost synonymous with manufacturing. Here modern industry had its genesis, and today the region contains one of the largest and most diversified industrial concentrations in the world. Factories employ from 25 to 40 per cent of its working population. Despite sharp competition from more recently developed areas, western Europe continues to produce an important share of the world's goods.

The broad Western European Manufacturing Belt, extending from northern Ireland to western Germany, is endowed with a number of favorable factors that have stimulated and consolidated industry. Numerous coal fields supply power, and a variety of raw materials is available. There is an abundance of highly-skilled labor with a rich background of experience dating back long before the Industrial Revolution. Transportation facilities are excellent with networks of railroads, highways, rivers, and canals; great ports are situated on the river estuaries and a "Marine Broadway" is at the front door. Domestic markets are large and outlets well-established abroad.

Manufacturing does not dominate throughout the belt, rather there are many major and minor districts, usually located on or near coal fields and in ports and transport centers. Eight such districts are recognized in the British Isles: (*1*) Northern Ireland, the most western district, specializing in ships and linen textiles, is centered at Belfast. (*2*) The Scottish Lowland is the industrial heart of Scotland with centers, dominated by Glasgow, on the Clyde River. Industries are varied, but shipbuilding is outstanding. (*3*) The Northeast England district consists of a number of iron and steel and shipbuilding cities along the lower courses of the rivers Tyne and Tees. Shipbuilding, significant here as it is in the former districts, exemplifies Britain's dependency upon commerce. Bordering the coal fields on the east side of the Pennine Mountains is (*4*) the Yorkshire sub-region. The emphasis is on woolen textiles at Bradford and Leeds; however, iron and steel are also important, especially at Sheffield, long known for its high-grade cutlery. (*5*) Lancashire, the cotton textile district, is west of the Pennines. Manchester, dominating the district, is contiguous to a number of smaller cities having textile specialization. (*6*) The Midland or the "Black Country" of England, south of the Pennines, manufactures nearly ever type of metal goods. Birmingham is the center. Shoes, hosiery, textiles, rubber goods, and electrical supplies provide diversification; large potteries are located

FIGURE 12-27. *Loading Douglas fir logs on a truck for movement out of the woods.* (Weyerhaeuser Timber Company.)

FIGURE 12-28. *Coal mining scene near Charleroi in the Sambre-Meuse valley of Belgium. The buildings at the pit heads and the slag piles are as typical of western European industrial areas as the factory smoke stacks.* (Belgian Tourist Office.)

FIGURE 12-29. *Barge traffic on the Rhine. Excellent transportation facilities are key factors in western Europe's industry.* (German Tourist Information Office.)

at and near Stoke-on-Trent. (*7*) South Wales and Bristol constitute a sub-region on the southwest coast. South Wales refines metal and tin-plates steel. Bristol's industries are based chiefly on products of colonial trade, such as tobacco, chocolate, and sugar. (*8*) Metropolitan London, the final British district, is the hub of the country's transportation and the great entrepôt of the world. Heavy industrial plants include shipyards, machine shops, chemical works, and oil refineries; nearly every type of light industry also occurs.

Three significant sub-regions stand out in France. (*1*) Paris, the largest and most important, has long been associated with luxury items such as style-setting clothes, jewelry, perfume, and other quality goods; however, the manufacture of engines and machinery, the refining of oil, and printing and publishing are also important. Many firms have located in Paris to capitalize on the city's reputation for quality production. (*2*) The Northern Industrial sub-region, containing the richest coal field of France, is the metallurgical and textile center and also produces glass and pottery and refines sugar. Lille, chiefly a textile city, is the major center. (*3*) The Eastern France sub-region, located around Nancy in the Moselle Valley, is a metallurgical district based on the Lorraine ore deposits. To the northeast is the Saar Basin, important for coal production and iron and steel.

The Low Countries are significant industrial nations despite their small size. Central Belgium contains the Sambre-Meuse district, where coal-production has fostered a line of industrial cities extending through the valley from Mons to Liége. The emphasis is upon metallurgy, chemicals, and pottery. Verviers, east of Liége, is Belgium's woolen textile and glass center. A second district, the Low Countries Manufacturing sub-region, extends from the Flanders Plain of Belgium into the Netherlands. Textiles lead in the Belgium section,

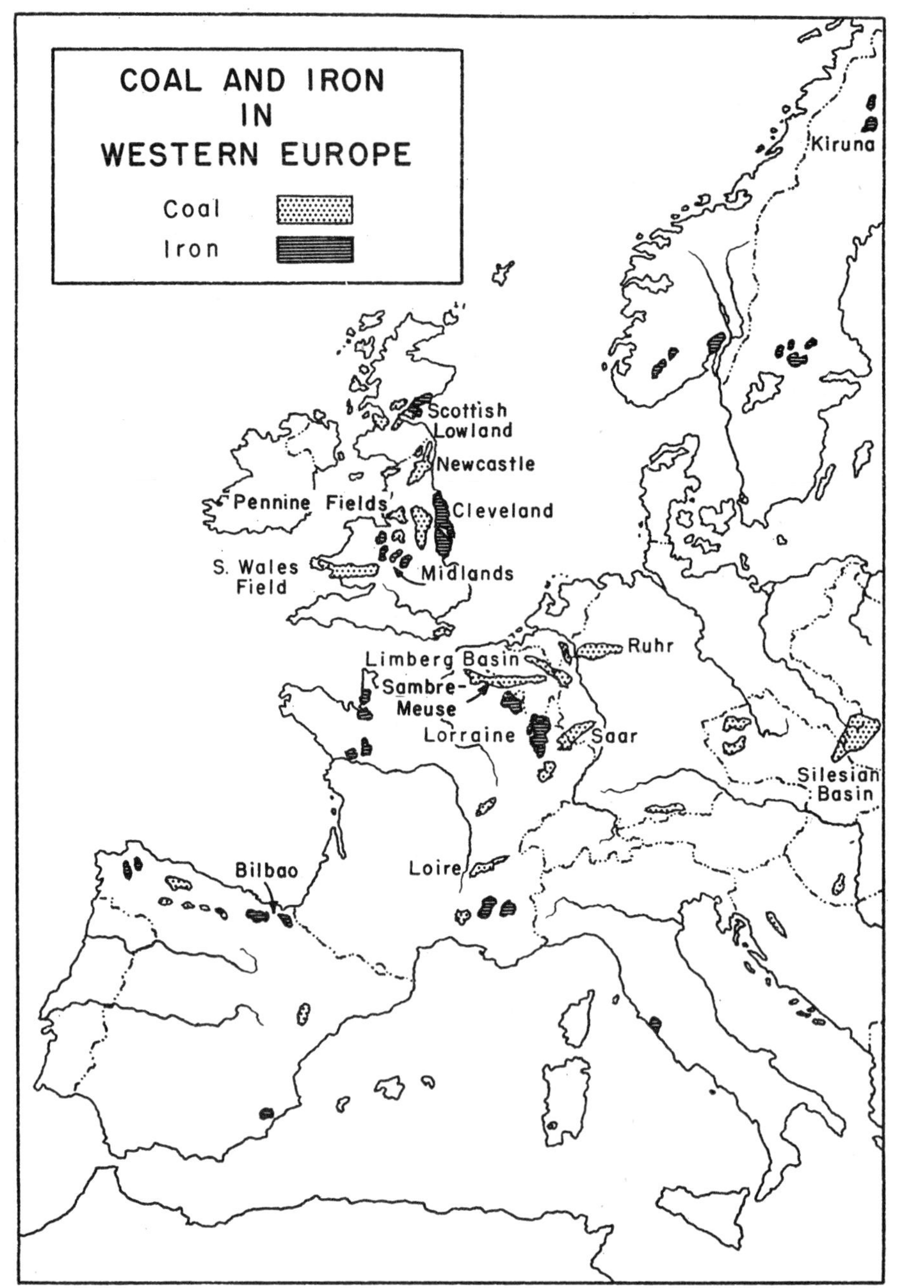

FIGURE 12-30. *Coal and iron in western Europe.*

FIGURE 12-31. *A skilled craftsman at a potter's wheel in Limoges, France—a world-famous pottery center. The great use of hand labor that characterizes much of French industry has given a distinctiveness in style and detail to French products, giving them a premium position in the luxury trade.* (French Embassy Press and Information Division.)

focused at Brussels, Ghent, and Bruges; Breda and Tilburg are the Dutch textile cities. Southeast of these centers is Eindhoven, the great electronics center. Much of the Netherlands' industry centers around the port of Rotterdam and is based on tropical raw materials such as sugar, copra, and rubber; however, chemicals, food-processing, textiles, and others are important, too.

Germany's most important industrial area is located in the Ruhr district, on western Europe's largest coal field. This is the greatest single concentration of heavy industry and coal mining in Europe, as well as in the world.[2] Here iron and steel are basic and a cluster of industrial cities, such as Essen, Dortmund, and Duisburg, manufactures every conceivable item of heavy equipment. Chemical industries are also noteworthy. Despite heavy damage by bombing raids in World War II, the district has made a rapid recovery, primarily due to the need for steel in western Europe.

These sub-regions by no means complete the list of industrial concentrations—only the most outstanding have been highlighted. Hundreds of smaller areas are scattered throughout western Europe. Furthermore, only the typical products of the districts are listed—a complete inventory would be almost endless.

The Pacific Northwest. Industry in the Pacific Northwest is based chiefly on the raw materials of the forest, farm, and sea, hydroelectric power, and a reservoir of skilled labor.

FIGURE 12-32. *Nitrate plant in east Norway. Cheap hydroelectric power is the advantage for this industry.* (Norwegian Information Office.)

[2] Van Valkenburg, Samuel, and Colbert C. Held, *Europe.* New York: John Wiley and Sons, Inc., 1953, 594.

FIGURE 12-33. *Integrated forest products mill at Springfield, Oregon. Here finished lumber, plywood, pulp, container board, and Pres-to-logs are manufactured. Former waste products are almost completely utilized.* (Weyerhaeuser Timber Company.)

Wood processing—in lumber mills, plywood plants, paper and pulp mills, and furniture factories—is the major industry. Lumber mills are scattered through the entire length of the area and are the most typical manufacturing plants. Some lumber mills have an enormous production, sawing as much as one million board-feet a day. Several are multiple-purpose plants producing lumber, pulp and paper, plywood, and often other products; such utilization of the saw log eliminates waste and corresponds to the complete utilization of the pig in modern packing plants (see Figure 12-33). Paper mills, located in response to large supplies of water and raw material, produce several grades of paper, ranging from paperboard to quality magazine paper.

The canning and freezing of fruits and vegetables is a significant industry, with plants distributed throughout the Puget-Willamette Lowland. Salmon canneries located on tidewater are scattered from Alaska to Astoria, Oregon. Cheap hydroelectric power has attracted aluminum plants to the Lower Columbia River area and to Tacoma. At Ruston, near Tacoma, is the largest combined smelter and refinery in the United States. Shipbuilding, the aircraft industry, wool textiles, and the manufacture of work and sports clothes are also important. The Puget Sound Lowland is the major area of industrial concentration and includes the cities of Vancouver, in British Columbia, and Bellingham, Seattle, Bremerton, and Tacoma, in Washington. The Portland-Vancouver metropolitan area on the Willamette and Columbia Rivers is the second large district.

Southern Hemisphere. Industry is minor by comparison in the Southern Hemisphere regions. All are handicapped by their remoteness from markets. Forest-based industries are dominant in Chile. Much of New Zealand and Australian industry is based on agriculture and forestry. Several huge pulp and paper mills are opening to use New Zealand Pinus radiata forests. Melbourne is the principal center of all the southern regions and does manufacture a variety of articles.

Tourism

Marine regions are endowed with a wealth of resources that foster tourism. Western Europe's assets include not only beaches, charming landscapes, historic sites, shrines, churches, and cities, but also a dense population. Culture and historical attractions vie with nature's contributions. All the countries have active promotional programs to entice the foreigner as well as the local inhabitant. Norway advertises "the Midnight Sun" and fiords. Colorful posters emphasize "Come to Britain." The "pull of Paris" is traditional.

Nature is the dominant tourist attraction in the Pacific Northwest. The ocean, lakes, streams, mountains, and forests, combined with cool summers, draw visitors from every part of the United States and Canada. Although the Pacific Northwest does not possess a large population, excellent transportation facilities have favored tourist movement into

FIGURE 12-34. *An automobile assembly plant at Melbourne, Australia.* (Australian News and Information Bureau.)

FIGURE 12-35. *Tourists in the Rhineland. This celebrated valley has many attractions for the European traveller— picturesque towns and cities, ancient castles, and steep slopes devoted to intensive viticulture.* (German Tourist Information Office.)

the area. Furthermore, there is considerable inter-regional travel. Tourism, the third-ranking industry in the region's economy, is growing rapidly.

Remoteness and small populations are the major handicaps of the Southern Hemisphere regions for tourism. Activity is largely limited to local participation. Superb alpine scenery and numerous glacial lakes have stimulated a resort trade in the lake district near Puerto Montt, Chile. New Zealand also possesses natural wonders such as Fiordland, mountains, and hot springs.

Urban centers

Industry and transportation functions have accounted for the development of many concentrations of cities in the western Europe area. The urban character of a high portion of the population is indicated by the fact that 60 per cent of the British are found in cities or urban clusters with over 50,000 persons. Greater London, commercial, governmental, industrial, and financial center, has more than eight million people. Five other cities have more than one-half million: Birmingham, Glasgow, Liverpool, Manchester, and Sheffield. There are at least 50 with populations ranging between 100,000 and 500,000.

Paris, with nearly three million, dominates the cities of the mainland, but there are many industrial centers in north France, Belgium, Netherlands, and west Germany. One of the major concentrations is found in the Ruhr District in the triangle formed by Duisburg-Hamborn, Cologne, and Dortmund. There are eight cities with populations between 250,000 and 500,000. Commerce and associated activities have promoted the growth of a number of large port cities such as Hamburg, Germany, with more than 1.6 million persons, at the head of the Elbe River estuary; Antwerp, main port of Belgium, on the Scheldt River, with about 500,000; Rotterdam, Netherlands, with nearly 700,000, an international transit harbor at the mouth of the Lek, a distributary of the Rhine; Amsterdam, Netherlands, economic center of the nation, with about 850,000 people, and a port by virtue of a canal to the sea; Copenhagen, Denmark, with over one million, commanding the gateway between the North and Baltic Seas; and Oslo, population nearly 450,000, capital and main port of Norway, located on a well-protected fiord in the southeast of the country. Brussels, nearly one million population, differs from most of those mentioned—it developed neither as a port nor industrial center, but rather as the political capital of Belgium. Later it developed considerable general manufacturing and financial and cultural functions. Small seagoing vessels can reach the city by way of a canal to the Scheldt River.

Four ports dominate the urban centers of the Pacific Northwest. From north to south they are: Vancouver, British Columbia, about 400,000; Seattle, Washington, nearly 500,000; Tacoma, Washington, about 150,000; and Portland, Oregon, approximately 400,000. Each owes its growth to strategic situation with respect to water and land transportation. The first three have excellent harbors on Puget Sound, a deep penetration of the Pacific Ocean into the land, where routes through the Cascade Mountains join

FIGURE 12-36. *London, England. Tower Bridge spanning the busy Thames River.* (Pan American World Airways.)

FIGURE 12-37. *Portland, Oregon. The panorama of the city looking eastward to Mt. Hood. The Willamette River bisects the city and provides a navigable waterway for ocean-going vessels from the Columbia River.* (Portland Chamber of Commerce.)

the north-south transportation lines. Portland, 90 miles inland, is situated on the Willamette River, a few miles upstream from its juncture with the Columbia. The latter, the great river of the region, allows ocean-going vessels to move inland to Portland and barge traffic to pass through the Cascades to the heart of the Columbia Basin; at the same time it provides a low level land route through the Cascades and Oregon Coast Range to the Pacific.

Melbourne, Australia, with about 1.5 million people, is the second largest city of the Southern Hemisphere regions. It has a fine position at the head of Port Phillip Bay, centrally situated on the southern lowland. More than one-third of the people of New Zealand live in the four major cities. Auckland, North Island, with a population of about 360,000, is the largest urban center. This commercial capital, located on a spacious harbor, serves the richest lowland. Wellington serves the southern lands of North Island. Christchurch on the Canterbury Plains and Dunedin in the Otago grazing area are the urban centers of South Island.

OUTLOOK

The cultural, political, and economic achievements of western Europe stand unmatched in world history and the influences of European civilization have reached all corners of the earth. It does not appear, however, that the future will be as glorious as the past. In some respects this region may be termed the victim of a maturing world. Much of the economic and population growth in years gone by was based on processing raw materials for youthful, industrially undeveloped areas. The twentieth century has witnessed a world-wide trend toward economic nationalism, with many nations attempting to establish a high degree of industrial self-sufficiency. The industrial nations of western Europe, therefore, have not only lost many former sources of raw materials and markets, but now have competitors for the sale of manufactured products on the remaining world markets. Additional problems in this region, which could function economically as a whole, result from the subdivision of the resources by national boundaries. One could well imagine the limitations that the multiple national ownership of Appalachian coal and Minnesota iron, with resulting tariff barriers, would have on the United States steel industry. Yet such conditions exist in western Europe; plentiful coal and iron are present, but no nation controls sufficient quantities of both.

In the future, western Europe will be striving to hold what she has gained—her industries, markets, raw material sources, and foreign trade. She will have to re-entrench, mustering all possible assets, pressing distinctive relative advantages in industry, developing local resources to optimum output, and intensifying agriculture even further. There will have to be a high degree of co-operation among the nations of the region for the good of all.

The Pacific Northwest is presently in the most rapid stage of development in its history. Agriculture is being intensified; plants for processing wood and wood fiber are increasing; hydroelectric power and ample water supplies are attracting other industries; and the recreation resources of the region are bringing in increasingly greater numbers of tourists. The region has a firm base in land, water, and biotic resources and present trends should continue.

The traditional problem of isolation will be long a deterrent for the Southern Hemisphere regions. Distance, rugged terrain, and wet, cool climate will continue to limit development in southern Chile. The best possibilities lie in increasing forest activities. Victoria is one of the most favorable parts of Australia and should develop as the nation progresses. New Zealand, while small in area, has possibilities in most phases of economic endeavor. There is room for intensification of agriculture, increased industrialization on the basis of water power and local raw material, and even a tourist activity.

SELECTED REFERENCES

Bacon, Lois B. et al., *Agricultural Geography of Europe and the Near East,* U.S.D.A. Miscellaneous Publication No. 665. Washington, D. C.: U. S. Government Printing Office, 1948.

Belshaw, Horace, ed., *New Zealand.* Berkeley, Calif.: University of California Press, 1947.

Freeman, Otis W., and Howard H. Martin, *The Pacific Northwest.* New York: John Wiley and Sons, Inc., 1954.

Highsmith, Richard M., Jr., and John L. Beh, "Tillamook Burn: The Regeneration of a Forest," *Scientific Monthly,* LXXV, No. 3, 1952, 139-148.

Highsmith, Richard M., Jr., ed., *Atlas of the Pacific Northwest—Resources and Development.* Corvallis, Ore.: Oregon State College, 1953.

Hills, Thoe L., "New Zealand Forestry in Transition," *Journal of Geography,* L, No. 7, 1951, 265-276.

Madigan, Thomas E., "Zuiderzeeland: The Province from under the Sea," *Journal of Geography,* LII, No. 7, 1953, 265-275.

Morgan, F. W., "Rotterdam and Waterways Approaches to the Rhine," *Economic Geography,* XXIV, No. 1, 1948, 1-18.

Ormsby, Hilda, *France, A Regional and Economic Geography.* New York: E. P. Dutton and Co., Inc., 1950.

Taylor, Griffith, "Hobart to Darwin: An Australian Traverse," *Geographical Review,* XL, No. 4, 1950, 548-574.

CHAPTER 13

Middle Latitude Highlands

NOWHERE ARE THE STUDIES OF nature and man more involved than in the mountains. Mountains are the most complex, spectacular, and majestic of the landforms of the earth. Here nature manifests her tremendous forces in earthquakes, volcanoes, landslides, and avalanches. Marked climatic changes occur with elevation, as well as from slope to slope. Remarkable contrasts of vegetation are found in a remarkably short space. The environment for the most part is inhospitable to man, but the mountain resources have sometimes attracted him. Valuable minerals and forest-clad slopes have stimulated extractive industries. Many attractions for recreation and tourism are present. Valley bottoms and slopes are cultivated and herds are pastured on the alpine meadows.

FIGURE 13-1. *Saint Gotthard Pass, the most famous and most important of the passes through the Swiss Alps. The difficulties of road building are clearly shown in this scene.* (Swiss National Tourist Office.)

Man has modified the mountain environment but the mountain environment has greatly conditioned his activities. His works are molded and dwarfed by the most imposing of earth's features.

Mountain influences

Climate and weather are universally influenced by mountains. Some highlands are so effective in blocking out precipitation that deserts are formed on lee sides whereas the heaviest precipitation in the world falls on windward slopes. Mountains act as barriers to man, animals, and plants. Mountains are hindrances to transportation. Roads and railroad construction are costly and require great engineering skill (see Figure 13-1). Isolation is a mountain trait often resulting in the preservation of old customs, languages, and habits. Mountain people are often conservative, industrious, individualistic, and independent. The several small independent states that still exist among their larger neighbors, such as Andorra, Nepal, San Marino, and Liechtenstein, are mountain countries. Mountains are used for political boundaries—the Pyrenees have been the boundary between France and Spain for centuries; the Himalayas separate India from Tibet. The influences of mountains upon nature and man are so extremely varied that generalizations fitting one area cannot always be applied to another.

Distribution

Highlands cover a significant portion of the earth's surface and are found on every continent. Study of a physical map of the world reveals that the great moun-

FIGURE 13-2. *A cog railroad in the Austrian Alps. The toothed rail, placed between the regular rails, allows open pinions on the driving axle of the locomotive to engage in the rail cogs and thus assists in ascending or checks speed in descending the steep mountain grades.* (Austrian State Tourist Department.)

tains tend to be located on the peripheries of the land masses. A rugged ring encircles the Pacific Ocean, and high mountains border the Mediterranean Sea and extend eastward through Eurasia. Four major cordilleran regions contain the principal highlands of the world: (*1*) the North American Cordillera, which includes the Alaska-British Columbia ranges, the Coast ranges, the Cascade-Sierra Nevada systems, the Basin ranges, and the Rocky Mountain and Sierra Madre systems; (*2*) the South America Andean Cordillera; (*3*) the Southern European Cordillera composed of the Atlas Mountains of North Africa, the mountains of Spain, the Pyrenees, Alps, and Carpathians; and (*4*) the Asian Cordillera, which fans eastward from the Pamir Knot to include the Himalaya and Kunlun mountains, the Tien Shan, and the intermediate plateaus and ranges, and extends westward in the Hindu Kush, Kopet Dag, Elbruz, and Caucasus Mountains.

Lower uplands frequently occur in isolation, detached from the great cordilleras. Some are ancient, and undoubtedly represent the roots of other cordilleras of earlier periods. They now often assume the form of hills or plateaus. Such uplands occur in eastern North and South America, northern and central Europe, eastern and southeastern Asia, and eastern Africa and Australia. In many cases the factor of isolation, usually associated with mountains, is not a great deterrent to man and the human occupation of these lower uplands is sometimes closely associated with that of neighboring lowlands. For this reason the lower uplands have been discussed mainly in the regions in which they occur.

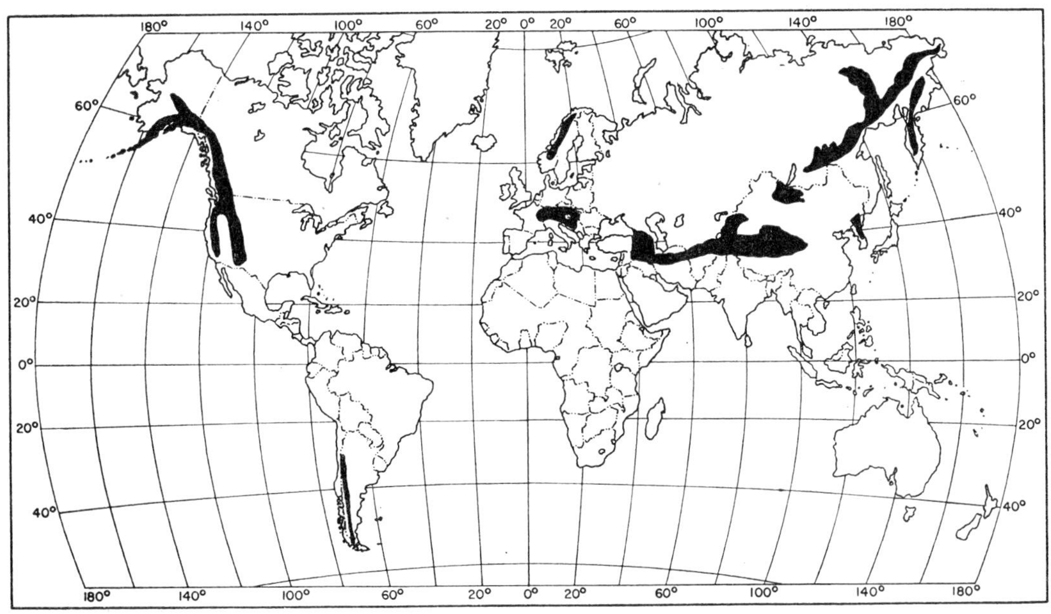

FIGURE 13-3. *The Middle Latitude Highlands.*

FIGURE 13-4. *A view of the Austrian Alps in Tyrol. These youthful mountains have been greatly modified by the work of ice.* (Austrian State Tourist Department.)

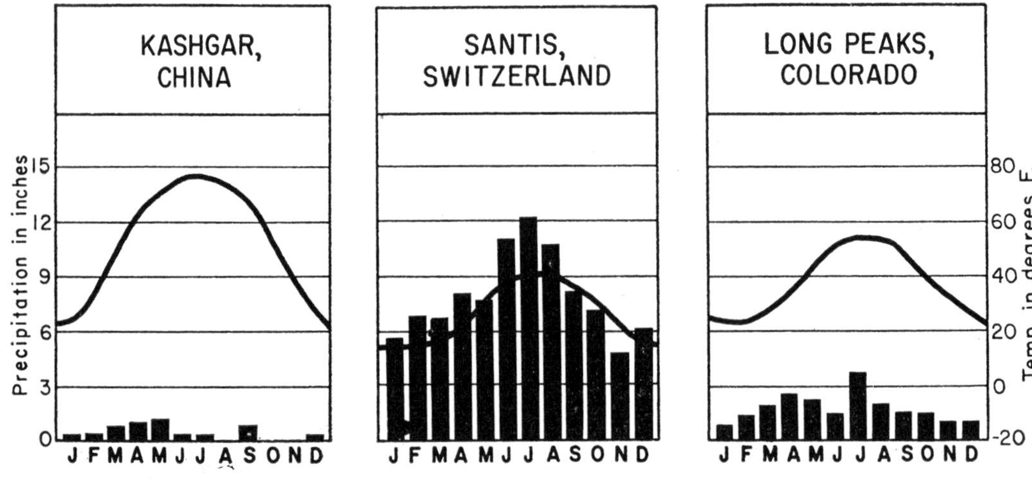

FIGURE 13-5. *Climatic graphs of Middle Latitude Highland stations.*

PHYSICAL ENVIRONMENT

Climate

The climatic pattern of the Middle Latitude Highlands, in very general terms, is similar to that of the surrounding lowlands. In reality, however, highlands have an endless variety of climates resulting from differences in latitude, altitude, continentality, mass, and exposure.

Temperature. Temperature decreases with altitude at the average rate of 3.3 degrees per 1000 feet of elevation. Other major controls operating in varying combinations and intensities make unconformity the general rule. For example, a 32° isotherm, or line of equal temperature, may be used as a reference. The higher the latitude of a mountain, the lower is the location of the 32° isotherm on its slope. A mountain in the interior of a continent has a much lower 32° isotherm than a coast or island mountain in the same latitude. The 32° isotherm is much higher on a large mountain mass than on small isolated elevations. Contrasts occur between sunny and shady slopes. South exposures in the Northern Hemisphere receive more direct sun rays and consequently more heat and sunshine than north slopes. North and south slopes are easily discernible in the spring when snow is melting, since a cover will remain much longer on the shady north side, particularly if forested. The contrasts between the two slopes have considerable effect on human occupancy—the sunny slopes are the favorite sites for settlement while the shady sides are often avoided.

Energy actually received at the land surface from the sun increases with elevation. Dust and water vapor, which intercept much of the incoming solar radiation, are concentrated at low elevations and above 3000 feet they have little influence. Insolation, therefore, reaches surfaces above this level with little loss. The air is only slightly warmed but heat-absorbing objects warm rapidly. Rock and soil surfaces in the sun will be as much as 40 to 50 degrees higher in temperature than similar surfaces in the shade. Cooling at night is about as rapid as daytime heating, therefore diurnal ranges are high. Evaporation rates are particularly high on slopes exposed to both sun and wind. Mountain climbers in the high elevations often experience considerable thirst.

Growing seasons, affected by the same controls as temperature, decrease rapidly with altitude. In some cases, a difference of 2000 feet in elevation means 15 days difference in harvest dates.[1]

Precipitation. Precipitation in the mountains is generally greater than on the neighbor-

[1] Peattie, Roderick, *Mountain Geography.* Cambridge, Mass.: Harvard University Press, 1936, 25.

ing lowlands. Thunderstorms are more frequent and are especially terrifying due to the reverberations. Snow is the characteristic winter precipitation and in high mountains may begin in early autumn and continue intermittently until late spring. High summits have a continuous cover—the lower boundary of this permanent ice and snow is known as the snow line. Snow covers on windward sides are often deep. The western slopes of the Sierra Nevadas in the United States average more than 400 inches a year. In one year a station there recorded a depth of 884 inches.

Snow is of special significance to mountain-dwellers. Winter transportation is facilitated by the use of sleds or skis. In some European countries, snow makes it possible to transport hay from small isolated pastures to barns in the main valleys. Loggers cutting on slopes utilize snow for log movement. Some winter sports depend on snow. Furthermore, it acts as a reservoir for water to be used in the lowlands for domestic, irrigation, and hydroelectric purposes. Conversely, snow has adverse effects. An early cover hazards the harvest of a crop and a slow-melting cover in spring causes a delay in crop planting. It blocks roads and rail lines. Masses of heavy snow sometimes avalanche down mountain slopes with great speed and force, destroying forests and occasionally obliterating villages. Thousands of avalanches occur each year in Switzerland. Only a slight vibration—a far-off train whistle or the clanging of a cow bell—may be the start of an avalanche.

Winds. Mountain and valley breezes are common diurnal phenomena in the highlands. A valley breeze is the movement of warmed air up the valley or up mountain sides by day, caused by warm air rising from valley floors and slopes. Mountain breezes occur at night when air near mountain sides cools and the chilled air flows down hillsides and valleys. Winds resulting from a flow of cold air down slope under the pull of gravity are known as *katabatic* winds. Foehn winds are also characteristic. These warm, dry winds quickly evaporate snow on mountain sides often allowing early spring planting and grazing. In the European Alps, certain crops such as grapes are restricted to slopes favored by foehn winds.

FIGURE 13-6. *A snow survey team in the Sierra Nevada. Data gathered by these crews will give information useful in flood control and water-use planning.* (United States Weather Bureau *and* Soil Conservation Service.)

Surface features

Mountains display an endless variety of forms; some have jagged crests and are sharp and narrow, some are broad and rounded, others are plateau-like, surmounted by conical peaks. The distinguishing feature of all is a preponderance of area in slope. Although steepness is a characteristic, slopes seldom exceed 35 degrees and most average 20 to 25 degrees. Age is reflected in mountain appearances—youthful mountains are sharp and steep whereas mature and old highlands, long exposed to the forces of weathering and erosion, appear more subdued.

The nature of highlands, as well as other landforms, is related to: (*1*) the kinds of earth materials or rocks that compose them; (*2*) the constructional forces that originally produced them; (*3*) the destructional forces at work to grade them down; and (*4*) their

FIGURE 13-7. *Majestic Mount Rainier, the highest of the line of young volcanic peaks that surmount the Cascade Mountains.* (United States Air Force.)

age, which determines the length of time the gradational processes have been at work. The influences of these factors are best demonstrated in the highlands.

Rock classes. Three classes of rocks constitute the earth's crust: igneous, sedimentary, and metamorphic. All are composed of minerals, but are formed in different ways. *Igneous* rocks, chief components of the earth's crust, have been solidified from molten magma that was pushed upward into the crust and sometimes onto the surface. Based upon mode of occurrence of igneous rocks, two subdivisions are recognized: (*1*) intrusive igneous rocks that solidify beneath the surface and are generally completely crystallized, such as granite; and (*2*) extrusive igneous rocks, formed by the ejections and molten magmas in quiet flows from fissures or by explosion from vents. The quiet flows produce lavas, of which the most common is the dark-colored basalt, and the explosive processes frequently produce fragmental rocks such as tuff and breccia.

The rocks at the surface are constantly under the attack of the atmospheric elements, as well as water, ice, and biotic agents. Down through the earth's history these weathering processes, which are both mechanical and chemical, tend to break up the rocks. Fragments are loosened and reduced in size; a mantle develops, which eventually may completely cover the coherent or solid rock below. Action of gravity, water, ice, and wind moves these materials from the place of their origin to other places on the earth. Such deposits are known as sediments and are mainly laid down in bodies of water, near ocean shorelines, or in lakes, later to be compacted into solid rock by pressure of the increasing weight and by the deposition of some cementing agent. Organic materials are sometimes compacted with the sediments or separately. Together these rocks formed by the consolidation of sediments are called *sedimentary.* They range from fine-grained limestone derivative of organic sediments and shale of fine-grained inorganic sediments, through medium-textured sandstone, to coarse and irregular conglomerates that resemble concrete.

Metamorphic rocks are those that have undergone change. The minerals and structural features of most rocks have developed under rather definite chemical and physical equilibrium. Heat, pressure, or both, brought about through crustal deformation or igneous intrusion, may change the stable conditions and cause minerals to recrystallize either as the same or as new minerals adjusted to the changed conditions. Water percolating through the rock bodies can also produce changes by removing some minerals in solution and replacing them with others. Nearly every common rock has a metamorphic equivalent. For example, metamorphosed shale becomes slate, limestone becomes marble, and granite becomes gneiss.

Rocks differ in their resistance to deformation, weathering, and erosion. Soft rocks such as shales most often give rise to gentle slopes, plains, and subdued relief features; however, when inclined steeply, deep dissection may occur. Those such as granite, being resistant to deformation, weathering, and erosion, tend to produce more enduring and bold landscapes. Thus the nature of the rocks, their thickness, and lateral extent have direct bearing upon the nature of the landforms of any given area.

Constructional forms. Four types of mountains—folded, faultblock, intrusive igneous, and volcanic—result from processes that derive their energy from within the earth. *Folded* mountains are produced by stresses and strains that cause the earth's crust to wrinkle and develop a series of great anticlines and synclines (see Figure 13-8). *Faultblock* mountains occur when strain beyond the elastic limits of the rocks causes actual fracturing and blocks are raised or lowered in reference to one another. *Intrusive igneous* mountains are formed when large masses of magma are forced upward into the earth's crust and cause the upper strata to be bowed-up, often in more or less circular pattern. The *volcanic* mountains result from the accumulations of molten materials that have poured out upon the surface. Eruptions from central vents produce individual cones or shield-like shapes; flows from fissures or numerous vents develop plateau-like uplands.

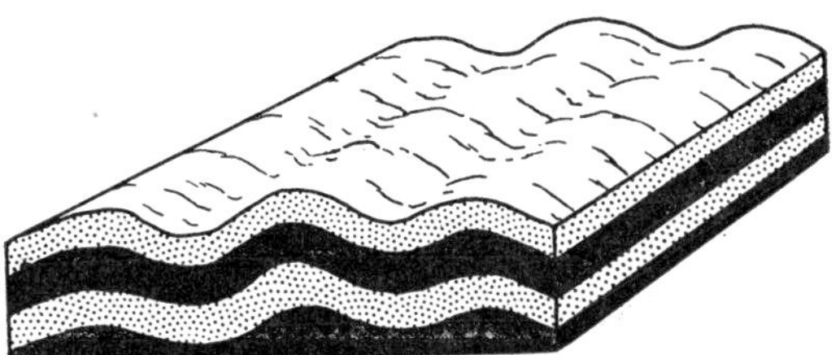

FIGURE 13-8. *Simple folding. The upfolds are called anticlines and the downfolds synclines.*

Destructional forms. Opposing the forces that derive their energy from within the earth are destructional forces that derive their energy from without and are at work to bring the land to a uniform low level. These processes, as noted, include the work of atmospheric elements, gravity, water, ice, wind, and plant and animal life. By the process of weathering, which includes mechanical disintegration and chemical decomposition, the

FIGURE 13-9. *A mountain glacier in the Austrian Alps.* (Austrian State Tourist Department.)

FIGURE 13-10. *A mountain valley before and after glaciation.* Left, *a youthful,* V-*shaped valley.* Right, *the glacier has scoured out the valley, producing a* U-*shape and sharpening the peaks.*

coherent rocks are prepared for removal by the processes of erosion that pick up the rock fragments and transport them for deposition in the lower areas.

Running water is the most potent agent of erosion. On a newly-elevated surface, run-off is in the form of a sheet of water. Soon it concentrates into rivulets that grow into valley-carving streams. Gradually the valleys grow longer, deeper, and wider until base level is reached and the strong interstream relief features are removed. The streams, too, acquire new characteristics. Their courses become less direct as the water searches continually for the lowest elevations; in the resulting meandering channels the current is lessening its velocity.

Mountain or alpine glaciers are destructional forces in some of the high mountains today and were more extensively developed during the Pleistocene Period. Glaciers are bodies of ice formed by great accumulations of snow (see Figure 13-9). They advance as tongues down valleys to points where melting equals forward progression. Moving slowly forward, a glacier carries along loose rock materials, which are dropped when an overload is obtained, deposited as a terminal moraine, or carried down the valley by the melt waters. These mountain glaciers have a tendency to produce U-shaped valleys, often leaving tributary valleys detrunked and hanging, with waterfalls cascading down the steep slopes (see Figure 13-10). Frequently the terminal moraine blocks the flow of water and causes the development of lakes, which sometimes occur in chains.

Influences of age. Although mountains appear to be permanent features from the point of view of the lifetime of man, in a broader view of the earth's history no landforms are static. Forces are constantly at work building up and tearing down the earth's surface features. Mountains may be young, mature, or old. In each stage they have distinctive qualities that influence their habitability and use by man. Young mountains are commonly sharp in their detail, their surfaces highly irregular, and their peaks often snow-covered the year around. Valleys are V-shaped with little room for settlement. Streams are swift and often adaptable to hydroelectric power development. Minerals, however, are frequently deeply-buried and out of reach by economic mining techniques.

Mature mountains, longer exposed to the action of the destruction forces, have lost their ruggedness. Elevations have been lowered and often even the highest peaks are below the timber line. Valleys are broader and slopes more rounded. Further lowering may continue until the mountains have been reduced to a series of low, rolling hills, or even to a near plain-like surface—they have then reached the stage of old age. The mature and old-age mountains have greater possibilities for settlement because the valleys are broader and slopes less steep. Frequently they are the location of important mineral deposits formed during mountain building and exposed by weathering and erosion.

Natural vegetation

All mountains display an altitudinal zonation of vegetation. A zone's width, elevation, variety of species, and character of cover depend chiefly on the same controls that affect climate. The vegetation of low altitudes is similar to the surrounding lowlands and changes slowly with elevation. If broadleafs constitute the lowest zone, they are gradually replaced by conifers. Grasslands or desert shrub at the base are also replaced, depending on amounts of precipitation and heights of mountains, by conifers. Where conifers form the base, such as in the Cascade Mountains of North America, only the species change with higher elevation. Tree growth ceases with lower temperatures and shorter summers. The boundary marking the termination of tree growth is known as the timber line. Its location is affected by amounts of moisture, exposure, wind, evaporation, and depth of snow. Some mountains, such as the Appalachians, do not extend high enough to have a treeless zone. Above the timber line is the alpine zone, which is subdivided into a shrub zone of stunted and gnarled trees bordering the timber line, followed by the meadow zone known as alps. The alps grade through tundra-like vegetation until bare rock and the snowline are reached. The Rocky Mountains of the United States exemplify altitudinal zonation in the middle latitudes. W. W. Robbins recognizes six zones of vegetation in northeastern Colorado: (*1*) steppe vegetation up to 6100 feet, (*2*) a narrow interrupted belt of chaparral or brushland, (*3*) yellow pine and Douglas fir zone from about 6100 to 8130 feet, (*4*) lodgepole pine zone, 8130 to 10,170 feet (see Figure 13-11), (*5*) Englemann spruce and balsam fir zone, 10,170 to 11,670 feet, and (*6*) the alpine zone above timber line.[2]

FIGURE 13-11. *Dense lodgepole pine stand on Beaverhead National Forest in Montana.* (United States Forest Service.)

Native animal life

Animals especially characteristic of Middle Latitude Highlands live in the alpine zone; animal life in the forests of the lower elevations in general is similar to species found in the contiguous lower areas. Alpine animals, however, frequently migrate to the forest zone during the winter or when food becomes scarce in the alpine pastures. Most alpine mammals are herbivorous, depending upon the forage of the high mountain

[2] Robbins, W. W., *Native Vegetation and Climate of Colorado in Their Relation to Agriculture.* Fort Collins, Colo.: Colorado Agricultural Experiment Station, 1917, Bulletin 224.

FIGURE 13-12. *Sheep grazing on a high mountain pasture in Wyoming.* (United States Forest Service.)

FIGURE 13-13. *Mountain sheep in the Tarryall Mountains of Colorado.* (Fish and Wildlife Service: E. P. Haddon.)

pasture. Coarse hair or thick fur protects them from winter cold. Many are able to survive at extremely high elevations; in Central Asia wild sheep and ibex live at about 19,000 feet and yaks even higher.[3] Many are sure-footed, climbing animals with strong, spreading hoofs. Species include the yak, musk deer, ibex, and wild sheep of Central Asia. Chamois and ibex are found in the Alps, Pyrenees, and Caucasus Mountains of Europe. Rocky Mountain bighorn sheep are the characteristic animals of the Rocky Mountains of North America. Several small rock-inhabiting species, such as the marmot and other rodents, are common in all regions.

FIGURE 13-14. *Male mountain goat.* (Fish and Wildlife Service: David L. Spencer.)

Soils

Mountain soils defy classification, owing to the scattered distribution of mature groups. Slope operates as a major factor in soil accumulation and only in the small pockets of flat land is development a response to climate and vegetation conditions; thus only patches can be classed as podzols, gray-brown soils, and the like. More commonly, the soils are immature, consisting of a shallow layer overlaying the rock formations and ranging in depth from one inch to one or two feet. Frequent exposures of the bed rock are common and the soil in general is composed of inorganic materials. They are, therefore, known as lithosols, from the Greek word *lithos,* meaning rock.

MAN IN THE MIDDLE LATITUDE HIGHLANDS

Mountains tend to repel the development of large and widespread population centers. "Man—like air and water—feels always the pull of gravity." [4] He prefers the plains, and it is only with increased effort and often deprivations that settlements in the highlands have been possible. In spite of adversities, some have chosen the more rigorous habitat for a variety of reasons. There are those who sought freedom, refuge, or seclusion; others, particularly in the Orient and Mediterranean Basin, have been forced up the slopes by overcrowding on the lowlands. Moreover, mountains are not always completely undesirable. There may be valuable resources of minerals, forests, and pastures. Recreation possibilities are often present. In the tropics, the highland environment frequently presents superior living conditions.

In general, nature places rigid limits on the supporting capacity of the Middle Latitude Highlands. Population is thinly spread and often absent. Noteworthy concentrations are found only in central and southern Europe and in eastern Asia. Although average density is low, there are the isolated areas in many mountain regions, usually in valleys or on plateaus, where, like the oases of the deserts, population numbers are large.

Everywhere numbers decrease sharply with elevation. For example, in Switzerland, the most famous highland country, the majority of the people live on the plateau between the

[3] Allee, W. E., and Karl P. Schmidt, *Ecological Animal Geography*. New York: John Wiley and Sons, Inc., 1951, 589.

[4] Semple, Ellen Churchill, *Influences of Geographic Environment.* New York: Henry Holt and Company, Inc., 1911, 521.

FIGURE 13-15. *A Swiss chalet. Notice the steep roof, storm shutters, and wide-projecting eaves—all for protection from the heavy snows.* (Swiss National Tourist Office.)

Jura Mountains on the north and the Alps on the south. The Alps have brought the nation much of its fame, but without the plateau, along with the great resourcefulness of the people, the country could not support its nearly five million people. In contrast, Tibet, a million square miles of plateaus and mountains with three-fourths of its area above 10,000 feet, supports only about three million people, and these live under great handicaps.

The range of economic opportunity is seldom as wide in the highland environment as on the plains. Man's adjustments frequently are not as complex nor as advanced. In fact, due to difficulties of travel and intercourse with the outside, mountains tend to promote backward cultures. The name "mountaineer" has long been synonymous with social and economic retardation. Only in a few areas have modern transportation and communication systems brought any upsurge in development.

Agriculture

The Middle Latitude Highlands are hostile to the widespread development of agriculture. Irregular surface with a sparsity of flat land limits farm sizes, shapes, and numbers, and leads to serious difficulties

FIGURE 13-16. *Hay harvest in the Tyrol. The mountain farmers must provide for their livestock, which are kept in stables during the long winter season.* (Austrian State Tourist Department.)

FIGURE 13-17. *Grapes are an important crop on the sunny slopes in many of the highlands of southern Germany.* (German Tourist Information Office.)

in the use of machinery as well as in the transport of products to markets. Soils are shallow, often stony, low in fertility, and susceptible to erosion. Climate, changing with altitude, slope and exposure, is found in variety, but a short growing season is a common handicap. The crop possibilities are distinctly limited, with coarse grains, hardy vegetables, tree fruits, and hay most adaptable. All of these normally cannot be grown in the same locality. However, on the subtropical margins of the Orient, climate allows the production of rice and other grains, vegetables, mulberries, tea, and a variety of fruits. Quality locations for tree crops and vineyards are found on many of the sunny south slopes facing the Mediterranean Sea.

Pressure of population on the plains of the Old World has caused terracing to be practiced as a means of increasing cultivation in the highland portions. It is common in China and Japan; it is practiced in the Himalayas and the Hindu Kush, as well as on the slopes of the Vosges and the Black Forest facing the Rhine River, and in the Alps. Terracing is little practiced, however, by the mountaineers of the newer lands. This system requires and develops an industrious and cooperative peasantry; the cultivators by necessity become high-quality gardeners.

Agriculture is elsewhere restricted primarily to the valleys where lesser slopes, milder climates, and better soils are conducive to production. Stream patterns usually are indicative of the population pattern. Narrow tentacles of population extending up the shoestring valleys of mountains bordering the lowlands, such as in the Willamette Valley of Oregon, denote the diminishing farmlands and increasing physical limitations to agriculture as well as most other activities.

Grazing

The pasturing of livestock on slopes, alpine meadows, and open-forest lands of the high elevations is a major agricultural activity in nearly all middle-latitude mountain lands. Each year the animals are driven or transported into the high pastures as soon as the snow cover disappears and forage is available. The movement of bands of sheep from the hot, dry plains of the Rhone delta to pastures in the French Alps is a picturesque sight.[5] Like a slowly moving gray cloud, the sheep begin their long journey. Trek-wise rams lead the procession, herders on horseback and scurrying sheep dogs guard the flanks, and the pack asses bring up the rear. A tinkling symphony accompanies the band since recognition bells with distinctive tones are worn by each type of animal. Movement of the band begins during the cool of the evening and the approximately 200-mile trip is accomplished in easy stages of 15 miles a night to accustom the sheep to the colder temperature and higher altitudes.

---

[5] For a vivid description of transhumance in southern France see Moyal, Maurice, "The Big Trek," *The Farm Quarterly,* Winter 1954, VIII, No. 4, 56-59 and 84-89.

FIGURE 13-18. *Sheep grazing in the Swiss Alps. Every summer thousands of sheep are brought from the lowlands to feed on the alpine pastures.* (Swiss National Tourist Office.)

FIGURE 13-19. *Farmland is scarce in Norway and must be devoted to food and winter feed crops. Therefore farmers take their livestock to the nearby mountain pastures for summer grazing.* (William Merle Blum.)

FIGURE 13-20. *Norwegian* saeter, *summer headquarters for herdsmen.* (Norwegian Information Service.)

FIGURE 13-21. *Loading ponderosa pine on the east slopes of the Cascades. Tractor logging is particularly adaptable in these more open stands of the pine forest.* (Weyerhaeuser Timber Company.)

The dairy cow, the most important animal in the small mountain villages of central Europe, provides milk, butter, and cheese for both home use and market. Many villagers have a ceremony when the cows are released from their long winter captivity in barns to begin their journey to the alps. The animals, carefully groomed and belled, present a picturesque sight as they wend their way up the slopes. Herders chosen by the villagers accompany the cattle to the high pasture and remain with them until late summer. The herders' main chores are milking and cheesemaking. When enough cheese is accumulated, it is brought to the village and prorated among the cattle-owners. Village youngsters in some communities make trips to the alps for the cheese and at the same time take food, tobacco, and other supplies to the herders. In the meantime the villagers below are busy with crops and hay.[6]

The Norwegian farmers who cultivate the narrow bench lands along the fiords send their livestock to *saeters* or summer dairies, in the high valleys above their farms (see Figures 13-19 and 13-20). There they often are tended by the children of the farm families. The saeter system is usually a farm family enterprise, in contrast to the method used by central European mountain villages. This system of transhumance is a planned adjust-

[6] The various systems of transhumance in Europe are quite complicated and the interested student should read Chapter 6 of Peattie, Roderick, *Mountain Geography*. Cambridge, Mass.: Harvard University Press, 1936.

ment whereby the farmer uses his limited farm land in the valley bottoms or on the benches for growing food crops and winter forage instead of pasture. Late snow covers, steep slopes, thin soil, and short growing seasons preclude the use of the high pasture for plow agriculture; but the high pastures ideally fit this special farming scheme and relieve the land-use pressure on the small holdings. In North America, the mountain pastures are the summer grazing grounds for livestock of the great plains and intermontane basins and valleys. Livestock are often shipped by truck or rail to these summer pastures.

Forest industries

Forests and mountains are almost synonymous; several mountain sections of Germany are called forests, such as the Schwarzwald (Black Forest) and Odenwald (Oden Forest). Forestry is associated with all Middle Latitude Highlands in Europe. Conifers are usually the chief commercial species. Many of the forest operations are small-scale and logging is often practiced by farmers during the winter. The most outstanding forest activity of the mountain regions is concentrated in western United States. Mature, high-quality timber covers slopes of the Coast Ranges, Cascade-Sierra Nevada Mountains, and the Rocky Mountains. Douglas fir, most important of the commercial trees, prefers slopes that receive heavy to moderate amounts of precipitation; particularly heavy stands are west of the summit of the Cascade Mountains. Western white pine is the most important species cut in northeastern Washington, northern Idaho, and western Montana. Large stands of Ponderosa pine are found on the leeward and drier sides of the Cascades. Several varieties of pine are associated with the Sierra-Nevada Mountains. The large mechanized operations in western United States contrast sharply with methods in Europe, where hand labor and horses furnish much of the power. Winter snows, often restricting work in the woods of western United States, are welcomed by European loggers, who cut a much smaller tree and utilize the snow for moving logs.

FIGURE 13-22. *An open pit iron mine in Styria, Austria. This mine has been operated for hundreds of years and today is still the chief source of ore for Austria's small steel industry.* (Austrian State Tourist Department.)

Mining

Metallic minerals are commonly found in the highlands. It is in these regions that weakness in the earth's crust has allowed magmas, formed in the depths, to intrude near the surface, later to be exposed by weathering and erosion. These magmas have often brought economic minerals which are sufficiently concentrated to be classed as ores and profitably mined. Mining is often the major reason for the existence of population in some of the highland areas. Owing to the importance of minerals in the modern industrial world, rich ore deposits attract men to isolated areas, and despite difficulties of transportation, food supply, and adverse living conditions, relatively large centers have developed.

The Rocky Mountains supply a major share of copper, silver, lead, zinc, and molybdenum in the United States. The Ural Mountains of the Soviet Union are highly mineralized and

FIGURE 13-23. *Ashcroft, a ghost town of Colorado. This former small mining community is typical of many centers that flourished in the Rockies during the early mining boom.* (State of Colorado Advertising and Publicity Department.)

provide a variety of metals, including large quantities of iron ore. Gold and other minerals are taken in considerable amounts from the highlands of southern Siberia.

Mining is based upon a non-renewable resource. Mineral deposits in time are exhausted, and the base for the mining community gone; abandonment follows. Black Hawk, Georgetown, and Central City are famous Colorado mining towns of the past which went through a short period of rapid and lively exploitation.

Water resource development

Mountains perform important roles in water resource distribution and development. They catch and store water and thus nourish and give direction and velocity to many of the world's streams. Artificial storage is facilitated by numerous deep valleys and canyons in which dams and large reservoirs can be constructed economically without damaging settlements or other developments. Thus water supplies for cities, irrigation, and other uses can be implemented. Damsites, regularity of stream flow, and favorable gradient also give the mountainous areas large hydroelectrical potentials. These are being developed in the more accessible sections where this form of generation competes favorably with other energy sources. More and more attention is being devoted to mountain watershed management by the progressive nations in the interest of obtaining long range and maximum benefits from their water resources.

FIGURE 13-24. *The Kaprun Dam in the Austrian province of Salzburg. This dam, now completed, is one of the greatest hydroelectric projects in Europe.* (Austrian State Tourist Department.)

Manufacturing

Raw materials having bulk, waste, and excessive weight are often processed or semi-processed near their sources to facilitate shipping and reduce freight costs. This principle is one of the major stimuli for manufacturing in mountainous areas and is exemplified by sawmills and mineral concentration plants and smelters. Further fabrication is usually outside the mountains. Bases for wide-scale industrial development and diversification are weak. Major handicaps include poor transportation, distance from markets, and shortages of skilled labor.

Handicrafts or home industries are often typical of mountainous areas where the long cold winters curtail outdoor activities. The mountain dwellers in Switzerland, Germany, and Austria are noted for fine wood carvings, cuckoo clocks, toys, laces, and embroidered goods. Handicrafts not only provide winter hobbies but supplement incomes.

Switzerland is an outstanding example of a small mountainous country that has achieved fame in the industrial world. Over one-third of the Swiss people are engaged in manufacturing activities. Coal and oil are lacking but the country has developed much of its great hydroelectric potential for power. Most of the raw materials have to be imported. The significant Swiss assets are skill and resourcefulness among the people. The manufacturing emphasis is on high-quality and high-value commodities. Industry is concentrated on the Swiss Plateau, where silk, cotton and wool textiles, agricultural and textile machinery, electric engines and turbines, and chemicals are manufactured. The Jura Mountains of Switzerland are the center of the world's clock and watch industries. Individual parts are often produced in home workshops. Swiss chocolate and cheese are also famous products. The varied manufactures are sold widely on world markets.

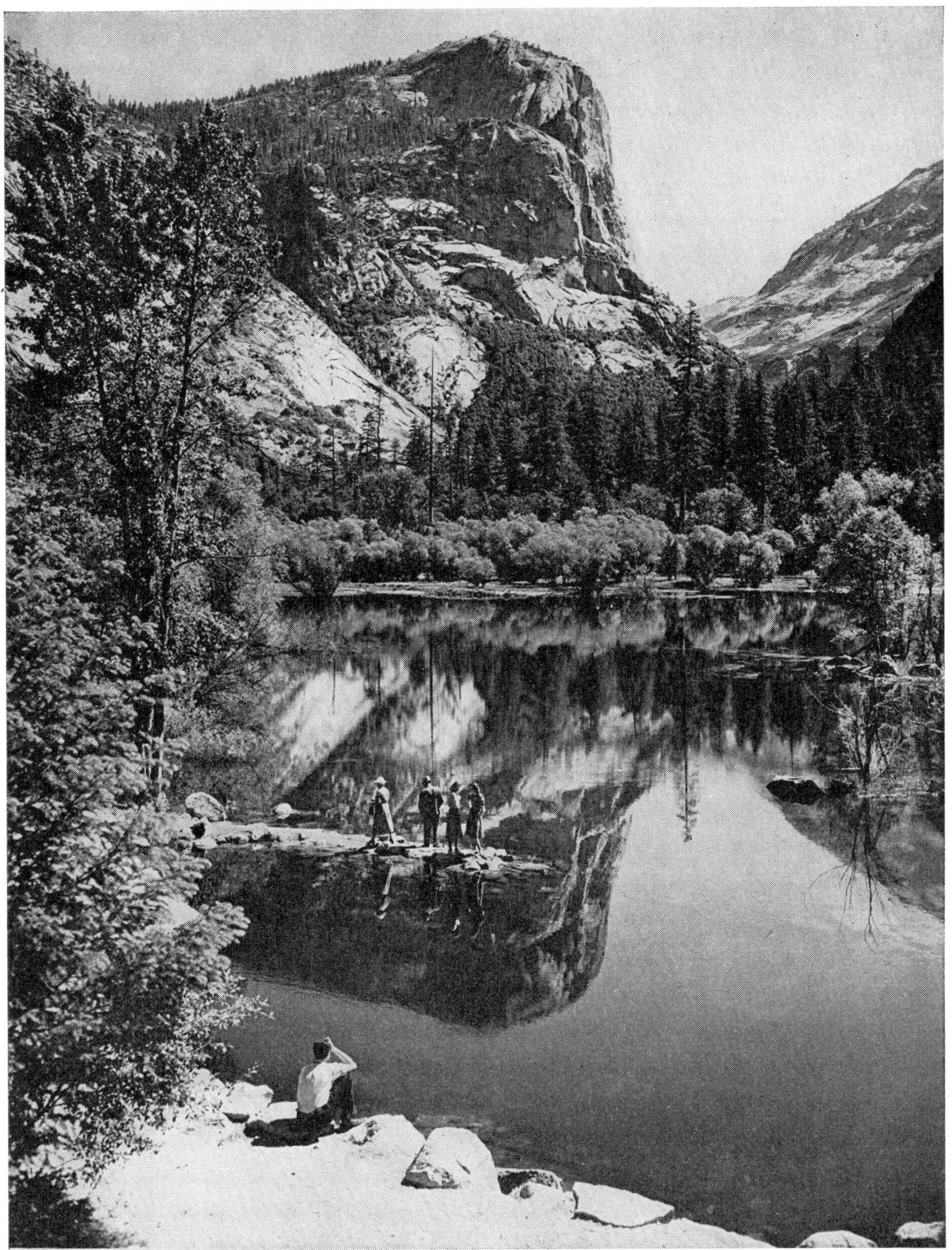

FIGURE 13-25. *Mirror Lake in Yosemite National Park. Thousands of tourists are attracted to this beautiful park in the Sierra Nevada Mountains. Half Dome is seen in the background.* (Sante Fe Railway.)

Tourism

A country which possesses mountains has a valuable tourist asset. Mountains offer spectacular scenery with forested slopes, colorful alpine meadows, streams, lakes, and glaciers and snowfields, as well as a cool, bracing summer climate. The sheer beauty of their winter landscape is unsurpassed. Forest and alpine trails appeal to the hiker; rugged peaks and slopes challenge the more adventurous climber. Fishing, hunting, and skiing attract the outdoor sportsman.

Resort centers are scattered throughout many of the mountain regions of the United States and Canada. Many in the West were first developed and promoted by railroad companies who realized the tourist potential. Canada and the United States have established large national parks that have stimulated the tourist industry. Many of these noted national parks are located in the western mountains. Two well-known western parks of Canada are Banff, containing beautiful Lake Louise, and Jasper National Park. In the United States, Yellowstone heads an imposing list of national parks which includes Mount Rainier, Crater Lake, Yosemite, Glacier, and the Grand Tetons. Although far from population concentrations, the parks are visited by thousands of travelers annually.

FIGURE 13-26. *One of the picturesque mountain villages in the Alps. Frequently, as in this view, the ancient church steeple stands as a prominent landmark. These villages have facilities for handling both winter and summer tourist business.* (Austrian State Tourist Department.)

The greatest economic value of many of the mountains in Europe, especially the Alps, lies in their tourist attractions. The livelihood of many small villages has been radically changed from a meager agricultural existence to a profitable tourist activity based on the feeding, housing, and guiding of visitors. Several small, obscure villages have become world famous, such as St. Moritz in Switzerland and the winter resort twin cities of Garmisch-Partenkirchen in Germany.

Switzerland is one of the major European tourist nations. The Swiss, through careful planning, have systematically developed their tourist activity. Railroads and good highways tap the mountain areas and scenic cable railroads have been constructed especially for tourists. Lodging accommodations fit all pocketbooks and the food and services are excellent. Success has been the outcome and the well-executed policies have made tourism a significant segment in the Swiss national economy.

Urban centers

As a general rule, the Middle Latitude Highland environment is not conducive to city growth. The few cities that do occur have developed as the result of mineral and forest exploitation, or commercial advantage derived from location at the junctions of mountain passes, or at the entrance to mountain passes where lowland routes come to focus. Butte, Montana, is an example of a mining city. Innsbruck, in the Inn Valley of Austria, illustrates the value of the crossing of routes through mountains; here the famous

FIGURE 13-27. *An aerial view of Butte, Montana, the town that copper built. Mine tunnels honeycomb the earth beneath the city. Copper workings can be seen in the background.* (Butte Chamber of Commerce.)

Brenner Pass from Italy to Bavaria meets the valley route from Switzerland to Vienna. The girdle of European cities both north and south of the Alps indicates the importance of the gateway location; none, however, is actually in the mountains.

Most of the cities of Switzerland are on the plateau. Geneva is the gateway city in the west and Basel in the northeast. Zurich, the largest city of the nation, is within the protecting walls of the mountains at the convergent point of north-south and east-west transportation. Bern, centrally located, is the capital. Manufacturing has contributed to the importance of all.

OUTLOOK

The Middle Latitude Highlands are so diverse in character that it is difficult to forecast a general future. In respect to neighboring lowlands all suffer from disadvantages of adverse slope, isolation, difficult transportation, and short growing seasons—these conditions in all probability will restrict major population growth in the highlands. This is not to infer that there cannot be further development; in fact some mountains have relatively good possibilities. These largely relate to the additional exploitation of forest, mineral, water, and scenery and recreation resources. Much of the increased activity will be for the benefit of the inhabitants of the nearby lowlands. In all cases development must be accompanied by wise management to sustain continuously the resource base and the economy.

It is doubtful that there will be any major increase in crop agriculture or in grazing activities. The suitable lands, for the most part, are already being utilized. In some cases there is overgrazing and in the interest of good range management and watershed protection livestock numbers should be decreased. Mining will continue to fluctuate in significance as deposits are exhausted and new discoveries developed.

SELECTED REFERENCES

Atwood, Wallace W., *The Rocky Mountains.* New York: The Vanguard Press, 1945.

Carrier, Else Haydon, *Water and Grass: A Study in Pastoral Economy of Southern Europe.* London: Christopher's, 1932.

Douglas, William O., *Beyond the High Himalayas.* Garden City: Doubleday and Company, Inc., 1952.

Foscue, Edwin J., "Gatlinburg: A Mountain Community," *Economic Geography,* XXI, 1945, 192-205.

Hinds, Norman E. A., *Geomorphology, the Evolution of Landscape.* New York: Prentice-Hall, Inc., 1943.

Hoffmeister, Harold A., "Central City Mining District," *Economic Geography,* XVI, 1940, 96-104.

Lackey, Earl E., "Mountain Passes in the Colorado Rockies," *Economic Geography,* XXV, 1949, 211-215.

Multon, Alice F. A., "Glockner-Kaprun Hydroelectric Project, Hohe Tauern, Austria," *Geographical Review,* XLI, No. 2, 1951, 332-334.

Peattie, Roderick, ed., *The Pacific Coast Ranges.* New York: The Vanguard Press, 1946.

CHAPTER 14

Subarctics

THE SUBARCTIC REGIONS ARE THE lands of the northern coniferous forests. Dark evergreens appear interminable, sharing the landscape with swamps and bogs, thousands of lakes, winding rivers, and rushing streams. The Subarctics are winter strongholds; summer is brief; spring and fall are fleeting. When winter grips the land, nature seems at rest. The ground is blanketed with snow, streams are stilled, lakes are paved with ice, frost hardens the soft, moist lowlands, birds have migrated, and most animals remain in hiding unless in search of food. The crash and thunder of breaking ice heralds the end of winter. The melting snow soon saturates the low, open lands, vegetation springs into life, countless insects fill the air, and birds return from the south.

FIGURE 14-1. *A scene in eastern Finland. Here is depicted the physical and cultural geography of the Subarctics—water, forest, milling, and only patches of agriculture.* (Finnish National Travel Office.)

FIGURE 14-2. *The Subarctics.*

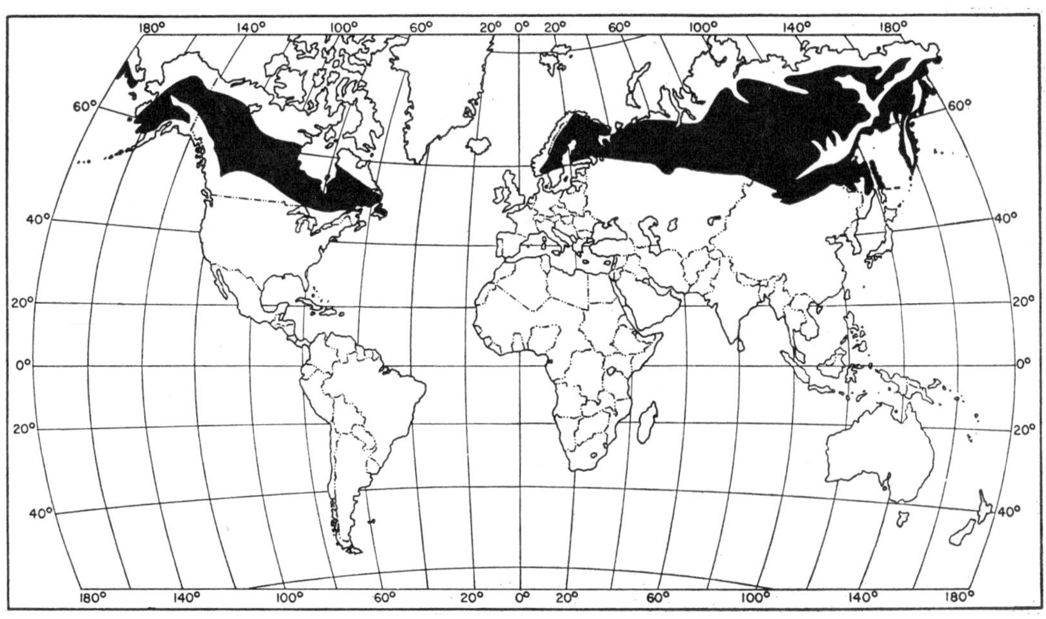

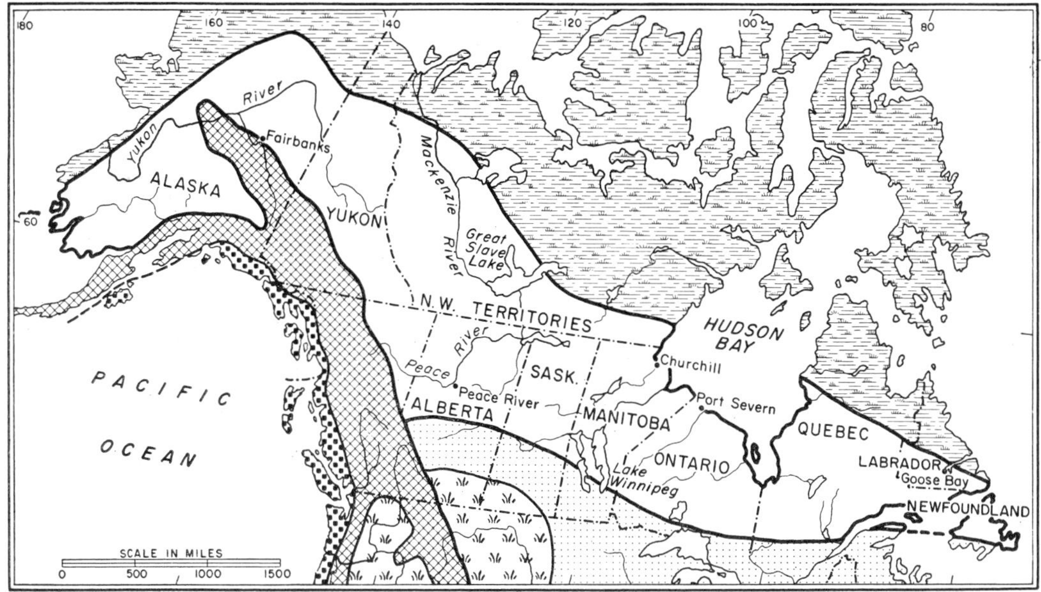

FIGURE 14-3. *The Subarctics of North America.*

Winter is the season for man's activity in the Subarctics. Ice and snow become highways for travel, and the air is clear of troublesome insects. Loggers, hunters, and trappers invade the forest, but numbers are small—man is always scarce and usually transient. Isolation keynotes the region; forests keynote the economy.

Location

Only the Northern Hemisphere continents have sufficient land masses in the high latitudes to allow development of Subarctic climates. The regions straddle the sixtieth parallel with extreme margins extending to latitudes 50° or 55° on the south and 65° or 70° on the north. The southern margin is the zone of contact with the Short Summer Humid Continental regions, and the poleward boundary is the 50° isotherm for the warmest month, which approximately marks the poleward limit of tree growth.

There are two large areas. In North America the Subarctic region, 10 to 15 degrees wide, stretches from the Pacific Ocean through Alaska and Canada to the St. Lawrence River Estuary and Newfoundland on the Atlantic Ocean. The Eurasian region extends from the Scandinavian Highlands across Sweden, Finland, and the Soviet Union terminating on the Pacific Ocean; eastward it progressively broadens as continentality increases and includes the bulk of Siberia.

PHYSICAL ENVIRONMENT

Climate

Extreme continentality marks the Subarctic climate and its seasonal temperature contrasts are the greatest on earth. "King Winter" rules for much of the year.

Temperature. Winters are long and severe; six months or more of the year are below freezing. January temperatures for North American inland stations average below zero and the extreme minimum of −80° has been recorded in the Yukon. Summers have about three months above 50°. July averages are about 60°, but daytime maxima sometimes

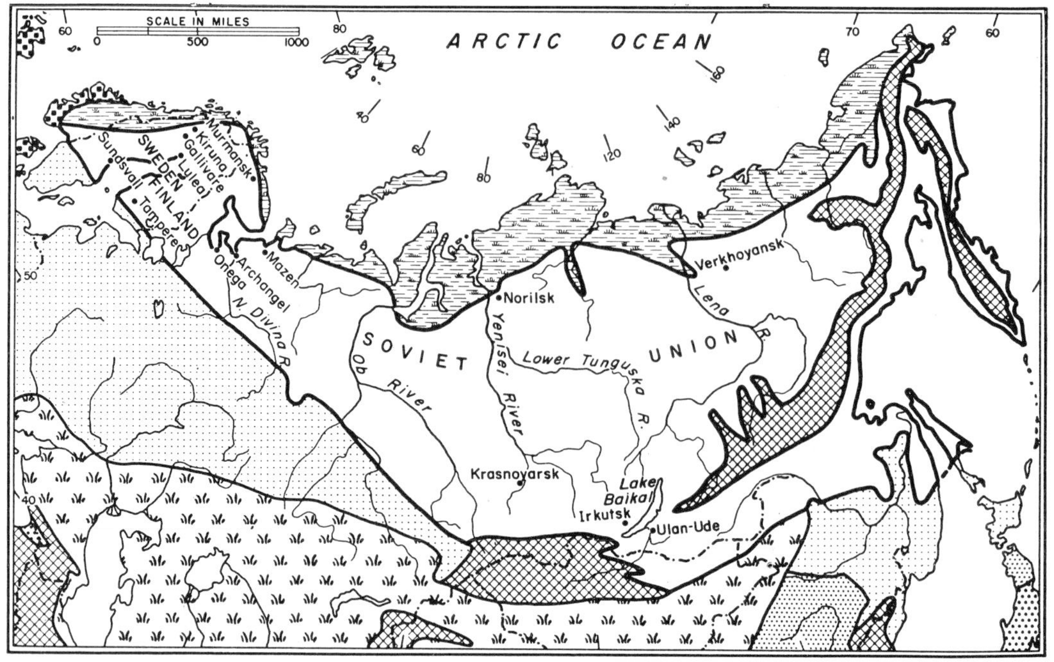

FIGURE 14-4. *The Subarctics of Eurasia.*

FIGURE 14-5. *The midnight sun in northern Finland. On the northern margin of the Subarctics the sun does not set during June and most of July.* (Finnish National Travel Office.)

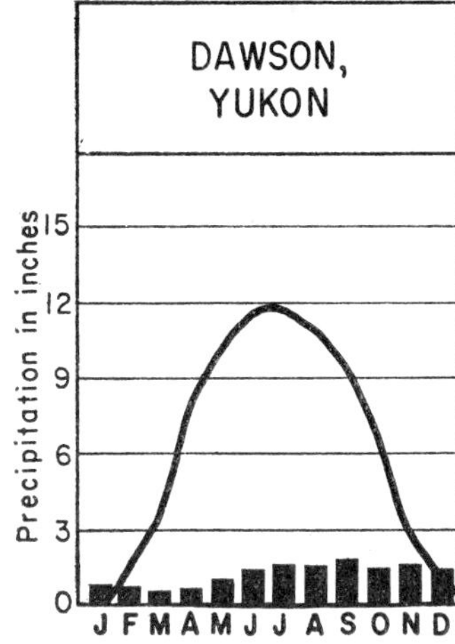

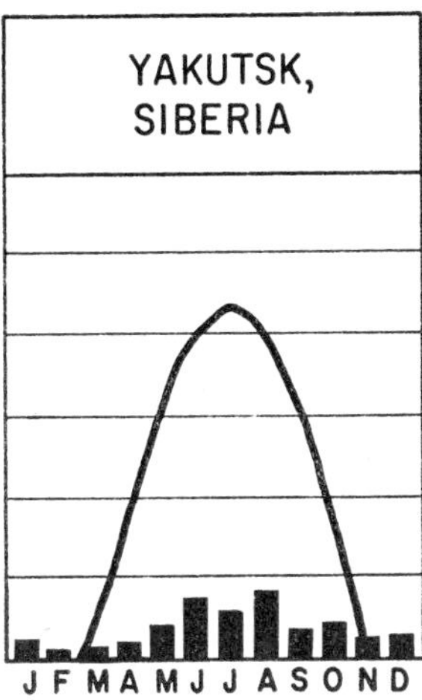

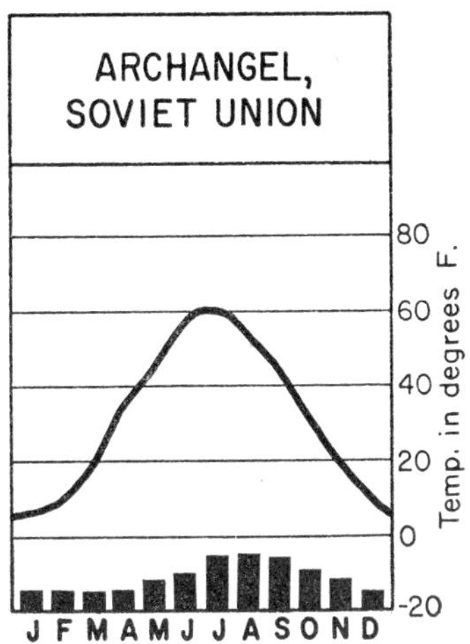

FIGURE 14-6. *Typical climatic graphs of Subarctic stations.*

exceed 90°. Coast areas modified by open water bodies have warmer winters and cooler summers. Annual ranges are high and in North America average 80 degrees. Growing seasons vary between 90 and 100 days on the southern boundaries and become increasingly shorter with poleward progression. Some favored areas in the north, such as the Mackenzie Valley, may have growing seasons of 50 to 75 days; however, frosts may occur any month. In the interior of Asia, winters are colder and summers warmer than in North America, due to greater continentality. Verkhoyansk in Siberia holds the record for the high average annual temperature range with a —58° in January and 59° in July—a difference of 117 degrees. Verkhoyansk has recorded a low of —93° and Oymyakon to the southeast has reported even colder temperatures. This Siberian area, the coldest on record in the world, is often called the "cold pole"—it is even colder than the arctic region.

Many hours of sunshine partly compensate for the shortness of summer in these regions, but the plant growth potentials are still low compared to regions farther south, owing to the lower intensity of heat and light. Summer days are long and on June 21 at 60° north latitude there are 18½ hours of continuous sunshine. However, this is reversed on December 22 when the sun shines about five or six hours.

Precipitation. Precipitation, resulting chiefly from cyclonic activity, ranges from 10 to 20 inches a year for most parts of the regions; however, northeastern Siberia, due to greater continentality, averages only five inches. The greater part comes during the summer months since winter air is too cold to contain much moisture. Snow, dry and granular, falls during the cold season, seldom to any great depth, but remains on the ground from five to seven months, receiving protection by the forest.

Surface features

The landforms of the Subarctic regions almost everywhere display evidence of long subjection to the forces of weathering and erosion. Continental glaciation usually has had a major role in shaping the present surface and hard crystalline rocks, representing the roots of older highlands, are present in large areas.

The North American region crosses five physiographic provinces: (*1*) the eastern half is included mainly in the Laurentian Uplands, an ancient highland of metamorphosed rock long exposed to both constructional and destructional forces. Today it appears as a rolling surface with numerous lakes, large stretches of marsh land, and scattered low mountains of resistant material. The entire region was

FIGURE 14-7. *A landscape near Simpson in the Mackenzie Valley.* (George Hunter, Ottawa.)

glaciated and in many sectors bed rock is exposed. (*2*) The southern margin of Hudson Bay is bordered by a lowland covered with sedimentary materials. (*3*) The Great Plains, the northern part of which is drained by the Mackenzie River, separates the Laurentian Upland from the Rocky Mountains. (*4*) The Rocky Mountains together with the Brooks Range form a continuous highland to the Arctic Ocean. (*5*) The westernmost province is the Yukon Plateau, which fills central Alaska. This broad upland surface is characterized by gently rolling topography in which the Yukon River system has cut valleys.

The Eurasian Subarctic, also extending across the entire continent, is composed of several physiographic units. The surface of the region is relatively uniform, differing principally in elevation; the major heights are found in the Urals and Far East. (*1*) The Fenno-Scandinavian shield in the west is an area of ancient crystalline rock, lowered by erosion to an uneven plain-like surface. Severe glaciation has in many places removed the soil covering, and unequal scouring and deposition have produced thousands of lakes (see Figure 14-10). (*2*) Eastward to the Urals is the northern portion of the Central Russian Lowland, divided into two parts by the drainage basins of the Dvina and Pechora Rivers. (*3*) The rounded Ural Mountains separate the Central Russian Lowland from the West Siberian Lowland, a large, flat, and poorly drained region through which the Ob River flows. (*4*) The Central Siberian Plateau, between the Yenisey and Lena Rivers, appears

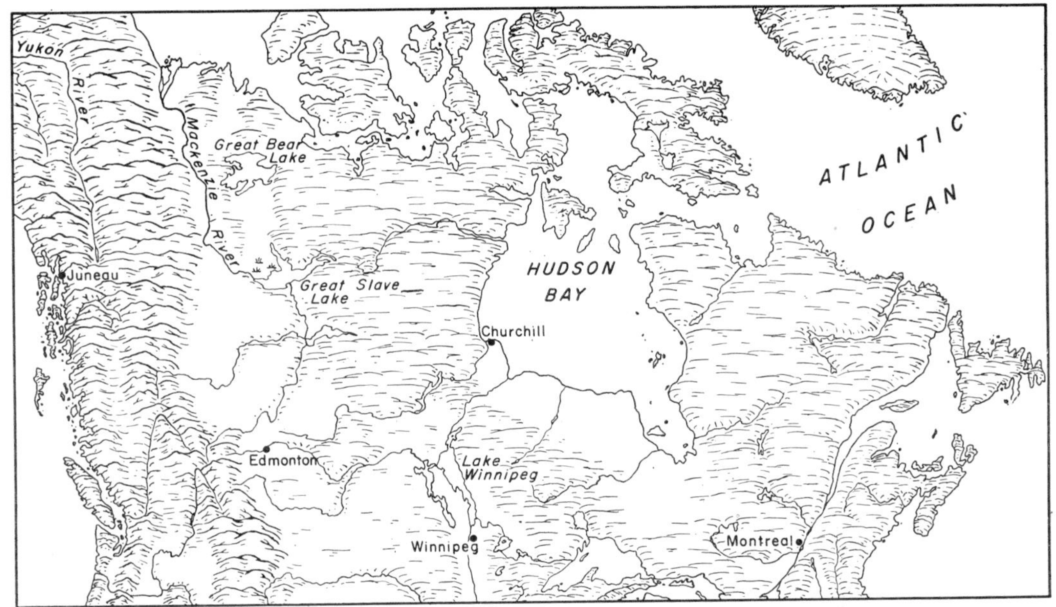

FIGURE 14-8. *Physiographic diagram of Canada.*

FIGURE 14-9. *Physiographic diagram of the Soviet Union.*

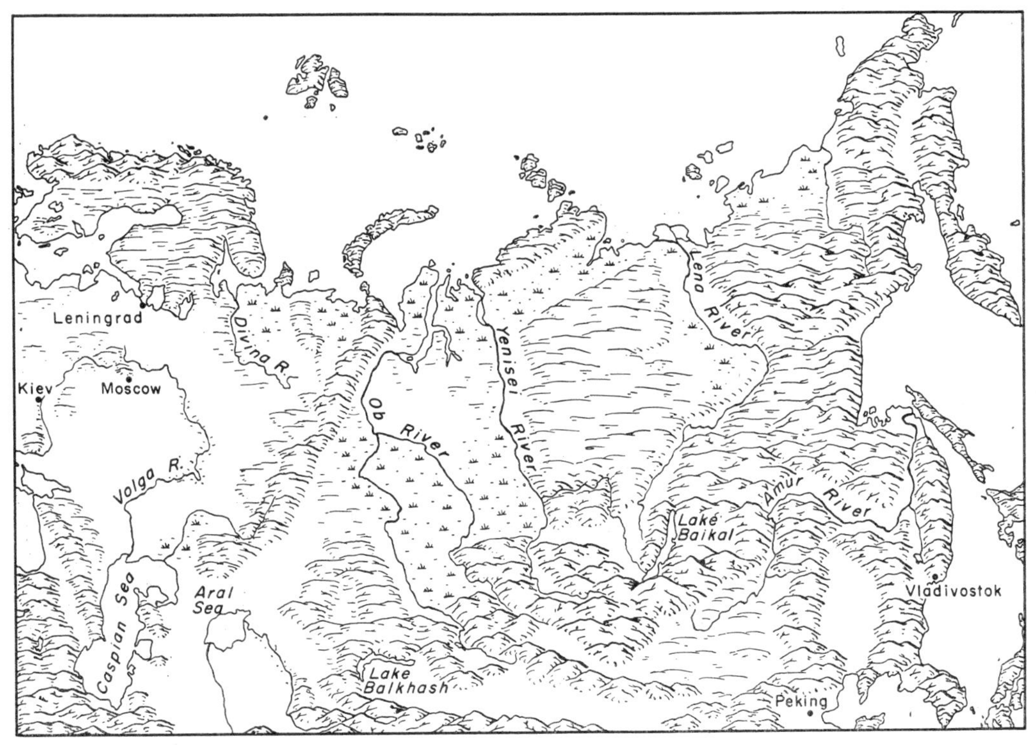

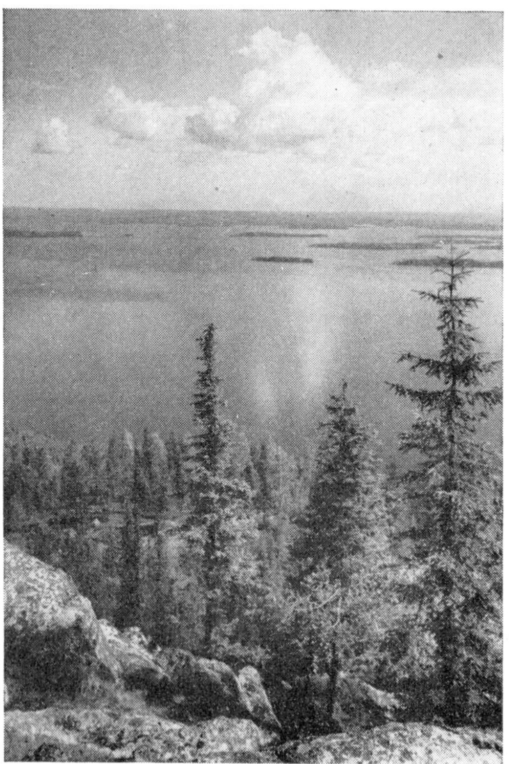

FIGURE 14-10. *The lake region in eastern Finland.* (Finnish National Travel Office.)

as a flat, but elevated, plain into which the streams have incised deep valleys. (5) Eastern Siberia is extremely mountainous.

The Ob, Yenisey, and Lena Rivers are three of the great streams of the world—in volume, length, and area of drainage basin. These rivers are ice-bound for the long winter season; at Yakutsk the Lena is frozen an average of 210 days per year. Their utility is further reduced by ice choking the lower courses; vast areas are inundated when the warm season thaw in the southern margins of their drainage basins sends large volumes of water poleward.

Natural vegetation

Stretching from coast to coast across the broad expanse of the Subarctic regions is the *taiga,* or northern coniferous forest, one of the greatest forest belts in the world. The forest cover is dominated by coniferous trees; spruce, larch, fir, and pine are the major species. Intermingled with the conifers, paralleling stream banks, or forming solitary clumps are willows, alder, aspen, and birch. The forest floors are quite clear with coverings of moss, lichens, and low bushes. The taiga has its largest trees and greatest forest densities on the southern margins and along river banks. Poleward, with diminishing sunlight intensity and growing season, the forest thins and the trees decrease in size until they are virtually dwarf bushes at the margin of the tundra. Tree growth everywhere is slow, since water at the roots is only available from three to five months a year. Trees 50 years old with diameters of only a few inches are common. The average size of conifers in the main portion of the Canadian taiga ranges from heights of 30 to 70 feet and from diameters of six inches to two feet.[1]

The taiga is not a continuous forest region. Where it borders the steppes on the southern margin, the forest is occasionally broken by open prairies. Scattered throughout the taiga are thousands of square miles of spaghnum moss swamps and muskeg, the accumulated remains of decayed vegetation. During the thaw of the summer months, the swamp and muskeg country is virtually a morass, infested with biting and stinging insects, and travel is practically inhibited.

Native animal life

An abundance of animal life is a characteristic feature of the Subarctic regions. A rich variety of species ranges through the stretches of open forest, which provides both food and protection. Caribou or reindeer, moose, and elk comprise the forest-browsers. The fur trade is based on beaver, fisher, fox, martin, mink, muskrat, otter, weasel or ermine, and wolverine. The

[1] See *Native Trees of Canada.* Ottawa: Forestry Branch, Department of Resources and Development, 1950.

FIGURE 14-11. *A bull moose in a natural meadow in the Subarctic forest.* (Fish and Wildlife Service: J. Malcolm Greany.)

prime winter pelts of these northern forest animals make the Subarctics the most important fur-producing regions in the world. Bears, wolves, lynx, squirrels, and hares are common. The forest is the habitat of numerous birds such as the grouse, woodpecker, and grosbeak. Streams and lakes are well stocked with game fish. Insect life is superabundant. In summer the muskegs, swamps, ponds, and the general moist condition of the lowlands provide numerous breeding places. Clouds of mosquitoes, stinging gnats, and black flies make life miserable for man and beast. Insects are one of the great drawbacks to living in the taiga.

The forest is the scene of two seasonal migrations. Great flocks of birds arrive from the south in the spring and depart with the approach of winter. Caribou, hares, and arctic birds, summer inhabitants of the tundra, invade the taiga in winter for the forest's protection and food.

Soils

The greatest development of podzol soils occurs in the Subarctic regions in response to the long sub-zero winters, cool, moist summers, and coniferous vegetation. Glaciation and imperfect drainage, however, have hindered the development of a uniform pattern. The best soils have formed in the sedimentary rock areas where breakdown is more rapid, in basins containing glacio-fluvial deposits of clays, on lacustrine plains, and along stream floodplains. Soil is often completely lacking where the glaciers scoured the surface, and stony in other areas where deposition occurred. In the marshes conditions for soil development are unfavorable and in some cases peat, several feet thick, has accumulated.

Permafrost—a condition of permanently-frozen subsoil—exists in parts of these regions, with probably the widest distribution in northeast Siberia. It causes many problems

FIGURE 14-12. *A Canada goose family. The honk and the V-shaped flight pattern of these migratory birds announce the approach of spring to the middle latitudes of North America.* (Malak, Ottawa.)

in construction of houses and roads, or in any digging or excavating. Frost-heaving ejects telephone poles from the ground and forms cracks in brick or concrete walls. With the advent of spring, thaw of the surface layer while the subsoil remains frozen causes a mushy mass of mud to form.[2]

MAN IN THE SUBARCTICS

The Subarctic regions are frontiers of settlement. The harsh climate, which is marginal for plant growth and unfavorable to easy living, together with the great distances to major centers of development, produce an environment that is unattractive to man. Thousands of square miles are entirely without people and nowhere are densities great. Much territory is sparsely occupied by relatively small numbers of native peoples who depend upon hunting, fishing, and fur trading for their living. The greatest white populations are found in the southern margin of the Eurasian region in Sweden, Finland, and European Russia. In the past 25 years, resource development has resulted in some settlement in the area between the Yenisey River and Lake Baykal. Canadians in the Subarctic are confined mainly to the southern fringe in eastern Canada. The average density for the realm as a whole does not exceed two persons per square mile.

Agriculture

These northlands offer little to attract the farmer. Long, bitterly cold winters, short, cool growing seasons, and soils generally thin and low in fertility restrict farming opportunities. Lack of transportation and distances to market place further limitations

[2] See Mirov, N. T., *Geography of Russia.* New York: John Wiley and Sons, Inc., 1951, Chapter 3.

FIGURE 14-13. *A rural Finnish steam bath or* sauna. *Water is thrown on the heated rocks to produce steam for the bathers, who sit on the raised platform. The cleansing effect of the sauna results from the sweating caused by the heat and the steam, and this is often stimulated by beating the body with birch twigs. There are about 350,000 rural saunas in Finland.* (Finnish National Travel Office.)

in the way of commercial agriculture. Long mid-summer days in part compensate for short seasons so that hardy species of vegetables, grains, hay, and pasture crops can be grown where soils are favorable. Potatoes, turnips, radishes, peas, lettuce, and cabbage, along with rye, oats, and small fruits, are usually the most significant enterprises, but agriculture is by no means widespread.

Canada has not yet exerted a major effort toward agricultural development in this region because of her relatively small population and the possession of other comparatively large productive areas. Three areas in her Subarctic region are showing considerable progress in the production of hardy grains and in animal industries—these are the Vermilion Area of north Alberta, the district north of Prince Albert in Saskatchewan, and the Clay Belt in the vicinity of Abitibi Lake near the Ontario-Quebec border.

Sweden, Finland, and the U.S.S.R. are giving more attention to the development of farming. A major share of the area of each of these countries is in the Subarctics and of necessity the better districts have had to be opened. Even so, agriculture is of small proportions and notable progress is being made only along the southern borders. In the Soviet Union, as the result of the development of mineral and forest resources, some advances have been made in establishing small food production bases to provide vegetables, meat, and milk to the workers.

FIGURE 14-14. *Fishing in one of the many lakes of central Finland. Many farmers supplement their diet and income by catching fish.* (Finnish National Travel Office.)

FIGURE 14-15. *A farm in Finland. Holdings average about 40 acres. Farmers attempt to attain self-sufficiency in food production. Rye, potatoes, hay, and livestock are the major enterprises. The crop shown is flax.* (Finnish National Travel Office.)

Forest industries

The coniferous forests of the Subarctic regions are one of the world's great sources of timber and pulpwood. The U.S.S.R. taiga alone contains 1.5 billion acres. Forests have a major role in the entire economy of each country that shares a part of the taiga. Canada, relying on stands of balsam fir and spruce, has become a world leader in newsprint production. Sweden, Finland, and U.S.S.R. account for the bulk of Eurasian surplus forest products.

Logging is concentrated in the accessible southern margins where trees are largest and stands are most dense. Logging operations in both Eurasia and North America are similar. The trees are harvested in the winter and are assembled along frozen stream banks by sled and tractor. The logs are floated downstream to the mills with the thawing of the river ice in the spring. At this time of year and in early summer, the surfaces of the lakes and rivers are covered by logs.

FIGURE 14-16. *Rivers play a major role in the forest activities of the Subarctics. During the months of spring and summer the timber is carried by the rivers from the forest to the mills.* (Swedish National Travel Office.)

Fur industry

Furs, not trees, were the earliest attractions of the northern forests. Long before man looked to the taiga for timber, the trapping of fur-bearing animals and the trading of pelts were the dominant and most lucrative activities. Despite centuries of exploitation, the furs of the taiga continue to be an important revenue source.

Winter is the season for trapping since furs are in their prime—longer, glossier, and thicker. The trapper must take all his supplies, which include food, blankets, traps, firearms, and ammunition, into the woods. He establishes a base camp near a stream or lake and sets his trap line. The entire winter is spent in checking the string of traps, hunting, and preparing the pelts for market. With the spring thaw he returns with his catch to a collecting center. In Canada the Hudson's Bay Company is still the major fur-trading organization.

Fur farms are becoming a significant source of furs. To be assured of a dependable supply of pelts, trappers began to keep foxes, captured during the warm season, in cages and to hold them until their pelts were prime. This method developed and stimulated the breeding of fur-bearing animals that has become a well-established and profitable activity. Animals most usually raised in captivity are fox and mink.

Mining

As easily accessible supplies in other regions are depleted and industrial needs multiply, these northern forest lands are becoming increasingly important as sources of minerals. Full information on the possibilities is not yet known; detailed geologic surveys have covered only small areas.

FIGURE 14-17. *Sorting timber in one of the many rivers of northern Sweden.* (Swedish National Travel Office.)

FIGURE 14-18. *An otter—one of the fur-bearers of the Subarctics.* (Fish and Wildlife Service: V. B. Scheffer.)

FIGURE 14-19. *A trapper with his team of dogs. This is one of the important modes of winter travel in the isolated Subarctics.* (Standard Oil Company of New Jersey.)

Chance prospecting, however, has revealed widespread occurrences of metals in the old hard-rock areas. The Laurentian Upland of Canada is known to be rich in minerals; the list includes iron, uranium, nickel, copper, cobalt, gold, and silver. Mining camps are being established to exploit these ores. Development of the iron deposits of Labrador are of particular significance.

Gold in the Yukon Valley was the first major attraction of Alaska and northwestern Canada. Although the more accessible and richer gravels were worked by the turn of this century, the activity continues as a profitable enterprise for a few large companies that use huge dredges.

One of the highest quality iron deposits in the world is in Sweden, north of the arctic circle. Sweden exports most of the iron ore from this district since she does not possess coking coal—her small steel industry cannot consume the total output from her mines. The mining activity has expanded since World War II and Sweden has become the largest supplier of iron ore on the international market. She now supplies most of the ore imported by the western European steel industry and some is shipped to the United States. Kiruna is the leading center; from there ore moves by rail to the ports of Narvik on the coast of Norway and to Luleå on the Gulf of Bothnia. Narvik, always ice-free, is the more important, allowing activity in winter as well as in the summer; it has the additional ad-

FIGURE 14-20. *The famous Kiruna iron mines.* (Swedish National Travel Office.)

vantages of being nearer to the mines as well as to the European markets.

In the past quarter-century, the Russians have conducted mineral explorations that have revealed valuable deposits, and several mining centers have developed. Particularly noteworthy is the center in the heart of the Kola Peninsula where two significant minerals are mined: apatite, a source of phosphate fertilizer, and nepheline, important for its potash content and use in aluminum and ceramic industries. In the same area, some iron and molybdenum are produced, and nickel is mined at Petsamo. Coal and petroleum are being exploited to some extent in the Pechora Basin. Undeveloped reserves of coal are present in the Yenisey and Lena Valleys, and iron is found along the Angara River. Large quantities of gold are mined in Yakutia, mainly along the Aldan and Kolyma Rivers. The settlement at Norilsk in the northern edge of the region near the Yenisey River is based upon the mining of nickel and related minerals.

Water resource development

Numerous streams and lakes provide these northlands with vast water resources that serve the regions in several ways. From the historic point of view, the transportation function has been most significant, furnishing the avenues of penetration for the trappers who have taken many millions of dollars worth of fur from the forest and marshes. The waterways are still used for this purpose and in addition provide the access routes and shipment arteries for the forest-based industries as well as others. With a minimum of excavation to connect lakes and streams, the Russians have constructed a Baltic to White Sea waterway which serves the heavy-duty needs of the forest and mines of the northwestern area. This canal system is also connected to the Volga system. Today Moscow, by a series of canals, rivers, and lakes, is connected to the Baltic, White, Caspian, and Black Seas.

Lack of coal and petroleum has encouraged

FIGURE 14-21. *A Diesel tug pushing a loaded barge down the Athabaska River.* (George Hunter, Ottawa.)

some development of hydroelectric power. Important generation facilities have been established in Ontario and Quebec, Canada, near the populated zone, and in Sweden, Finland, and the adjacent part of the Soviet Union. The potentials are high because of the many natural storages, numerous rapids and falls, and the presence of hard-rock surfaces which minimize sediments and provide firm foundations for dam construction. Distance to major consuming centers is the principal deterrent of more widespread development at the present time.

Use for industrial water supply is of great local importance. Pulp and paper plants frequently are located on streams which supply the transportation facility for bringing in the logs, produce the needed power, and furnish the large quantities of water needed in the process.

Manufacturing

Industry in the Subarctics is based on forest products—timber and pulpwood—and an abundance of hydroelectric power. These two factors have made the regions leaders in pulp and paper production.

Canada tops the world in the manufacture of pulp; paper and pulp production is the major Canadian industry. Numerous pulp and paper mills, as well as sawmills, are located along the south edge of the forest and along tributary streams of the St. Lawrence River in Quebec and Ontario. Two of Canada's largest paper mills are at Corner Brook and Grand Falls, Newfoundland. Cheap hydroelectric power has stimulated a second industry—the production of aluminum from imported bauxite. The largest aluminum plant

FIGURE 14-22. *The power house for the Aluminum Company of Canada's Arvida plant. Large quantities of cheap hydroelectric power and access to both tidewater and freshwater navigation have made the Saguenay district the ideal center for the Canadian aluminum industry.* (Malak, Ottawa.)

in the world is located at Arvida, Quebec, on the Saguenay River.

Forest-based industries in Sweden are located at river mouths along the Gulf of Bothnia, with the greatest concentrations around Sundsvall and Harnosand. Sawmills, pulp and paper plants and other woodworking factories are scattered along the west and south coasts of Finland. The industrial center of Finland is at Tampere, which has some diversification, manufacturing in addition to wood products, textiles, shoes, and metal goods. In the northwestern U.S.S.R., rafts of logs move downstream to sawmills, woodworking plants, and pulp mills at Archangel, Onega, and Mezen. Petrozavodsk has diverse forest-based industries, including a ski factory that produces an important share of the nation's skis; there is also a small steel works, and engines and equipment for the forest industry are manufactured. Sawmills are scattered along the rivers traversing the forest in Siberia. There are a number of small industrial settlements along the Trans-Siberian Railroad between Krasnoyarsk and Lake Baykal utilizing local coal, iron, other minerals and forest resources for varied manufactures.

Urban centers

The urban needs of the Subarctic regions are small. As a result there are few compact settlements and only in Eurasia do any exceed 10,000 in population. Most are resource exploitation centers and result from favorable advantages for mining, milling, assembly, and trans-shipment. Such are the Soviet Union centers along the Baltic-White Sea Canal, and along the Trans-Siberian Railroad. Murmansk is the most northern large city in the world with a population of about 150,000. Its ice-free fiord harbor provides the Soviet Union with a gateway to the open Atlantic. Murmansk also serves as the terminus of the Northern Sea Route, the summer route through the Arctic Ocean to the Pacific. The city is connected to Leningrad by

900 miles of rail line. Archangel, with a population of about 300,000, is the largest city in the entire realm. Its situation at the mouth of the navigable Dvina River, which provides access to a vast forested area, has resulted in its growth and importance for timber concentration and milling. Irkutsk, with about 300,000 people, is the largest city of a number of centers along the Trans-Siberian Railroad. It is an old settlement which has recently expanded as the result of industrialization; situated at the head of the Angara Valley near Lake Baykal, it is within easy reach of a variety of minerals, power, and forest resources.

Fairbanks, serving the Yukon area of Alaska, is the largest center within the North American region, with about 6000 inhabitants. Several slightly larger centers are located within the margins of the Short Summer Humid Continental region.

OUTLOOK

The rigors of climate probably destine the Subarctics to a continued role of a pioneer fringe. Agriculture is severely limited by physical impediments; the farmer who braves these lands operates under as much risk as those who attempt to farm in the marginal drylands. Only the most favorable areas, largely those presently containing some settlement, have immediate future prospects. There is much to be learned about cultivation in this restrictive environment before agriculture becomes economically feasible.

The development of extensive large-scale manufacturing suffers from inaccessibility, limited resources, labor, and markets as well as competition from areas more favorably situated. Manufacturing will thus be geared to the processing of materials at hand, or to the utilization of large quantities of cheap hydroelectric power. Forest-based and metallurgical industries have a sound future.

The resources of forest, water, minerals, and furs keynote the future of the Subarctics.

SELECTED REFERENCES

Berg, L. S., *The Natural Regions of the U.S.S.R.* New York: The Macmillan Company, 1950.

Carlson, Lucille, "The Mining District of Kiruna Stad, Sweden," *Scientific Monthly,* LXXIV, No. 2, 1952, 76-83.

Collinder, Bjorn, *The Lapps.* Princeton, N. J.: Princeton University Press, 1949.

Cressey, George B., *How Strong Is Russia?* Syracuse, N. Y.: Syracuse University Press, 1954.

Englund, Eric, "Peat-Land Farming in Finland," *Foreign Agriculture,* XIV, No. 11, 1950, 246-249.

Miller, E. Willard, "Agricultural Development in Interior Alaska," *Scientific Monthly,* LXXIII, No. 4, 1951, 245-254.

Polyakallio, Onni, "Farming Under the Midnight Sun," *Foreign Agriculture,* XIV, No. 4, 1950, 82-85.

Reeds, L. G., "Land Utilization in Central Ontario," *Economic Geography,* XXII, No. 4, 1946, 289-306.

Stone, Kirk H., "Populating Alaska: The United States Phase," *Geographical Review,* XLII, No. 3, 1952, 384-404.

Van Cleef, E., "Finland, Bridge to the Atlantic," *Journal of Geography,* XLVIII, No. 3, 1949, 99-105.

Webster, C. J., "The Growth of the Soviet Arctic and Subarctic," *Arctic,* IV, No. 1, 1951, 24-45.

CHAPTER 15

Polar Lands

THE BARREN LANDS OR TUNDRA OF the far north and the ice caps of the poles constitute the Polar Lands. Nowhere on earth are winters so long and summers so short. Ice and snow are eternal on the ice caps, and the aspects of summer are almost ephemeral on the tundra. Nowhere on earth does the sun remain continuously above the horizon for as many months and nowhere is its heating less effective. Conversely, no other lands are as long deprived of sunlight. Darkness and light divide the year more than the day. Nature provides two compensations for the bleak and barren landscapes and the long dark winters. In the season of maximum warmth, the tundra displays a mosaic of color when the flowering plants make their hasty appearance, and in winter the

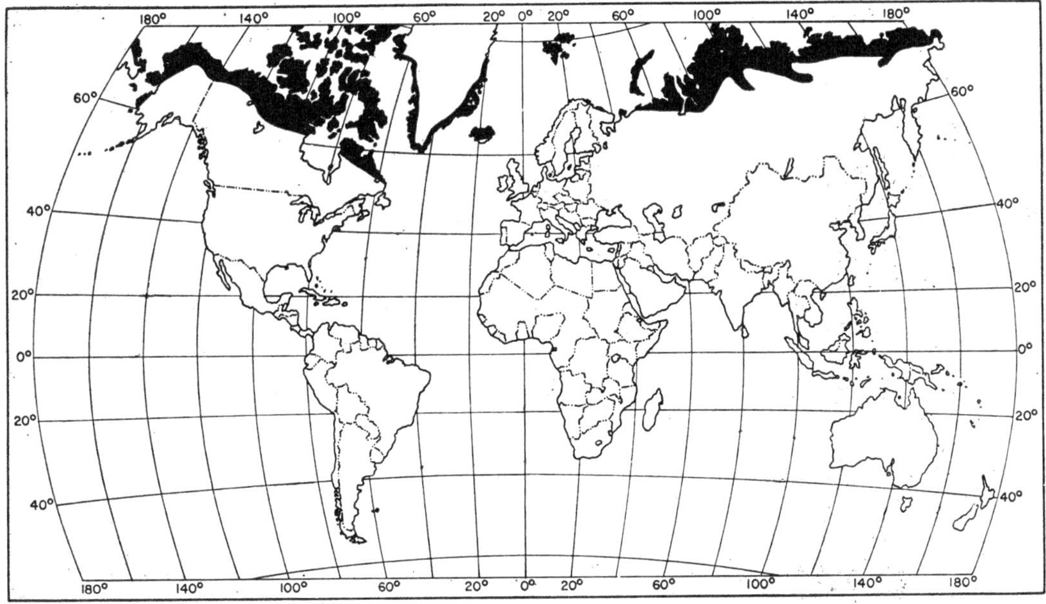

FIGURE 15-1. *The Polar Lands of the Northern Hemisphere.*

FIGURE 15-2. *The Polar Lands of North America.*

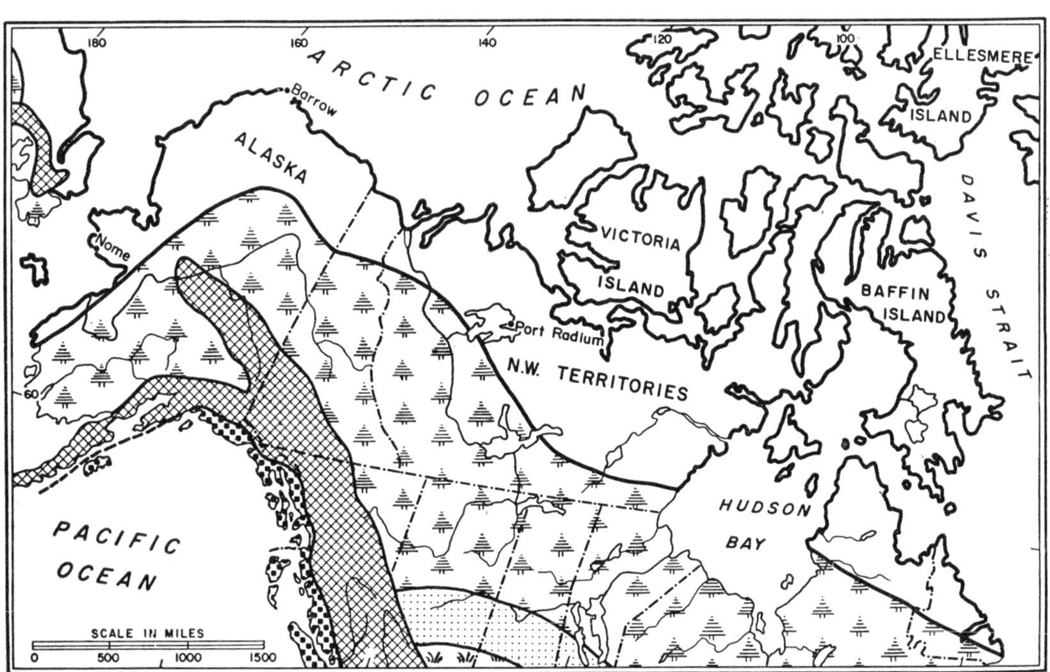

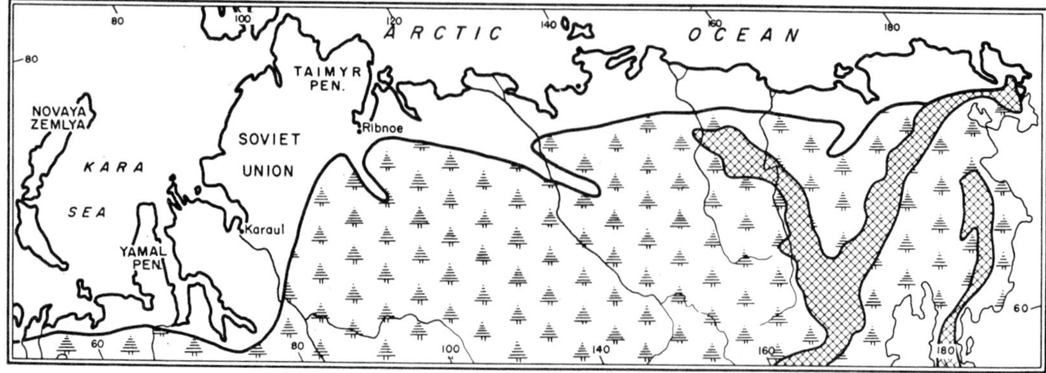

FIGURE 15-3. *The Polar Lands of Eurasia.*

skies are brightened by the parading colors of the auroras.

Resemblances can be seen between the Polar Lands and the Tropical Deserts. Both are characterized by scanty precipitation, scanty vegetation, and barren expanses; both are largely uninhabited. One is a desert of drought—the other a desert of cold. But in the Polar Lands man finds no oases!

Location

As their name implies, the Polar Lands are situated in the high latitudes, mainly poleward of 65°. East of Hudson Bay in Canada, however, the tundra bends southward to about latitude 55°. The equatorward margins are marked by the warmest month isotherm of 50°, which approximately denotes the cold boundary of tree growth. It is common to subdivide these regions into the tundra and the ice caps.

Tundra. The tundra is the high latitude cold frontier of vegetation. The warmest month isotherms of 50° and 32° mark, respectively, the equatorward and poleward boundaries. It is found preponderantly in the Northern Hemisphere fringing the Arctic Ocean. Belts of tundra stretch along the margins of North America and Eurasia, and include the coast of Greenland and other arctic islands. Small and fragmented areas occur along the coast of Antarctica.

Ice caps. The polar lands of perennial ice reach the greatest development in Antarctica where all of the land mass except a few coastal strips is included. In the Northern Hemisphere the interior of Greenland and the ocean within the vicinity of the North Pole are perpetually frozen.

PHYSICAL ENVIRONMENT

Climate

The tundra and the ice caps are divided by the 32° isotherm for the warmest month. The tundra possesses the last vestiges of summer whereas the ice cap is a land of eternal frost.

Tundra. Winters are long and bitterly cold, with about nine months averaging below freezing. January and February have the lowest averages, in the neighborhood of −30° to −40°. Location has considerable effect on winter temperatures and stations near the coasts are 10 to 20 degrees or more higher than inland stations and are also much cooler in summer. Summers are cool and short but days are long. Average monthly temperatures never reach 50°; however, daily maxima during the warmest month may be as high as 70° or more. The tundra has many hours of sunshine during the summer since the sun is above the horizon for two or three months. The sun, however, is low and the incoming rays are oblique and have little effect as warming

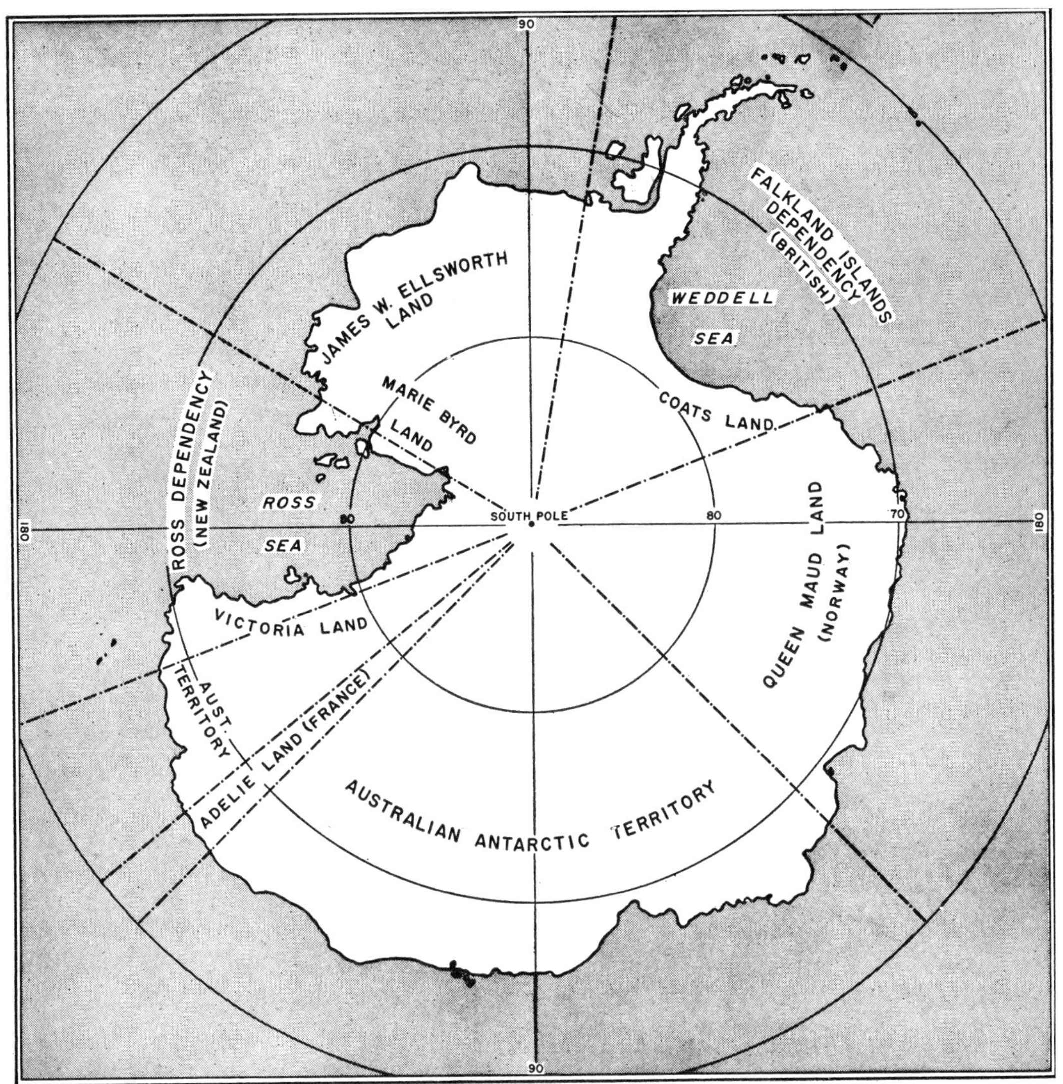

FIGURE 15-4. *Antarctica.*

agents since much of the energy is consumed in melting snow and ice and evaporating water. Furthermore, much of the insolation is reflected from the ice and snow surfaces. The region has a period of darkness during the winter when the sun does not make its appearance, but when the sun is below the horizon during these two or three months, the region is not completely dark. There are long periods of twilight following the disappearance of the sun and preceding its return. Light is furnished in this twilight interim by the reflection of celestial bodies on the white ice and snow and by the glowing green or red curtains of the aurora borealis. Precipitation, chiefly of cyclonic origin, is light, averaging about ten inches throughout the tundra as a whole. The maxima comes during the warm season. During this short season, some rain falls; however, snow prevails much of the time. The tundra snow is dry and powdery. The snow does not reach great depths, and

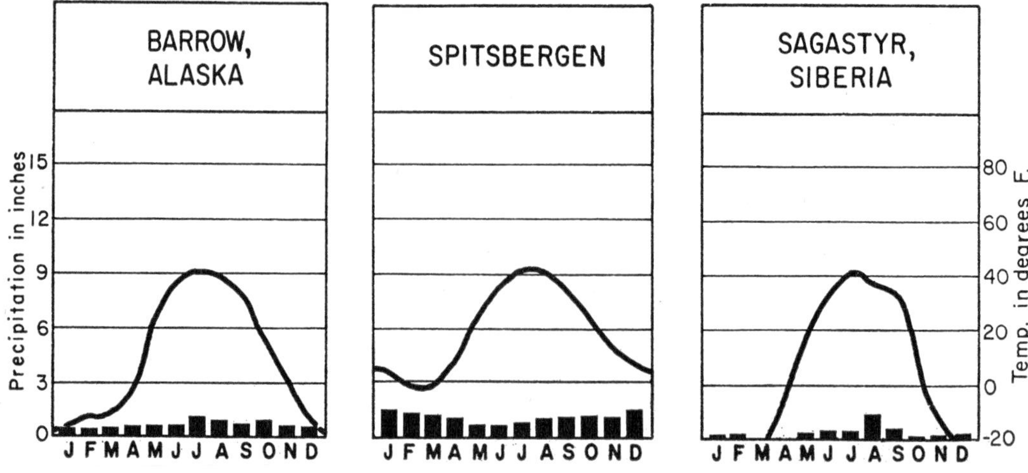

FIGURE 15-5. *Typical climatic graphs for Polar Land stations.*

due to strong winds and the lack of protecting vegetation, there are large expanses bare of snow even in winter.

Ice caps. The North and South Poles are the two points on the earth's surface having six months of sunlight and six months of darkness. Equatorward from the poles, the length of continuous light and darkness changes with latitude. March 21st at the North Pole marks the sun's first appearance on the horizon. The barely visible sun follows a circular path around the horizon without setting or rising. It continues to appear higher in the sky until about June 21st, when the entire area within the arctic circle is bathed in light. Following the summer solstice, the sun gradually sinks in the heavens until, on about September 22nd, it disappears below the horizon. About the 22nd of December, the entire area within the arctic circle is covered by darkness. The exact opposite occurs at the South Pole. The winter six months when the sun is below the horizon is not a period of complete darkness. Twilight exists for part of the period and celestial bodies and the aurora borealis (aurora australis at the South Pole) furnish subdued light.

The arctic ice cap covers a number of islands, whereas Antarctica is presumably a single land mass of about five million square miles. Climate data for both ice caps are fragmentary. Ice caps have the lowest annual average temperature on earth; the average of the warmest month is below 32°. Temperatures recorded in interior Greenland from November through March averaged —43°. May, June, and July were the warm months with about a 6° average; however, coasts may occasionally have daily maxima above freezing.

The cold air prevailing over ice caps holds little water vapor, consequently precipitation is small in amount and occurs as powdery, dry snow. Little melting allows the snow to accumulate and in time it becomes loose, granular ice, or *névé,* and solid glacier ice. Both ice caps experience violent blizzards, especially in winter.

Surface features

The landforms of the Polar regions range from low coastal plains to high ice plateaus, often surmounted by glaciated mountains. In North America the Laurentian Uplands reach the Arctic Coast throughout much of the eastern portion of the continent; here they are low in elevation with relatively slight relief, and often bordered by coastal plains. Fairly wide plains are found along the northern fringe of Alaska and in the Mackenzie River area of Canada. The western islands of the Arctic Archipelago are low, but the eastern islands appear plateau-like and are

FIGURE 15-6. *A summer view of the Alaskan tundra.* (United States Geological Survey.)

surmounted by ice-scoured low mountains and hills, many of which are partially covered with glaciers. Greenland, the largest of the world's islands, is a high plateau of 5000 to 8000 feet in elevation. Except around the coast, it is covered by a vast ice sheet held within fringing mountain walls.

Flat to rolling plains and low plateaus border the arctic coast of Eurasia. The narrow Fenno-Scandinavian portion appears as a dissected plain 500 to 700 feet in elevation, dropping sharply to the Barents Sea. The sea penetrates the land in long, narrow fiords. A low, relatively featureless lowland fringes the shore of the Arctic eastward to the Kolyma River. It is broken only by the Ural Mountains and plateau-like elevations in the Kanin Peninsula, Timan Mountains, and Yamal and Taimyr Peninsulas; rarely do these elevations reach 1000 feet above sea level.

In the Southern Hemisphere the continent of Antarctica harbors the world's largest ice sheet. The ice, for the greater part, rises steeply from the sea and levels out to a rather flat interior with an average elevation of 6000 feet. Inland from the Pacific Ocean, heights reach 10,000 feet or more.

Natural vegetation

Conditions for vegetation in the tundra are far from ideal. Periods of growth are short, and during the warm season the ground is saturated with water. Despite these handicaps, the tundra has a wealth of vegetation.

The natural cover has three broad divisions: (*1*) The bush tundra, bordering the taiga, is composed of scrubby alders, birches, and willows only a few feet in height. (*2*) The grass tundra, beyond the fringe of dwarf trees, occupies the largest area and is most typical. This cover includes mosses, lichens, sedges, flowering plants, and an occasional low bush. (*3*) The desert tundra on the poleward margin consists of small islands of vegetation growing in the pockets of soil scattered among the bare rock surfaces.

The vegetation pattern of the tundra is a near counterpart of a high mountain alp, the area between the tree line and the permanent snow. During the short summer, plant life is quickened by the warmth. Taking advantage of their brief stay in the sun, plants speed through the various stages of growth. Flowers

FIGURE 15-7. *A winter view of the Alaskan tundra.* (United States Geological Survey.)

FIGURE 15-8. *A herd of caribou in the Alaskan tundra.* (Fish and Wildlife Service: Edward F. Chatelain.)

FIGURE 15-9. *A domesticated reindeer in the grass tundra of Alaska.* (Fish and Wildlife Service: V. D. Scheffer.)

burst into bloom on the heels of the departing snow and the bleakness of the landscape is replaced by a colorful carpet of low-flowering plants, poppies, lilies, buttercups, and violets.

Native animal life

The majority of animal life in the Polar regions inhabits the tundra lands. Species include the musk ox, reindeer or caribou, wolf, arctic fox and hare, and lemming. Millions of insects, especially the mosquito, swarm through the air during the warm season. Several species of birds, such as the ptarmigan and the arctic owl, inhabit the tundra throughout the year and populations are swelled by the great summer migrations from the south. Rookeries along many rocky coasts are crowded with bird life and water bodies are invaded by waterfowl.

All warm-blooded animals of the Polar regions have developed means of conserving body heat in order to combat the severe low temperatures.[1] All are equipped with thick fur or feathers. Mammals usually have a silky fur and a thick wooly undercoat. The long hair of the reindeer, which is thicker at the end than at the root, forms an airtight coat. Thick layers of fat provide insulation against loss of heat and act as food reserves for winter. White coloration, typical in winter, radiates less heat and acts as camouflage.

Land animals are almost lacking on the ice caps, but sea life is abundant here as well as along tundra shores. In the arctic are polar bears, walruses, whales, and seals. The Otary

[1] For an excellent description of animal life, see Allee, W. E., and Karl P. Schmidt, *Ecological Animal Geography*. New York: John Wiley and Sons, Inc., 1951, Chapter 25.

FIGURE 15-10. *Reindeer, the wealth of Lapland. The reindeer has long been domesticated in northern Eurasia.* (Finnish National Travel Office.)

seal of the Pribilof Islands is prized for its fur and the Arctic seal is hunted for its oil and skin. Sea elephants and whales inhabit the seas of the South Polar region. Whaling is the major activity in the Antarctic waters, which are the world's principal whaling grounds. Breeding colonies of birds are present at both ice caps. The penguin is the typical bird species of Antarctica.

Soils

Soils occur only in the tundra portions of the Polar regions. Even here the forming processes work very slowly and barren rock surfaces are common. The tundra soils are characterized by high accumulations of organic matter caused by the extreme retardation of chemical and biological breakdown. As a result, they usually have a peaty surface overlaying a compact subsoil, which in many areas is permanently frozen. Despite low precipitation, the soil is supersaturated with water during the short summer because of low evaporation and poor drainage. Most areas are suitable only as pasturage for reindeer or caribou. The soils of the better-drained, south-facing slopes offer limited possibilities for a few hardy crops that will mature in an extremely short growing period.

MAN IN THE POLAR LANDS

Opportunities for man are indeed small in the Polar Lands. Most areas are as devoid of people as the driest deserts and environments are equally unattractive. Harsh conditions of severe climate, ground that is frozen for most or all of the year, scanty vegetation, and a dependence on animal life compel the few dwellers of these cold lands to exert constant effort to survive. Less than 100,000 people live in these regions, all in the Northern Hemisphere. None are agriculturalists and all are more or less migratory.

The few nomadic people living in the Eurasian tundra are engaged chiefly in reindeer tending and hunting, especially for sea mammals. Sometimes there is a division of labor with various male members of the family alternately hunting and herding. The reindeer are pastured on the mosses, lichens, and low plants of the tundra during the short, warm season, but in winter are driven to the edge of the taiga where the animals are about to expose snow-covered forage plants with their shovel-like hoofs. Furthermore, the nomads prefer the forested areas in winter since the trees provide fuel and protection from the arctic winds. Reindeer furnish meat, milk, and hides and are used as draft animals (see Figure 15-10). Another domestic animal is the sled dog. In teams of 10 to 14 they are capable of pulling loads up to a ton, and can average from two to four miles an hour, depending upon snow and weather conditions.

The tundra in North America is occupied chiefly by the Eskimos, who live by hunting and fishing. Reindeer were introduced from Eurasia to provide a more dependable food supply, but the experiment has not been too successful. The Eskimo is an excellent hunter and fisherman, and animals are the key to his life—supplying food, heat, light, shelter, and transportation. There is a great dependency upon sea life, especially the seal. The Eskimo's boat, the kayak, is the epitome of seaworthiness. Housing consists of sod igloos, stone huts, or crude shelters made of skin supported by driftwood or whale bones. Temporary snow-block igloos are constructed for shelter during winter hunting trips. Dogs are the only domestic animal and are used in hunting and for transportation. The Eskimo has made an excellent adjustment to his harsh and unattractive environment. Eskimos living around the Mackenzie River delta and in Alaska have acquired a veneer of western culture due to their many contacts with Canadian traders and American government workers and servicemen.

Although there may be differences in racial background among Polar peoples, the restricting environment has imposed many similarities in culture. Clothing, food, tools, utensils, and shelter types are quite the same from one tribe to another.

White man has avoided the Polar Lands. His contacts have been largely in the interests of commerce with the natives, exploitation of aquatic life, military security, and scientific experiments. The airplane has made possible exploration of large areas that were unknown but a few years ago, and has given new significance to these lands in terms of national security. Advancing knowledge of weather and climate has assigned importance to the arctic region's relationships with the middle latitudes. Weather observation stations have been established within the arctic circle.

Since 1930, the Soviet Union has directed some efforts toward development of her arctic fringe. Several "reindeer farms" have been established and native peoples organized into collectives for systematic and improved use of the tundra pasturages. A number of small ports are operated along the coast for shipment of timber, minerals, and furs from the forest lands to the south over the Northern Sea route. During the brief summer, several scores of ships serve these ports, some making the complete trip from Murmansk to Vladivostok.

FIGURE 15-11. *Eskimo children await their parents, who are attending Sunday morning Eskimo service at All Saints Cathedral, Aklavik, Northwest Territories. Note the mixture of western and traditional Eskimo clothing. Aklavik, on the Mackenzie River delta, serves a district containing about 1600 white persons, Eskimos, and Indians. It is still a center of fur trade, but it also plays an important part in the air and water transportation systems of the Far North. Hospital care and educational services are now available to all the population, including the roving groups of Eskimos well outside the limits of the district.* (George Hunter, Ottawa.)

OUTLOOK

Man is the world's most adaptable creature—his range of living is from the equator to the poles. He has achieved his greatest development, economic and cultural, in the intermediate lands; here too, he is present in greatest numbers. Up to now the areas of extremes—those too hot, too wet, too dry, too high, too rugged, too remote, or too cold —rarely have attracted large concentrations on a permanent basis.

Of all the restrictive environments, the Polar Lands offer the least to attract man. Their meager resources and extremely harsh environment indicate scattered and limited possibilities for the future.

SELECTED REFERENCES

"Canada Counts Its Caribou," *National Geographic Magazine,* CII, No. 8, 1952, 261-268.

Gruber, Ruth, *I Went to the Soviet Arctic.* New York: Viking Press, Inc., 1944.

"Resources of the Arctic," *Focus,* II, February 15, 1952.

Richards, E. A., *Arctic Mood.* Caldwell, Idaho: The Caxton Printers, Ltd., 1949.

Roucek, Joseph, "The Geopolitics of Greenland," *Journal of Geography,* L, No. 6, 1951, 239-246.

Sommers, Lawrence M., "Svalbard: Norway's Arctic Frontier," *Scientific Monthly,* LXXIV, No. 6, 1952, 338-345.

Stefansson, Vilhjalmur, *Arctic Manual.* New York: The Macmillan Company, 1944.

Stefansson, Vilhjalmur, *The Friendly Arctic.* New York: The Macmillan Company, 1943.

Taylor, Griffith, ed., *Geography in the Twentieth Century.* New York: Philosophical Library, 1951, Chapter XII ("Geography and the Arctic Lands"), and Chapter XIII ("Exploration of Antarctica").

Tweedsmuir, Lord John N.S.B., *Hudson's Bay Trader.* New York: W. W. Norton and Company, Inc., 1951.

Index